ENCYCLOPEDIA
SCIENCE
SUPPLEMENT

A Modern Science Anthology for the Family

1983

This edition of the YEARBOOK is published for use as a supplement to
THE FUNK & WAGNALLS NEW ENCYCLOPEDIA
THE NEW ILLUSTRATED COLUMBIA ENCYCLOPEDIA

DISTRIBUTED BY FUNK & WAGNALLS, INC.

ISBN 0-7172-1513-X
Library of Congress Catalog Card Number 64-7603

 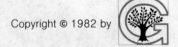

ACKNOWLEDGMENTS

Sources of articles appear below, including those reprinted
with the kind permission of publications and organizations.

THE VIEW FROM IO, Page 6: Reprinted by permission of *Astronomy* magazine; © 1981 by AstroMedia Corp.

A LAST LOOK AT SATURN, Page 11: Reprinted with permission from *Sky & Telescope,* November 1981; © Sky Publishing Corporation.

QUASARS, Page 20: Reprinted by permission of *Astronomy* magazine; © 1981 by AstroMedia Corp.

ASTEROIDS, Page 27: Reprinted by permission of *Astronomy* magazine; © 1981 by AstroMedia Corp.

THE BEAUTIFUL PEOPLE, Page 40: © 1981 by The New York Times Company. Reprinted by permission.

YOU ARE WHAT YOU EAT, Page 43: Reprinted from *Psychology Today* magazine; copyright © 1981 Ziff-Davis Publishing Company.

AUTISM: A WORLD APART, Page 48: Reprinted with permission from *Science News,* the weekly news magazine of science; © 1981 by Science Services, Inc.

HASSLES, Page 55: Reprinted from *Psychology Today* magazine; copyright © Ziff-Davis Publishing Company.

TEENAGE SUICIDE, page 61: Reprinted by permission of *The Wall Street Journal;* © Dow Jones & Company, Inc. 1981. All Rights Reserved.

LIFE AT THE END OF THE EARTH, Page 68: Reprinted by permission of the author. Article first appeared in *Smithsonian* magazine.

MONOCLONAL ANTIBODIES, Page 75: Reprinted by permission of *The Wall Street Journal;* © Dow Jones & Company, Inc. 1981. All Rights Reserved.

THE FLY IN OUR FRUIT, Page 80: Copyright 1981 by the National Wildlife Federation. Reprinted from the November–December 1981 issue of *International Wildlife* magazine.

CHOCOLATE GROWS ON TREES, Page 83: Reprinted by permission of the author. Article first appeared in *Horticulture* magazine, November 1981.

COMPUTER GAMES, Page 94: Reprinted by permission of the author. Article first appeared in *Smithsonian* magazine.

COMPUTER MUSIC, Page 104: Reprinted with permission from *New Scientist* magazine.

RUBIK'S CUBE, Page 109: Reprinted with permission from the May 1981 *Reader's Digest.* Copyright © 1981 by the Reader's Digest Assn., Inc.

THE MONTE CARLO METHOD, Page 112: Reprinted from the *Mathematics Teacher,* May 1981 (vol. 74, pp. 327–34), Copyright 1981 by the National Council of Teachers of Mathematics. Used by permission.

DESERT BUILDERS, Page 120: Reprinted by permission of the author. Article first appeared in *Smithsonian* magazine.

TAKING AIM AT TORNADOES, Page 127: © 1980 by The New York Times Company. Reprinted by permission.

LIFE OF A SNOW CRYSTAL, Page 131: Reprinted by permission of the author. Article first appeared in *Country Journal* magazine, December 1981.

SOLAR-HEATED HOUSES, Page 144: Reprinted by permission from Blair & Ketchum's *Country Journal.* © November 1981 Country Journal Publications Co. Inc. All rights reserved.

PEATLANDS, Page 151: Reprinted with permission from *Sierra* magazine, published by the Sierra Club, 530 Bush, San Francisco, California 94108.

WHAT A DRAG!, Page 156: Reprinted by permission of the author. Article first appeared in *Technology Illustrated,* October–November 1981.

DOWN, Page 161: Reprinted by permission of the author. Article first appeared in *Country Journal,* November 1981.

ELECTRICITY FROM THE WIND, Page 167: Reprinted by permission from Blair & Ketchum's *Country Journal.* © July 1980 Country Journal Publications Co. Inc. All rights reserved.

TEN ENDANGERED HABITATS, Page 174: Copyright 1981 by the National Wildlife Federation. Reprinted from the October–November 1981 issue of *National Wildlife* magazine.

OUR TROUBLED LAKES, Page 186: Reprinted by permission of the author. Article first appeared in *The New York Times Magazine,* September 20, 1981.

NUCLEAR WASTE DISPOSAL, Page 194: Reprinted with permission from *Science News,* the weekly news magazine of science; © 1981, 1982 by Science Services Inc.

RIVER IN A STRAIGHTJACKET, Page 202: Reprinted by permission of the author. Article first appeared in *American Forests.*

SCIENCE ANNUAL STAFF

EDITORIAL

MANUFACTURING

GROLIER INCORPORATED

CONTENTS

ASTRONOMY & SPACE SCIENCE

BEHAVIORAL SCIENCES

BIOLOGY

COMPUTERS & MATHEMATICS

EARTH SCIENCE

ENERGY

THE ENVIRONMENT

HEALTH & DISEASE

PAST, PRESENT, & FUTURE

PHYSICAL SCIENCES

TECHNOLOGY

WILDLIFE

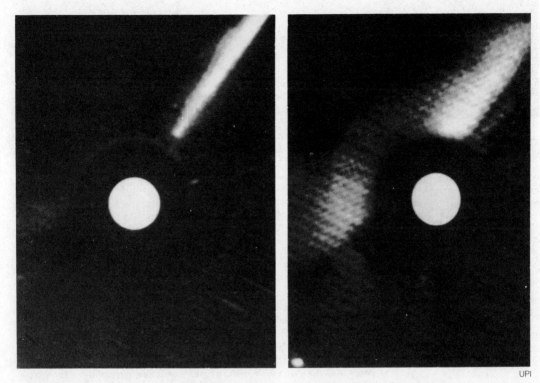

UPI

In late 1981, scientists reported that a comet streaked toward collision with the sun in 1979 (at left), scattering cometary debris in an immense halo that rose millions of kilometers above the solar surface.

ASTRONOMY & SPACE SCIENCE

The Pioneer Venus orbiter provided this global view of the planet. The huge volcanic region, Beta, and Ishtar, the high mountain range above it, are seen on the right.

ASTRONOMY & SPACE SCIENCE
REVIEW OF THE YEAR

The most spectacular news in astronomy and space science during 1981 was again Saturn—this time as seen by the Voyager 2 flyby. New findings and analyses of previously obtained data also revealed more details about the solar system, our galaxy, and the universe. The U.S. manned space program scored a major achievement—its first in several years—with the successful flight of the space shuttle, while the Soviets continued visits to its space station Salyut and launched an interplanetary probe due to land on Venus in early 1982.

The Solar System. U.S. and Soviet probe studies continued to reveal more about our nearest planetary neighbors. Scientists concluded that while Venus may have had lots of water during its first few hundred million years, the water was more likely vapor than liquid ocean. They base this on measurements of the ratio of deuterium to hydrogen on Venus made by the U.S. Pioneer Multiprobe. The Pioneer Venus orbiter also provided data on Venusian weather. Frederick L. Scarf of TRW Incorporated suggests that observed "whistlers" on Venus are probably associated with volcanoes in the northern hemisphere Beta region and with the continent-sized Aphrodite headland. Scarf and William J. Borucki of the NASA Ames Research Center also suggest that Venus has the same lightning levels as earth—an idea disputed by Soviet V. A. Krasnopolsky whose study of Venera lander data suggests that there is more lightning on Venus than on earth. ■ Mars history was also elucidated a bit more—thanks to pictures provided by the Viking orbiter. It seems that earlier locations of the poles on Mars are now near the planet's equator and that the present poles were established after the huge Tharsis rise was formed on the planet's surface.

A large array of antennas are used by The Group for Decametric Radio Astronomy at an observatory in Nancy, France, to study solar and planetary decametric emissions.

Group for Decametric Radio Astronomy, Meudon Observatory

Continued analysis of observations of Jupiter and its environs made by the U.S. Pioneer probe (1976) and Voyager 2 (1979) revealed further details about the planet. Jupiter's magnetotail is believed to be a long, fat cylinder with a length equivalent to about 10,000 times the radius of Jupiter and a width of about 400 radii. It points away from the sun or perhaps sideways and may form in long filaments. Saturn probably passes through this large magnetotail from time to time. ■ Alex Dessler of Rice University suggests a new model to explain several of Jupiter's oddities. He suggests that there is a large weak spot in the northern hemisphere of Jupiter's magnetic field. Io, Jupiter's volcanically active satellite, ejects sulfur and oxygen that form a doughnut-shaped region around Jupiter. The doughnut bulges outward on one side and dips inward on the other. Electric current flowing along Jupiter's magnetic field lines is enhanced in these regions and creates the unusual radio bursts that have been observed. ■ And Jupiter will be in for even more study—this time from earth. The Group for Decametric Radio Astronomy of Meudon Observatory in France has finished a ground-based telescope to study Jupiter. Containing 144 helical (spiral) antennas, the telescope is about 100 times more sensitive than other similar telescopes and can track Jupiter for up to ten hours a day, rather than just for a few minutes.

Saturn revealed some of its secrets but kept other of its mysteries unsolved as Voyager 2 completed its flyby in August 1981. (See "A Last Look at Saturn," on page 11.)

The peculiar object, called Chiron, discovered by astronomer Charles Kowal in 1977 in the region between Saturn and Uranus was also studied during the year. It could be satellitelike or it could be asteroidlike, though it is far from the normal region for asteroids and is larger, some 310 to 400 kilometers (approximately 195 to 250 miles) across, than most asteroids. Orbital analyses indicate that it has come into the solar system from the "Oort cloud," the region beyond Pluto where comets may originate. ■ An unidentified comet apparently fell into the sun. Donald J. Michels and colleagues at the U.S. Naval Research Laboratory recently found evidence on a photograph made on August 30, 1979. ■ And Neptune may have a small additional satellite—about 100 kilometers (60 miles) across—so say University of Arizona observers.

Our Galaxy—the Milky Way. Several new objects formed or were recognized in the Milky Way during the year. The object GL 618 may, for example, be the site of a new planetary nebula forming. The object is ejecting an atmosphere, forming a nebula, and collapsing into a small hot white dwarf. ■ The hottest known white dwarf may also have been found. It is part of BE Ursae Majoris, now thought to be a white dwarf with a cool companion, not an eclipsing binary as previously supposed. Work on pulsars continues. Although each pulsar is unique, pulsars do have some features in common. Their pulsing periods range from 33 milliseconds to 4.2 seconds and they shut down after a few million years. Probably a new pulsar is born every 180 years or so. There are probably about 500,000 to 1,000,000 in the Milky Way alone.

The Universe. Quasars, those unusual starlike objects, were again the object of much study. Although many scientists disagreed with the 1968 explanation by Jeno and Madeleine Barothy that quasars might be optical illusions caused by a gravitational lens, theoretical support for this suggestion has been provided recently. The general theory of relativity predicts that light rays from a distant object bend as they pass through the gravitational field of a dense, heavy object. In the proper conditions, a dense object acts as a lens and creates several images, sometimes amplified, of a distant object. Perhaps quasars are created by the passing of light through a galaxy or other similarly massive object. And quasars have been found in association with galaxies—quasar 3C345, near another quasar, may be sustained by a rich cluster of galaxies, and there is a cluster of quasars near the galaxy M82, according to recent observational reports.

The mass of the star R 136a in the center of the Tarantula Nebula in the Large Magellanic Cloud, one of the galaxies nearest ours, was calculated to be 3,000 times that of the sun. This makes it the most massive star ever found. The mass was deduced from the brightness and class of the star using ultraviolet observations.

The perennial question of whether the universe is open or closed remains. Recent studies concentrate on neutrinos and whether they have mass. (Neutrinos are elementary particles that have long been thought to be massless.) Some researchers, analyzing data on known neutrino lifetimes and on how much of the mass of the universe is known, conclude that the universe is open and will expand outward infinitely. Others disagree, pointing out that if a species of neutrino is found to have mass— and one is suspected to exist—then the total mass of the universe would be enough for the universe to be closed—expanding for a certain time and then collapsing. ■ The age of the universe was also studied. Some investigators, using data on optical galaxies associated with radio sources, recalculated the age of the universe at 18,000,000,000 years—much older than previous estimates.

UPI

A scientist stands beneath one of the world's largest telescopes, which will be used to survey the southern sky from Siding Spring Observatory in New South Wales, Australia.

The space shuttle Columbia, the first reusable, manned spacecraft ever flown, is seen here making a perfect landing at Edwards Air Force Base in California.

NASA

NASA

Space twins called Dynamics Explorer satellites are being used to study the magnetosphere, ionosphere, and other energy sources responsible for auroral displays and radio interference.

The Palomar Sky Survey is being updated. Originally made between 1949 and 1957 this greatest of all surveys of the sky is being repeated. The new study will have four times the sensitivity of the first survey and will include full coverage of the southern sky.

Katherine Haramundanis

The Space Shuttle. On April 12, 1981, a revolutionary new spaceship was launched into an orbit of earth. This was the space shuttle Columbia, the first reusable manned space vehicle ever flown. Its inaugural flight, after nine years of development and testing at a cost of $10,000,000,-000 was the highlight of the year in space flight.

The Columbia, a winged vehicle the size of a DC-9 jetliner, was piloted by John W. Young and Robert L. Crippen—the first U.S. astronauts to fly in space since 1975. They tested the craft's maneuverability and performance during a 54½ hour mission from liftoff at the Kennedy Space Center in Florida to landing on the desert at Edwards Air Force Base in California, on April 14, 1981.

A second Columbia mission followed in November 1981. Astronauts Joe H. Engle and Richard H. Truly rode the Columbia into orbit on November 12, the first flight of a used spacecraft. Their plans for a five-day mission were frustrated by a fuel-cell failure, forcing an early return on November 14, 1981. Nevertheless, the U.S. National Aeronautics and Space Administration (NASA) said that 90 per cent of the mission objectives were achieved, including operation of the shuttle's first scientific payload and tests of a remotely-controlled mechanical arm.

Two more test flights of Columbia are scheduled before the shuttle is expected to be ready for regular operation missions. The second of four planned shuttles—the Challenger—should be delivered to NASA in the summer of 1982. (See "The Space Shuttle," on page 34.)

Other U.S. Space Work. Unmanned U.S. operations in space featured the Voyager 2 flyby of Saturn. The spacecraft came within 100,000 kilometers (63,000 miles) of the planet's cloud tops on August 25, 1981 and examined in detail the surfaces of most of the known satellites of Saturn. Voyager 2 is now cruising toward a 1986 rendezvous with Uranus.

Two scientific missions were launched during 1981. On August 3 a Delta rocket deposited two Dynamics Explorer satellites in separate polar orbits to observe how energy from the sun enters the earth's atmosphere and interacts with the earth's magnetic field. On October 6, 1981 a Solar Mesosphere Explorer satellite was placed in orbit for detailed studies of the sun's effect on the formation and destruction of ozone in the earth's upper atmosphere.

Other U.S. missions—a total of 18 were launched in 1981—included communications, weather, navigation, and military reconnaissance sat-

NASA

The Solar Mesosphere Explorer is an atmospheric research satellite designed to study the photochemical and transport processes associated with atmospheric ozone concentrations.

ellites. ■ Two aging satellites came to the end of their lives: the High Energy Astronomy Observatory (HEAO) 2 ran out of control gas in June, and HEAO-3 in August. ■ Looking to the future, NASA designated the Johns Hopkins University as the site for the Space Telescope Institute, where scientific operations of the telescope will be directed after the huge instrument with its 94-inch (240-centimeter) mirror is placed in orbit by the shuttle in 1985.

Soviet Space Work. The Soviet Union continued its brisk launching rate—98 in 1981, only one short of its record in 1976. More than one-half of these were military reconnaissance satellites, but Soviet emphasis on long-duration manned flight also remained strong.

On March 12 two cosmonauts, Vladimir Kovalyonok and Viktor Savinykh, were launched aboard Soyuz T-4, which docked with the Salyut 6 space station that has been in orbit since 1977. They remained in space 75 days, until May 26, receiving short visits by two pairs of cosmonauts. (Eighteen crews have now occupied Salyut 6.) On March 22 Vladimir Dzhanibekov and a Mongolian pilot Jugderdemidiyn Gurragcha, were launched on a six-day mission in Soyuz 39. Another six-day mission, by Leonid Popov and the Rumanian cosmonaut Dumitru Prunariu on Soyuz 40, also included a visit to the space station. In June, a 30,000-pound unmanned vehicle, designated Cosmos 1267, linked up with Salyut 6 in what U.S. space experts believe was a test in assembling large space structures from modules.

Tass from Sovfoto

Soviet Union cosmonauts Vladimir Kovalyonok (top), commander, and flight engineer Viktor Savinykh, remained in space for 75 days in 1981 aboard the spacecraft Soyuz T-4.

The only two new interplanetary probes were Soviet—Venera 13 and 14. Launched separately in late October and early November 1981, the spacecraft were expected to reach Venus in March 1982 and deploy landers, one targeted for the Venusian lowlands and another for the highlands. (A U.S. spacecraft, Pioneer Venus 1, continued to orbit Venus and return data.)

European Space Activities. Western Europe moved ahead with its efforts to develop an independent launching capability. The European Space Agency (ESA), an 11-nation consortium, fired its Ariane rocket on a successful third flight on June 19, 1981, thus setting the program back on track after a 1980 rocket failure. The Ariane, launched from a base in French Guiana, placed two spacecraft in orbit—Europe's Meteosat 2, a weather satellite, and India'a Apple communications test satellite. Then, on December 20, another Ariane was equally successful, thrusting into orbit the European Maritime Communications Satellite (Marecs A). Following these two tests, ESA declared the Ariane launchers qualified for full operations. The rocket is a three-stage system using conventional technology and designed, unlike the U.S. space shuttle, to destroy itself in the process of boosting payloads into orbit. With Ariane the Europeans expect to seize a share of the growing business in launching communications satellites as well as expand their scientific exploration of space. A private company known as Arianespace, owned by European banks, aerospace companies, and the French government, has been established to operate the rocket program.

The Ariane, successfully launched and tested by the European Space Agency, is a rocket that self-destructs upon boosting payloads into orbit.

ESA

Space Activities of Other Countries. China, India, and Japan also conducted satellite launchings in 1981 using their own rockets. China successfully boosted three experimental satellites into orbit with a single rocket on September 19. India launched its fourth satellite, Rehina 2, with a small rocket on May 31. Japan used its rocket to launch three satellites—Kiku 3, an engineering test vehicle, and Astro A for solar studies, in February; and Mimawari 2, a meteorological satellite, in August.

John Noble Wilford

© William Hartmann

The sun casts a dull, reddish glow over Io's barren landscape from behind the ringed planet Jupiter, where it is almost totally obscured in eclipse.

© William Hartmann

Io's thin surface covering of sulfur-dioxide ice is evaporated in minutes by the heat of the mid-morning sun. Note the volcano in the background.

THE VIEW FROM IO

by William K. Hartmann

WHAT will those pioneers see—those lucky humans who step out of the first manned lander on Io and shuffle across the cindery surface to place a seismograph on some outcropping? We've already learned that the skies and surface of Io hold some of the most stunning visual effects in the solar system, though few of us will live long enough to see the pictures from the first robot lander. But, from the preliminary reconnaissance of the U.S. Voyager missions to Jupiter, we now know enough that we can travel to Io via our imagination.

BIZARRE WORLD

What distinguishes Io and makes it a world of dramatic sky and landscape? First and foremost, it simply isn't like other planets or the rest of Jupiter's moons. Even though they turned out to be strange worlds (at least by the standards of those of us who grew up breathing air, walking on a surface of silicate soil, dangling our toes in liquid water pools), nothing had prepared us for Io. It may qualify as the most bizarre of the nearly two dozen worlds we've seen at close range.

The sodium torus glows in the sky over Io's colorful plains of volcanic rubble. The plains may heat up to −145° C (−230° F) in the afternoon sun.

Toward sunset, Jupiter is a full disk of tannish and orange hues in the sky. When night falls, the temperature plunges as low as −195°C (−320°F).

From space, Io is mottled with orange, yellow, red, and white patches, and pocked with blackish spots. One Voyager team scientist remarked that although he didn't know what was wrong with Io, it looked as though it could be fixed with a shot of penicillin. Another remarked that Io looks like one of those planets we used to laugh at in grade "B" sci-fi thrillers.

VOLCANOS . . . AND MORE VOLCANOS

Io has volcanos. Voyager 1 "saw" a total of eight plumes shooting 70 to 280 kilometers (nearly 50 to 180 miles) above the surface, raining material across as much as 1000 kilometers (600 miles) of Io's surface. The plumes erupt—with incredible violence— from Io's volcanic vents at velocities of 1,800 to 3,600 kilometers (1,100 to 2,200 miles) per hour. Four months later, when Voyager 2 flew by Io, at least six of these volcanos were still active.

The blackish colored spots are volcanic calderas, the irregularly-shaped holes left by many volcanic eruptions. Flows of many-colored material have poured onto the surface and spread across large areas. So many simultaneous eruptions—at a level of volcanic activity unheard of on earth—qualify Io as the most volcanic body in the solar system.

The surface color of Io is thought to come not from the ice or rock of other worlds, but from sulfur and sulfurous compounds vented from Io's interior. The colors

© William Hartmann

Io's landscape is illuminated more brilliantly by the last quarter of Jupiter in the night sky than the glow of 200 quarter moons on our planet.

include the familiar yellow sulfur of earth's volcanic areas. However, because the color of sulfur and its compounds depends on temperature as well as composition, virtually every shade of red, orange, yellow, and brown is represented on Io's surface.

Furthermore, Io does not have one important kind of feature which we have come to expect on planets—craters. Billions of years ago, Io was surely as cratered as the other moons and planets, but the fall of ash and flow of sulfur lava could bury every trace of an Io crater in a million years at most.

AN IO DAY

Think of what you might expect if you were aboard a spacecraft that had just landed on Io. First the sky: Io keeps one side toward Jupiter, just as the moon keeps one side toward earth. This means that Jupiter must dominate the sky as seen from one side of Io, and always hangs in the same sector. From Io, Jupiter is enormous: it covers 1,600 times as much of the ionian sky as the moon does in our earthly sky.

Io's day, that is, the interval from one sunrise to the next, is equal to its "year," or the period of revolution around Jupiter— about 42 hours. Each "day," the interval from sunrise to sunset, lasts about 21 hours. But because Jupiter covers such a large part of the sky, the sun spends about 6 per cent of each day, nearly 2½ hours, in total eclipse behind Jupiter.

Suppose we were to spend a whole "day" on Io. What would we see? Let's start in the morning, at some place where the sun is behind the great mass of Jupiter in the sky, and Io's landscape is in darkness.

9 A.M., LOCAL IO TIME

The atmosphere of Jupiter is back-lit, and shows up as a dull-glowing, sunset-red ring in the sky. This, in turn, illuminates the scene before us with a dull red glow. Because Io has negligible atmosphere, the sky is space-black. On the ground is something we didn't see from orbit: a thin coating of snow or frost glistening in the faint light. With the light of the sun cut off, the ground is cold, and something has frozen on it.

10:00 A.M., LOCAL IO TIME

Finally the eclipse ends. As the sun emerges from behind Jupiter, it begins to warm the frigid landscape. The temperature "soars" toward 125 Kelvin (−145° Celsius, or −230° Fahrenheit). We suddenly realize that Io is manifesting yet another phenomenon: the "post-eclipse" brightening.

In the mid-1960's, astronomers Alan Binder and Dale Cruikshank monitored the brightness of Io before and after its eclipses, hoping to discover whether Io had an atmosphere. Their reasoning was that during the cold eclipse period, clouds, fog, or frost might condense and last for a few minutes after the eclipse, causing Io to be brighter than usual for those few minutes. Sure enough, they found that Io was often lighter than usual for 10 to 15 minutes after an eclipse. As other observers checked this result, it became clear that it did not happen after every eclipse—only sometimes. This shed doubt on the phenomenon, and when later data showed Io has virtually no atmosphere, the phenomenon was put on the back burner reserved for unresolved curiosities.

Voyager, however, may have provided an explanation. Among the volcanic materials erupted on Io is believed to be sulfur dioxide. Sulfur dioxide can condense into a whitish frost or snow when the temperature drops. Calculations suggest that if several large volcanos happen to be erupting during an eclipse, enough sulfur dioxide might condense on the orange or red volcanic plain to brighten the overall appearance of Io. Thus, for just a few minutes after the eclipse ends, we see a light-colored sulfur-dioxide frost deposit covering the surface in front of us.

3:00 P.M., LOCAL IO TIME

Some 10½ earth hours later, Io has moved a quarter of an orbit around Jupiter. The frost has long since burned off under the sun, and the yellows and oranges of Io's normal surface are prominent. Jupiter is now lit from the side by the sun, in the phase resembling earth's "first quarter" moon. Then we notice another of Io's surprises: a faint yellowish glow in the sky, first discovered from earth by Harvard astronomer Robert Brown.

A large, thin, gas cloud of sodium, sulfur, and other atoms surrounds Io. Io orbits inside the Van Allen radiation belts around Jupiter, and energetic atoms trapped in the belts strike Io's surface and knock atoms loose. Other atoms are spewed into space by Io's volcanic eruptions. As they escape Io, these atoms diffuse out into a cloud. This cloud is many Io-diameters wide and stretches forward and backward along Io's orbit. Where sunlight strikes the atoms, it excites them, and they absorb energy momentarily, then re-emit it at the same wavelength. Sodium atoms, in particular, absorb and re-emit the yellow light of "sodium D."

Now the physics gets complex: the sun's atmosphere absorbs much of the sodium D light leaving the sun, so that this wavelength is almost absent in the light coming from the

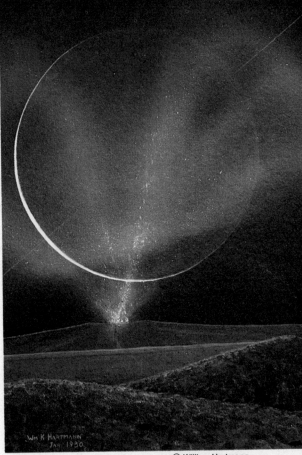

© William Hartmann

Just before dawn, a volcano on Io's darkened surface erupts, shooting a plume of sulfurous ash and gas high into the sky. Jupiter is just a crescent.

sun. We would expect that sodium atoms would not be excited, and therefore would not glow. However, when Io is moving toward or away from the sun (as it is one-fourth and three-fourths of the way around the orbit from the "noon" position), the sodium atoms absorb sunlight of slightly longer or shorter wavelength than the solar sodium D line, and there is plenty of sunlight at those wavelengths. Therefore, at the quarter positions in the orbit, Io's sodium cloud glows an unmistakable faint yellow. In brightness, it resembles a moderately bright aurora on earth.

9 P.M., LOCAL IO TIME

About 10½ earth hours later, Io is halfway around the orbit, between Jupiter and the sun. The sodium glow is now gone from

In a scene from the movie "Outland," actor Sean Connery plays the part of a Federal district marshal who has been assigned to a hermetically-sealed mining camp on Io.

the sky. Jupiter is "full"—a dazzling yellow, orange, and tan disk with complex ever-changing cloud patterns, like the famous Red Spot storm system.

By coincidence, the 10½-hour period needed for Io's quarter-trip around Jupiter is nearly equal to Jupiter's rotation period, so Jupiter displays the same cloud patterns again—except for the changes due to the weather systems on the massive planet. As we face Jupiter, the sun is at our back, and the vivid landscape is illuminated by the low sun as shadows stretch away from us toward the huge planet.

3 A.M., LOCAL IO TIME

The sun has set at our location. We have now traveled three-fourths of the way around the orbit and Jupiter is in its "third quarter" phase. Again we see the yellow sodium glow in the sky, perhaps a bit brighter now—depending on the amount of volcanic gas emitted in the last few days. In the cold of night, some sulfur-dioxide frost may have formed again, but it's hard to see it because the landscape is illuminated only by the dull yellow light of Jupiter itself.

6 A.M., LOCAL IO TIME

Perhaps just before dawn, a nearby volcano erupts. Jupiter is a crescent in the sky. We gaze in awe as the volcanic plume shoots up from the darkened surface, where we are, and into the light of the sun. How high is the plume? Maybe 100 kilometers (60 miles)—perhaps 200 (120 miles). The delicate traceries of sulfurous ash and gas glow in the predawn sky, while the shadow of Io falls across the lower part of the plume.

A REAL VISIT SOMEDAY

So far no one has stood on the plains of Io to see the views or feel the ground tremble as the volcanos explode. But if we humans do manage to establish a viable planetary economy, if we don't blow ourselves up or imprison ourselves forever on a resource-exhausted planet, the day may come when, heavily shielded from Jupiter's radiation environment, humans will see the sights of Io—not through spacecraft instruments or paintings, but with their own eyes □

SELECTED READINGS

"Far-out eruptive volcanoes (Io)" by S. P. Maran. *Natural History,* September 1980.

"Io: ground-based observations of hot spots" by W. M. Sinton and others. *Science,* November 28, 1980.

"Io: longitudinal distribution of SO$_2$ frost" by R. M. Nelson. *Science,* November 14, 1980.

"Volcanic origin of eruptive plumes on Io" by A. F. Cook. *Science,* March 27, 1981.

False-color images taken by Voyager 1 (left) and Voyager 2 (right) show how features in Saturn's northern hemisphere have changed in the nine months between encounters.

A LAST LOOK AT SATURN

by J. Kelly Beatty

NOW we see Phoebe, Saturn's outermost satellite. Although it looks much like other small objects in orbit around Saturn, Phoebe is really quite unusual. First, its surface is very dark, reflecting only about five per cent of the sunlight that strikes it. Second, this moon travels east to west (retrograde) along an orbit that is highly inclined to Saturn's equator and almost four times farther away from its parent planet than its nearest neighbor, Iapetus. None of Saturn's other satellites have these characteristics, and most astronomers believe that Phoebe is probably a visitor that strayed too close to Saturn and became captured by the giant planet's gravitational field.

The scientists who planned Voyager 2's dash past Saturn on August 25, 1981, knew all of this about Phoebe long before the encounter. Even so, they went to great pains to photograph the moon, and from the images they learned that it is round, considerably larger than expected—about 220 kilometers (125 miles) across—and rotates with a period of 9–10 hours. Bradford Smith, the leader of Voyager's imaging-science team, was surprised by Phoebe's roundness, which is unusual for small bodies. Given that property and the moon's distinctive dark surface, he says, Voyager 2 may have stumbled upon the encrusted nucleus of a gigantic comet.

As with all of Voyager's investigations, this close-up of Phoebe required years of careful preparation. Yet, for all their planning, the scientists consider themselves fortunate to have Phoebe's image in hand. A malfunction in Voyager's scan platform almost eliminated their one chance to see this remote body.

A DEEP-SPACE MISSION

Launched almost exactly four years before its 1981 encounter with Saturn, Voyager 2 approached the planet on a trajectory cho-

Courtesy of Jet Propulsion Laboratory

The spectrum of colors in Saturn's ring system suggests variations in chemical composition from one region to another.

sen to complement the one taken earlier by Voyager 1. In particular, a number of satellites seen poorly by Voyager 1 were photographed from much closer range. A mammoth reprogramming effort after the first flyby assigned more of the precious hours near closest approach to observations of the unexpectedly dynamic ring system.

Voyager 2 traveled 2,228,957,024 kilometers (1,385,073,894 miles) to reach Saturn, at an average speed of nearly 64,000 kilometers (40,000 miles) per hour. During that time the primary communications receiver failed, its backup refused to remain locked onto one frequency, and a chipful of computer memory was lost. Despite these problems, the spacecraft operated well as it cruised from Jupiter to Saturn, and by encounter day mission personnel seemed confident of success. The spacecraft's targeting was so accurate—within 66 kilometers (41 miles) of its aim point—that a comparable feat would entail sinking an 800-kilometer (500-mile) putt (allowing the golfer a few trajectory corrections along the way).

The errant scan platform cost two Voyager science teams dearly: crucial ultraviolet measurements were lost during an occultation of the sun, and the imaging team will have to make do without the five highest-resolution mosaics planned for satellites Tethys and Enceladus. Even so, the spacecraft garnered upwards of one trillion bits of data about Saturn and its system, yielding the preliminary results presented here. Imaging scientist Richard Terrile smiled and sighed, "It's like drinking out of a fire hose; there's so much data coming in so fast."

RING MADNESS

It became obvious even before the first encounter that the rings of Saturn were more involved than anyone had anticipated. The outer F ring and spokelike streaks in the B ring were perhaps the biggest surprises, but the system as a whole was far more intricate than suggested by even the most suspect observations of terrestrial observers. Voyager 1 had recorded some 500–1,000 discrete ring features, and several investigators doubted that the second spacecraft would reveal finer dissections despite its closer, better-illuminated approach. They were wrong.

When the spacecraft's photopolarimeter tracked the light of the star Delta Scorpii, as the ring system passed through the line of sight, it found that even on a scale of 100 meters (yards) the rings are anything but featureless. The reemergence of Delta Scorpii from behind the A ring happened so abruptly that the photopolarimeter, viewing the edge of the ring at an oblique angle, could barely respond fast enough to record a nearly instantaneous jump in the signal. From this, scientists have estimated that the A ring is no more than 150 meters (yards) thick; 100 meters (yards) being more likely.

In more down-to-earth terms, a phonograph record would have to be more than 4 kilometers (2.5 miles) across to match the A ring's ratio of diameter to thickness. Earth-based observers have set the proper limit on thickness at one kilometer (0.6 mile), but that corresponds to the thickest cross-section—thinner spots are easily possible.

The explosion of fine detail sent theorists scurrying to find explanations of all the bands, gaps, waves, kinks, and general chaos they had seen. Ironically, in a broader context the rings still exhibit enough regional similarity to retain and extend the classical designations given them by telescopic observers. Moving outward from Saturn, these are D, C, B, A, F, G, and E.

Voyager 2 largely ignored some rings to concentrate its efforts on a few compelling enigmas that remained from the first flyby. For example, the D ring was glimpsed only briefly on this pass ("It is quite invisible from earth," says Smith), as was G. Most of the time allotted to rings fell to C, B, A, and F, with special emphasis on the dynamic complexity of the B ring, the spokes, and Cassini's division, the approximately 3,500-kilometer (2,200-mile) gap between rings A and B.

SEARCH FOR MOONLETS

As the spacecraft approached Saturn, investigators armed themselves with four possible explanations for the rings' appearance: resonances with external satellites, gravitational instabilities within the rings, density waves propagating through the system, and small embedded satellites ("moonlets") sweeping out particles along their paths. The idea of satellite resonances, or gravitational interactions, has long played a key role in ring models, but it is not a complete answer. Instabilities and waves may prove important, but these are not well understood.

By most accounts, the favorite hypothesis going in was one involving embedded moonlets. From detailed theoretical studies by several researchers, it was thought that small satellites could influence ring particles in their vicinity—through subtle gravitational interactions, creating clear gaps much wider than the satellites' diameters. Two slots in Cassini's division, observed by Voyager 1, seemed particularly well suited to this idea. Moonlets about 30 kilometers (20 miles) across would perform the sweeping nicely. With little time remaining before Voyager 2's encounter, the imaging team frantically reworked their picture-taking sequence to include a "movie" of sorts that would monitor these gaps for the implied objects.

Early checks of the time-lapse images turned up nothing. Smith was shaken by the news: "We were so certain that embedded satellites would be there." More analysis, and more bad news: with 90 per cent of the images totally scrutinized, researcher Jeffrey Cuzzi reported that nothing larger than about 5 kilometers (3 miles) across could be found. The theory was in trouble, said Smith. "We find ourselves at a point we had hoped not to be. We are now looking desperately for other solutions."

RESONANCE COUPLINGS

By that point, a number of team members had examined some of the most promising resonant locations within the rings, particularly a location calculated to be in a 2:1 lock with Mimas. At that distance, a particle orbiting the planet completes exactly two revolutions in the time Mimas completes one. Thus the particle always feels the great-

This computer-enhanced image shows the Encke Division as a dark gap in the golden A ring. The Cassini division appears blue at lower right.
Courtesy of Jet Propulsion Laboratory

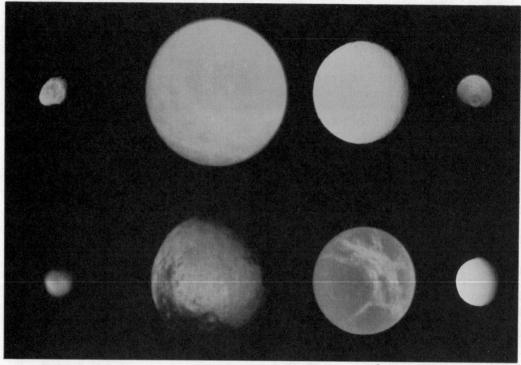

Eight of Saturn's satellites are shown to scale (from top left to bottom right): Hyperion, Rhea, Tethys, Mimas, Phoebe, Iapetus, Dione, and Enceladus.

est tug from Mimas at the same location along its orbit. This resonance has been invoked often to explain Cassini's division, and Voyager 1 refined the location of the resonance to somewhere near the gap's inner edge.

The surprising conclusion from Voyager 2 is that the resonance is most effective on the outer edge of the B ring. There gravitational forces apparently distort its boundary into a giant ellipse that precesses in space every 22½ hours (one orbital period of Mimas). The push-pull action of the rotating ellipse pumps energy into the rings, and the images show that the major axis of the elliptical edge points 90° away from Mimas—exactly opposite the sense of tides in the earth-moon system. "One of the neatest things we've found!" exulted a team member.

Other resonant locations may ultimately be certified within the rings, but investigators need to determine the exact distances of specific ring features from Saturn. However, Allan Cook, who has been attacking the resonance problem with Fred Franklin, says

such couplings cannot possibly explain everything seen in the system. Meanwhile, strong evidence has begun to emerge for the existence of wave phenomena within Cassini's division and elsewhere. The Voyager investigators now speak in terms of a combination of interrelated mechanisms to create alternating ringlets and "gaplets."

B'S SPOKES

Among Voyager 1's many revelations, the identification of crosscutting streaks, or spokes, within the B ring was perhaps the most mystifying. These features appear dark when viewed by reflected (backscattered) light and bright in the forwardscattered direction. This combination indicates powder-size dust or ice grains. Voyager 2 even recorded them on the underside of the B ring, raising the question of whether they occur on both sides or simply show through from the ring's illuminated side. The evidence is not yet conclusive, but Terrile confides. "I'd put money down that we're seeing dark-side spokes illuminated by Saturnshine."

Aided by improved viewing angles and ring illumination during the approach, Voyager 2's time-lapse movie revealed the features evolving from frame to frame. It was as if some source were painting them onto the B ring over the course of 15 minutes to an hour. "I feel that the spokes are trying to tell us something," commented Smith after one of the first screenings.

The scientists' working hypothesis holds that the spokes form radially to Saturn, then shear out as if they were orbiting ring particles. Terrile hopes to find a spoke with a radial trailing edge in consecutive images, thereby linking the creative process to the planet itself. If he succeeds, it may mean that electromagnetic sources charge microscopic grains in the B ring and trigger the spokes' formation.

F RING

Not forgotten in Voyager 2's reconnaissance was the F ring, discovered by Pioneer 11 during its 1979 rendezvous. Although some high-resolution coverage of the ring was lost during the flyby, three particular segments tracked by the spacecraft show none of the twisted and braided craziness observed by Voyager 1. Kinks of perturbed material were expected near F's attendant moons, 1980 S 26 and 1980 S 27. These "shepherd moons" straddle the ring and have been thought to provide the gravitational forces necessary to keep the wispy ring cohesive. But the ring appears undisturbed by the presence of the moons. And that, together with the faint glow of material found well inside the most obvious ring strands, may pose complications for the generally accepted "guardian satellite" method for narrowly confining the ring.

MAGNETIC BUBBLE

Saturn's magnetic field surrounds the planet as a voluminous bubble that extends away from the sun something akin to a wind sock. Outside this magnetosphere is the domain of the solar wind, a plasma of protons, electrons, and heavier ions that spews from the solar atmosphere at 400 kilometers (250 miles) per second. When it reaches Saturn's (or any other) magnetosphere, the wind's response is—literally—one of shock, as it abruptly changes direction to avoid an electromagnetic "collision." This chaotic redirection occurs in a zone called the bow shock. At Saturn the average location of the bow shock is 1,800,000 kilometers (1,125,000 miles) from the planet. The edge of the magnetosphere itself usually lies some 500,000 kilometers (312,500 miles) closer to Saturn, but both features ebb and flow with changes in the solar-wind's intensity.

Inside the Saturnian magnetosphere, field lines twirl around the magnetic axis, becoming more concentrated near the planet. Magnetospheres are largely vacuous, even more so than interplanetary space, but are not totally empty. For instance, some solar wind manages to leak in, preferentially at the magnetic poles where the magnetosphere is most vulnerable. Satellites, rings, and other sources add contributions which, if they become ionized, are lashed by the rotating magnetic field lines and entrained by them, in the manner of the earth's Van Allen belts.

A color composite of Titan shows distinct bands of color, which are associated with cloud circulation in the Saturnian moon's atmosphere.
Courtesy of Jet Propulsion Laboratory

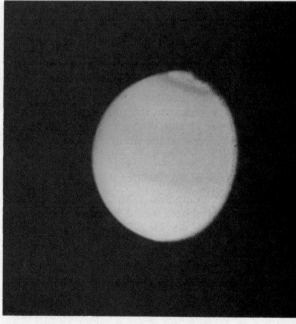

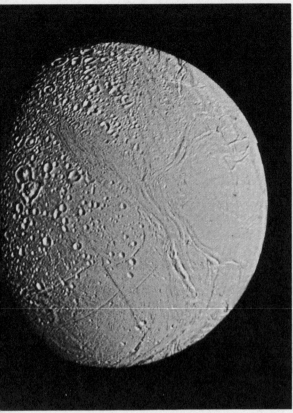

Courtesy of Jet Propulsion Laboratory

This high-resolution image of Enceladus, Saturn's brightest and smoothest moon, shows ancient craters, grooves, and other surface details.

Such trapped radiation creates a complex and energetic electromagnetic environment within the boundaries of the magnetosphere. During its August 1981 flyby, Voyager 2 spent five days crossing this near-void, tuning in its detectors to a wide range of particle energies and radiation frequencies. Yet, despite the previous soundings of Pioneer 11 and Voyager 1, project scientists now agree that the situation is more complicated than they had suspected.

TWO SPECIAL TORUSES

A composite sketch of the Saturnian magnetosphere would begin with Titan, an enormous satellite with a dense atmosphere of mostly nitrogen. Titan lies 1,222,000 kilometers (763,750 miles) from Saturn, distant enough to become exposed to the solar wind roughly 20 per cent of the time. During the remainder, it lies inside Saturn's magnetosphere and provides a source of both neutral and ionized molecules from its upper atmosphere. Ultraviolet studies during all three flybys of Saturn noted the presence of a huge torus, or doughnut-shaped ring, of neutral hydrogen extending inward from Titan to the orbit of the satellite Rhea. Titan has been implicated as the most likely source of this torus.

Another torus—this one containing charged plasma—lies inside Rhea's orbit. The plasma's ions and electrons spiral up and down magnetic field lines like beads on a string, all the while moving with the field as it rotates with Saturn. The spiraling plasma is itself magnetic and contributes to the local magnetic field.

ODD RADIO NOISES

Once inside the orbit of the satellite Dione, both Voyagers detected at least two distinct kinds of radio noise that could not reach the spacecraft when it was outside the plasma torus. One signal, involving frequencies of a few kilohertz, apparently emanates from regions adjacent to Mimas, Enceladus, and other inner satellites. The other, much more impulsive and powerful in nature, may well originate as massive electrostatic discharges within the ring system. The radio spectra of these percussive pops reminded one scientist of terrestrial lightning, but he noted two important differences: the Saturnian source is 10,000–100,000 times more powerful, and it was not detected visually.

One other electromagnetic disturbance was discovered that should keep Voyager scientists busy for some time. As the spacecraft crossed the ring plane, it passed through what one shocked investigator termed a ring of charged dust impacting at 13 kilometers (8 miles) per second, causing some of its sensors to jump orders of magnitude.

AND SATELLITES, TOO

While others concerned themselves with whizzing particles, swirling clouds, and exotic ring phenomena, the geologists among Voyager's scientists were preoccupied with high-resolution images of three major satellites (Enceladus, Tethys, and Iapetus), the first good images of eight smaller bodies, and another set extending the coverage of Titan begun with Voyager 1. None of them even seemed disappointed that the scan-platform trouble had cost them five mosaics of Tethys and Enceladus. With images of 17 satellites in hand, there was enough new data to keep everyone happy. (And latest analyses of Voyager 2 data suggest there are at least 21 satellites in the Saturnian family.)

TITAN

Like its predecessor, Voyager 2 encountered Titan before it passed Saturn. Smith called it "a rather uninspiring orange ball," even though some subtle atmospheric changes had apparently taken place between the two flybys. But photopolarimeter experimenters were elated by Titan, hailing it as "one of the most fantastic bodies in the solar system."

What brings joy to some and yawns to others is the dense atmosphere surrounding Titan. The first Voyager passed within 4,000 kilometers (2,500 miles) of the cloud tops and learned that the atmospheric pressure at the moon's surface is more than 1½ times greater than on the earth. The opaque hazes are laced with at least 10 organic compounds, including propane, acetylene, and hydrogen cyanide. Recently, Robert Samuelson and his colleagues reevaluated Voyager 1's infrared data, which suggests that the predominantly nitrogen-methane atmosphere may also contain up to 12 per cent argon and a minute amount of molecular hydrogen.

Titan's orange color arises from droplets or crystals suspended some 100 to 200 kilometers (60 to 125 miles) above the surface—a level well-suited to inspection by the photopolarimeter. Two separate populations of spherical particles at different altitudes provide good matches to Voyager's observations, but other indications point to particles of a third size or even to nonspherical, heter-

A false-color representation of Saturn's northern hemisphere reveals turbulent weather, including flowing spots with anti-cyclonic rotation and ribbonlike jet streams.

Courtesy of Jet Propulsion Laboratory

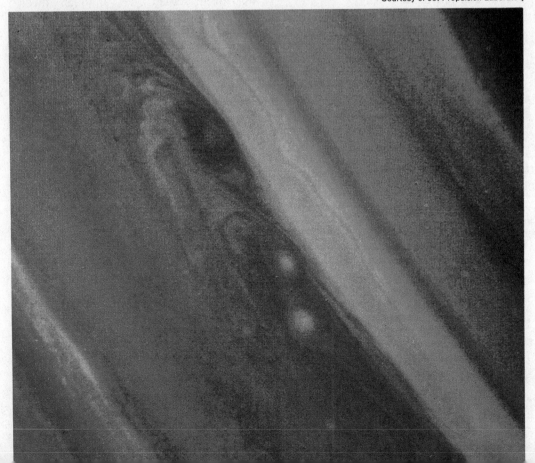

Courtesy of Jet Propulsion Laboratory

Fine strands are visible in Saturn's mysterious F ring in this computer representation of a stellar occultation profile compiled by Voyager 2.

ogeneous mixtures. "This is a dilemma first faced by Pioneer 11," notes team member Robert West, who is working with others on computer models that will try to fit the data to the right combination of particle sizes, shapes, and vertical distribution.

Another approach to the nature of Titan's hazes has been under way for some time at Cornell University. There Carl Sagan and Bishun Khare simply take a simulated atmosphere (in this case, nitrogen and methane), energize the mixture with sparks or radiation, and watch what happens. So far they have been able to produce almost all of the gases found in Titan's atmosphere. They believe that the basic component of Titan's haze is a very complex hydrocarbon chain, which Sagan terms a "tholin" (derived from the Greek work for tar).

TETHYS AND ENCELADUS

If Titan was visually unimpressive, other Saturnian moons surveyed at close range by Voyager 2 offered a wealth of exciting detail. Tethys has an ancient, cratered surface with one major distinguishing feature: an enormous rift that extends roughly 270° around the satellite. On other worlds such a feature would imply dynamic internal activity. But Tethys' fracture probably occurred very early in its lifetime, as the watery

interior froze and expanded, breaking the overlying crust of ice. Such expansion would have added five to ten per cent to the total surface area—just about matching that contained within the rift zone.

Voyager 2 revealed a more complex geologic history on Enceladus, an inner moon comparable in size to Mimas. Geologist Laurence Soderblom finds at least five distinct evolutionary episodes recorded in its surface, from ancient cratered plains to patches lacking any discernible craters at all. Some sections are reminiscent of grooved terrain on Ganymede, one of Jupiter's icy satellites. But the craterless areas, estimated to be no more than 100,000,000 years old, may be most indicative of Enceladus' history. Soderblom makes this observation: "The important point is that 100,000,000 years is only about two per cent of all geologic history. It's very unlikely that a planet would be active geologically for 98 per cent of its history and abruptly stop. It's much more likely that Enceladus is still active today."

Just exactly what "active" means has not been settled yet, although theorist Charles Yoder calculates that tidal heating induced by Saturn and the satellite Dione could play a significant role. Several researchers have proposed resurfacing mechanisms that range from methane geysers to pockets of subsurface water that occasionally breach overlying crusts of thin ice. Soderblom's conclusion that Enceladus is active also finds support in the tenuous E ring surrounding the satellite and concentrated near its orbit. To clinch the connection, astronomers will have to study the E ring from earth and verify that its particles consist of water ice, which would implicate Enceladus as their ongoing source.

IAPETUS

The outermost of Saturn's large satellites is Iapetus, an object that has eluded explanation since its discovery in 1671. What astronomers find so puzzling about this body was apparent then and is obvious from its photographs now—one half of Iapetus is bright, reflecting about 50 per cent of the light that falls on it, and the other is near-black, reflecting only four or five per cent. Moreover, the dark hemisphere neatly coincides with the half of Iapetus that faces the forward direction of orbital motion.

Voyager scientists offered three possible explanations for this strangeness. The satellite is known to be mostly ice, and the dark material could have erupted to the surface from within. This idea would explain dark-filled craters seen in the bright hemisphere, but makes the leading hemisphere's coating a matter of coincidence. Perhaps Iapetus long ago acquired an even layer of bright frost over a dark surface. With time, collisions and sputtering by high-energy particles on the forward-facing half would erode away the frost and reexpose the dark surface below.

Or did the satellite acquire its dark surface from some exterior source? Specifically, Phoebe lies outside the orbit of Iapetus and is comparably dark. Material blasted from Phoebe's surface during impacts by other objects would eventually spiral toward Saturn, and some would accumulate on Iapetus' leading hemisphere. Yet this scenario fails to provide adequately for the dark-floored craters.

Each theory has its proponents, but even Voyager 2's much-improved imagery may not be good enough for the scientists to reach a consensus. One point is certain: the dark material on Iapetus is very dark and slightly red, a combination matched only by certain organic materials—particularly those found occasionally in carbonaceous chondrite meteorites. Or, as radio scientist Von Eshleman put it, "the possibility that a portion of Iapetus is as dark as pitch ... is because it's pitch."

YEARS OF UNCERTAINTY

During the evenings nearest to the Voyager 2 flyby, Brad Smith watched Saturn close to within three degrees of Venus and Jupiter—by astronomical coincidence, this same trio converged in the morning twilight during the Voyager 1 encounter with Saturn in November 1980. And as Saturn hung low in the evening twilight, Smith reflected on the changes Voyager has brought to planetary science: "I've spent 10 to 20 years trying to eke out just a little bit more information from ground-based telescopes and it's a very

Courtesy of Jet Propulsion Laboratory

Multiple ringlets look like threads running through Encke's division, a narrow gap in the outer A ring.

difficult task. Saturn is a billion miles away—a very, very difficult object to observe. So for me, it's enormously exciting to see something close up that I've tried so hard to see over the years."

Voyager will provide the scientific fodder for hundreds of researchers over the next few years, but Smith's attention is already turning to the targets that lie ahead. Voyager 2 is now on its way to Uranus, due to arrive in 1986. If Saturn is difficult to observe, Uranus and Neptune lie somewhere near impossible. "Do you realize," he points out, "that these planets are no larger in a telescope than Jupiter's Great Red Spot?" Knowing how that feature appeared through Voyager's television eyes, one can only imagine anxiously what surprises await us at Uranus □

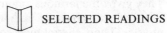 SELECTED READINGS

"Saturn's surprises" by A. P. Ingersoll. *Natural History,* September 1981.

"Voyager 2: all eyes and ears for Saturn" by J. Eberhart. *Science News,* August 15, 1981.

"Voyager 1 at Saturn" by Richard Berry. *Astronomy,* January 1981.

NEW QSO
(Z=2.0)

QUASAR 3C273

1 ARC-MIN

In this X-ray picture, history's most famous quasar—3C273—appears at lower right. A faint quasar, believed to be nearly 12,000,000,000 light-years away, is at upper left.

QUASARS

by David Shafferr and Gregory Shields

QUASARS fascinate. You can hardly pick up a book or periodical without finding yourself immersed in quasars, jets, megaparsecs (a measure of very great distances), and other jargon of professional astronomers. Clearly something very exciting is going on, but what is it? Why are those tiny points of light called quasars so all-mighty interesting?

Consider this: quasars are the most powerful sources of energy in the entire universe. They give off enormous amounts of power in most of the kinds of radiation known to physics. Their energy may come from giant black holes. And they may allow us to probe out to vast distances in space and back to remote times in the history of the universe.

Naturally, the details don't stand out clearly. There's a lot to be unraveled yet.

Even now, nearly 20 years after their discovery, we still lack a basic understanding of them. However, astronomers have made a tantalizing measure of progress. Before the end of the 1980's, this picture should clear up considerably, thanks to improved instruments such as the Space Telescope. Thanks, also, to the perseverance of theorists who aren't going to be happy until they've solved the mysteries of the quasars. Eventually, perhaps by the end of the century, we'll arrive at a thorough understanding of one of nature's most remarkable creations.

THE RADIO BEGINNINGS

The discovery of quasars was a coup for radio astronomers. As that branch of astronomy developed in the late 1940's and the

1950's, most radio sources were found to be broad, extended sources of emission. Nevertheless, a few resembled the point sources that stars look like in an optical telescope. Finally, radio telescopes became good enough to pinpoint the objects so that astronomers could find them in conventional optical instruments. These radio sources looked exactly like ordinary stars. But when these objects' spectra were studied, astronomers were dumbfounded. The spectra were totally unfamiliar.

A spectrum (pl. spectra) is the rainbow spread of colors seen when light passes through a prism. The spectrum of visible light ranges from red at one end to violet at the other end. Light acts like a wave, and its wavelength is the distance between crests of the wave. When a chemical element is heated so that it glows, it emits light at specific wavelengths. These wavelengths appear as one or more lines of certain colors of the spectrum. Study of the spectrum of light emitted by a star or other object can therefore reveal a great deal about the elements present in the object.

The spectra of the newly discovered radio sources showed emission lines of hot gases that didn't seem to correspond to any known substance. Obviously differing from the normal stars they superficially resembled, these weird "stars" got dubbed quasi-stellar radio objects. This mouthful was quickly shortened to "QSO" or "quasar."

Years passed. In 1963, a major breakthrough came when astronomer Maarten Schmidt found the spectral lines in the radio source 3C 273 were normal lines of hydrogen gas—but displaced toward the red end of the spectrum by an astoundingly large amount. Those unknown spectral lines which had so confused scientists were just those of ordinary elements—like hydrogen—extraordinarily displaced.

HOW FAR AWAY?

Astronomers call spectral displacements toward the red part of the spectrum *redshifts;* those towards the blue, *blueshifts.* They express the change as a decimal fraction; 3C 273's redshift was 0.158, meaning that each line in the spectrum was displaced 15.8 per cent toward the red relative to the laboratory standard.

A redshift or a blueshift indicates a radial velocity, a relative volocity between us, the observers, and the object in our line of sight. For example, light from the sun's east side is slightly blueshifted because that side is rotating toward us; light from the sun's western edge is slightly redshifted because that side is rotating away from us. The radial velocities of stars in a cluster help to tell an astronomer about the internal motions of a

A tremendously powerful quasar, surrounded by stars and clusters of galaxies, shoots out linear jets of material from its hyperenergetic core.

Artwork by Mark Paternostro

During its 30-month mission which began in November 1978, the Einstein Observatory took over 5,000 X-ray pictures of the skies while orbiting above earth's atmosphere.

cluster. But the cosmological use for radial velocities is mind-boggling.

In the 1920's U.S. cosmologist Edwin Hubble observed that the most distant galaxies had the largest redshifts. This finding established a cornerstone of modern cosmology—namely, the idea that the universe is expanding. Hubble also realized that the observations could be inverted—that redshifts could provide a means of determining relative distances to galaxies. Their "absolute" distances have been increased greatly since Hubble's day, but his principle stands unshaken: the farther away an object is, the greater its redshift. Over the years since, the redshift has become a convenient cosmic yardstick for astronomers.

3C 273's redshift of 0.158 corresponds to a recession velocity of some 47,000 kilometers (nearly 30,000 miles) per second and suggests a distance of just under 3,000,000,-000 light-years. A light-year is a measure of distance used in astronomy. One light-year is equal to approximately 9,600,000,000,000 kilometers (6,000,000,000,000 miles). Soon, observers found other quasars having lines of normal elements displaced by even higher redshifts.

But there's a catch: how can we be sure that quasars obey a Hubble Law founded on galaxies? If some other mechanism were at work, quasars might not really lie at the huge distances their redshifts imply. This very problem is the nub of a controversy among astronomers. A minority feel that quasars' redshifts are not "cosmological,"—that is, quasars are relatively nearby and their redshifts are produced in some unknown way. Most astronomers, however, believe that the observations show quasars are a type of galaxy—admittedly unusual—and therefore obey Hubble's Law.

ENORMOUS POWER

If the majority of astronomers are right—that quasars are distant—then quasars' power is stupendous. Considering the radio energy alone, we find quasars that release enough energy in one second to supply the present U.S. energy demand for a billion billion years. What can power such prodigious outputs?

Astronomers believe that cosmic-ray electrons generate the radio waves we observe from quasars. As these electrons move at nearly the speed of light (300,000 kilometers, or 187,500 miles, per second) around the object, through regions of space pervaded by the objects' magnetic fields, they emit radio energy. Astrophysicists call this emission process *synchrotron radiation.*

TINY, HOT CENTERS

The radio waves from many quasars pour out of a very small volume at the center of the quasar. These emission centers have diameters ranging from a few to a few dozen light-years. Compared to full-blown galaxies, these tiny sources are "compact." Galaxy-size sources or larger are called "extended."

Radio telescopes used singly have notoriously poor resolution when compared with optical telescopes, so to study these very small sources, radio astronomers had to exercise some ingenuity. They have hooked up radio antennas separated by thousands of kilometers (miles) to provide very high resolution. This powerful technique is called VLBI, short for Very Long Baseline Interferometry. It gives the resolution of a radio dish antenna thousands of kilometers (miles) across.

The VLBI-determined structure of quasar 3C 345 shows a radio source around 50 or 60 light-years across with an emission region extending out to one side of the compact central region. Like 3C 345, about half the quasars studied in detail show a paradoxical phenomenon of expansion.

Measurements taken since the 1970's show that the angular size of 3C 345's source has increased greatly. This provokes problems because when we use the redshift of 3C 345 to compute its distance, the source appears to be expanding at about seven times the speed of light. The widely accepted theory of relativity flatly rules this out. There has to be some other explanation.

Fortunately, several straightforward interpretations—based on optical illusions that occur when things move close to, but still slower than, the speed of light—are possible.

LIGHTHOUSE EFFECT

One candidate is the so-called "flash-light" or "lighthouse" effect. Picture a flashlight sending out a beam of light while rotating. As the beam sweeps past distant clouds of gas or dust, they'll light up briefly. The more distant the clouds or the faster the beam rotates, the swifter the lit patch will appear to move. Eventually it could "travel" faster than the speed of light.

Beaming effects in radio sources are common. Radio and optical emission from quasar 3C 273 shows a prominent linear jet; the radio jet in galaxy NGC-6251 is even more spectacular. More than 1,000,000 light-years long, the jet shows that the energy source has been squirting a stream of material—mostly hot gas—in the same direction

High-resolution radio interferometry has revealed that quasars are not simple point-sources of emission, but have lobes and other intricate details.

Artwork by Mark Paternostro

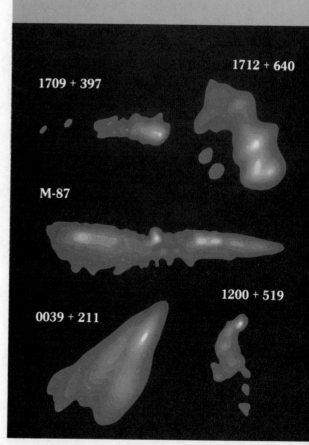

The Structure of Quasars

1712 + 640

1709 + 397

M-87

1200 + 519

0039 + 211

for at least 1,000,000 years. Any attempt to explain quasars must also explain the jets.

Many quasars and most radio galaxies also have extended sources of radio emission with sizes up to a few million light-years. The emission usually appears as two roughly equal components, or lobes, on opposite sides of the central object, as we see in the object known as Cygnus A. The radio lobes and the central object are almost perfectly lined up over a distance of several hundred thousand to a million or more light-years. No one is quite sure how the extended components are created or how they remain so well defined, but it appears that they are regions where the material ejected in the jets from the nucleus is plowing through the space between galaxies.

In maps of Cygnus A and many other sources, there is a very small and weak radio source right in the middle of the parent galaxy or quasar. These nuclear sources are elongated and line up with the extended emission. Some of the energy of the nuclear jets channels its way out to the radio lobes in streams of highly-magnetized material. If this theory is correct, the extended sources have been built up slowly over millions of years as energy and material ejected from the central source "piles up" around the quasar.

YOU NAME IT, QUASARS MAKE IT

Radio waves are not the only kind of radiation emanating from quasars. They also emit infrared, optical, ultraviolet, X-ray, and gamma-ray radiation.

Because the radiation at these wavelengths may have vital clues to understanding quasars hidden in it, and because our atmosphere hinders observations at ultraviolet, X-ray, gamma-ray, and some infrared wavelengths, astronomers must send their instruments above it. The recent Einstein satellite, for example, carries an X-ray telescope to study quasars.

But still the question nags: how can one source generate all these various types of radiation? A promising theory proposes that the emission at infrared and all shorter wavelengths comes from a compact region at the center of the quasar, perhaps about one light-year across. It calls for swarms of cos-

mic ray electrons immersed in strong magnetic fields to emit infrared waves by means of the synchrotron radiation process. The synchrotron process also generates radio waves with less energetic electrons and weaker magnetic fields.

The rest, optical through gamma-ray radiation, comes from another process called Compton scattering. Many of those infrared particles, smashing their way outward from the central source, will collide with the cosmic ray electrons and get reflected or scattered. Because the cosmic rays are energetic and moving at nearly the speed of light, most of the scattered infrared radiation is given a tremendous blueshift. Such violent scattering can upgrade infrared radiation into X-radiation.

THE QUASAR COOKBOOK

Where do the cosmic rays and magnetic fields come from? There isn't any wholly satisfactory answer to this question, but two ideas seem at least plausible. One proposes that some central powerhouse throws off fast-moving jets of gas. Where these jets collide with the surrounding gas, the resulting turbulence might produce both magnetic fields and the cosmic rays.

The other idea suggests that quasars may contain a massive spinning object such as a rotating giant star or an accretion disk of gas spiraling into a black hole. The magnetic fields attached to this material would rotate, making cosmic dynamos to generate immense power. This in turn could accelerate charged particles up to cosmic ray energies, and additionally, power the jets beamed out at right angles to the accretion disk.

The optical and ultraviolet spectra of quasars show emission lines from hot ionized gas, lying typically a few light-years from the center of the quasar. Naturally, the gas becomes heated as the ultraviolet and X-ray radiation streams through. Cosmic rays and violent collisions of moving clouds of gas may well add to the uproar.

Evidence for violent action comes from emission lines in quasar spectra. Because the lines are broad, instead of sharp and distinct, astronomers think that their light comes from many gas clouds moving at speeds of up to 10,000 kilometers (6,000 miles) per second relative to the center of the quasar. Since some of the clouds' light is redshifted, and some is blueshifted with respect to the quasar itself, the result is exactly the broad feature we see. As a best guess, astrophysicists suppose that some force, perhaps radiation pressure, is driving the gas clouds away from the energy source.

By studying quasar emission lines, astronomers hope to find out about the chemical composition of quasar material just as the composition of stars is inferred from their spectra. The first results suggest that quasars arise from the same mixture of chemical elements normally present in galactic nuclei. This adds weight to the idea that quasars and galaxies are members of the same family.

THE ENERGY CRISIS

But what lies in the center of a quasar? What ultimately powers all the activity? Quasars are so remote the answers remain obscure, but observation still can rule out many theories. What observations does a theory have to fit?

Considering the size of the radio lobes, a typical quasar must shine for many millions of years. For the sake of argument, let's assume that a quasar can extract energy from its fuel very efficiently. The processes that appear efficient enough include matter-antimatter annihilation and gravitational energy. Because we have no evidence for significant amounts of antimatter in the visible universe, most astronomers guess that quasars run on gravitational energy. Extracting gravitational energy from matter basically involves a supermassive star or a giant black hole. Black-hole models are especially popular right now since the masses called for are so great as to leave few other options.

In the nucleus of a galaxy, gas from dying stars might go into orbit around a black hole to form a flattened accretion disk somewhat resembling Saturn's ring. Friction in the disk would cause the gas to spiral into the black hole, generating heat and immense floods of radiation in the process. A lot of astronomers are busily engaged in the search for evidence to confirm or rule out this intriguing theory.

The Arecibo Observatory is part of the National Astronomy and Ionosphere Center, which is operated by Cornell University under contract with the National Science Foundation.

One clue lies in the suspiciously quasar-like behavior that occurs in the nuclei of some nearby galaxies called Seyfert galaxies. But Seyferts are rather tame. Still, astronomers hope that quasars are essentially brilliant Seyfert nuclei, so that Seyferts, then, can provide a bridge to the distant quasars.

PERSPECTIVES ON THE UNIVERSE

Because quasars are so bright, we can see them from distances of many billions of light-years. The light from distant quasars has been en route to earth for billions of years, or, in other words, for a large fraction of the age of the universe. In this way quasars give us a look into the past.

In the realm of space near us, there are only a few quasars. When we look far away, we look into the past because the light has traveled so long to reach us. Apparently, there were many more quasars when the universe was younger, 5,000,000,000 to 10,000,-000,000 years ago, than there are today. Were all galaxies once quasars? We don't know.

You can get another perspective on quasar distances by using a result from the Big Bang model of the universe. According to the Big-Bang theory, the universe was born with a gigantic explosion that sent matter hurtling outward. As the universe expands, widely separated galaxies move farther and farther apart. The "scale" of the universe therefore increases as it expands. It turns out that for a quasar of redshift 3.5, receding at 91 per cent the speed of light, the scale of the universe today is four and a half times larger than it was when the quasar emitted the light we see from it.

Studying quasars may help to answer the important questions of whether the universe will expand forever or will re-contract, and whether it has infinite or finite extent. If the universe contains sufficient matter, the gravitational self-attraction of the matter will at some point slow the present expansion to a halt. A contraction would then follow that might end only when everything crushes out of existence in a fiery implosion, or inward explosion.

Observing distant quasars may eventually allow us to compare the expansion rate of the universe billions of years ago with the present rate. Today, this cosmic crystal ball is only a hope. Modern instruments and theories leave too many uncertainties for reliable measurement. However, as the story unfolds and our understanding of quasars improves, an answer may yet be found □

 SELECTED READINGS

"Gravity lenses: a focus on cosmic twins" by E. Galco and N. Cohen. *Astronomy,* July 1981.
"Quasars confirmed" by S. P. Maran. *Natural History,* February 1980.
"When is a quasar a galaxy?" *Astronomy,* May 1981.

This aerial photograph of the Very Large Array (VLA) Radio Telescope was taken looking down its southwestern arm. The yellow structure is the Antenna Assembly Building.

National Radio Astronomy Observatory

ASTEROIDS

by Joel Davis

GIUSEPPE PIAZZI wasn't even looking for them—he was compiling a star map and catalog. But on the first night of the first year of the 19th century, he found them.

What he discovered was the first of the asteroids, those flying mountains that ring the sun between Mars and Jupiter. Unwittingly, Piazzi had upstaged a worldwide effort to find what many astronomers were convinced was a missing fifth planet.

From antiquity on, only five planets besides earth were known: Mercury, Venus, Mars, Jupiter, and Saturn. These five "classical planets" remained the only ones known until 1781, when the German-born English astronomer William Herschel accidently discovered Uranus. But even before that astronomers had looked at the arrangement of the planets and pondered. The large, empty gap lying between Mars and Jupiter intrigued many, including the famous German astronomer-mathematician Johannes Kepler. In 1596 he had published a treatise in which he wrote: "Between Mars and Jupiter I place a planet." He was the first astronomer of note to state publicly that a planet must exist in that mysterious gap.

TITIUS AND HIS CURIOUS LAW

More than a century and a half passed before the German mathematician Johann Titius published a detailed study of the relationship between the distances of the planets from the sun. It included the first formulation of the now-famous *Titius-Bode Law.* (The German astronomer Johann Bode got his name tacked onto it because he cleverly popularized Titius' discovery and effectively made it his own for a long time.)

The Titius-Bode Law is really quite simple. Titius started by dividing the distance from the sun to Saturn (the farthest-known planet at the time) into 100 equal parts. "Mercury is four such parts away from the Sun," Titius wrote. "Venus is $4 + 3 = 7$ of them, Earth is $4 + 6 = 10$, Mars $4 + 12 = 16$." Titius continued the series by

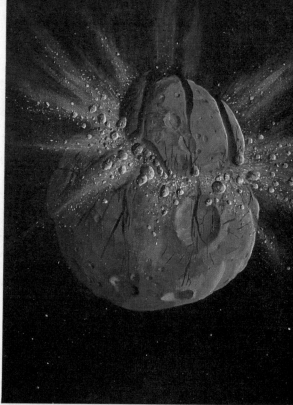

© William K. Hartmann

Occasionally one asteroid slams into another. Both then break into smaller fragments, many of which fall onto earth as meteorites.

making the second factor in each successive equation double the previous one: from 12 to 24, 24 to 48, 48 to 96, and so on. The sums he thus arrived at were 4, 7, 10, 16, 28, 52, and 100. Continuing the sequence yields 196, 388, and 772 ($4 + 192$, $4 + 384$, and $4 + 768$). All very simple.

The notable thing about this numerology is that when these numbers are divided by ten, they correspond remarkably well to the actual distances from the sun of the first six planets, taking the "astronomical unit" (AU) as a measuring stick. The astronomical unit is the average distance at which the earth orbits the sun, or approximately 149,-600,000 kilometers (93,000,000 miles). Mercury in fact orbits 0.38 AU from the sun; Venus 0.72 AU; Earth, 1.0 AU (of course); Mars 1.52 AU's; Jupiter 5.2 AU's; and Saturn 9.54 AU's.

The problem came with the fifth number of the series, 28. There just wasn't any planet between Mars and Jupiter, 2.8 AU's from the sun. So, despite its appeal, the

Titius-Bode Law remained not much more than an arithmetical curiosity.

Then Herschel discovered Uranus in 1781.

Uranus' average distance from the sun in astronomical units is 19.18; the Titius-Bode Law had predicted a planet 196 units—that is, 19.6 AU's—from the sun.

Uranus fit. (Well, almost. But few were prepared to quibble over the 0.42 AU difference.) That was enough for some astronomers. If it worked for Uranus, then there had to be a still-undiscovered planet at 28 units, between Mars and Jupiter, just as Kepler predicted in 1596. The hunt was on.

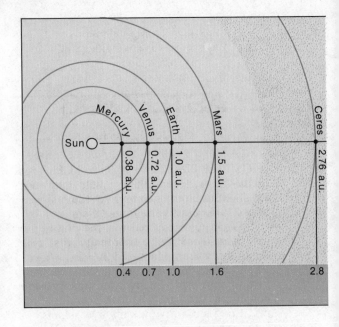

Some day astronauts may travel to asteroids. This view shows a space ship reaching a small Apollo-Amor asteroid not far from the earth-moon system.

© William K. Hartmann

THE "CELESTIAL POLICE" ORGANIZE

The German astronomer Baron Franz von Zach tried to compute the orbit of the missing planet—and failed. In 1796 an astronomical congress was held at Gotha, Germany and French astronomer Joseph de Lalande suggested an all-out crash program to find the missing planet.

In 1800, at a conference in Lilienthal, de Lalande, von Zach, and other astronomers pushed the plan into action. The sky was divided in 24 different zones, each "policed" by an astronomer keeping watch for the missing planet. Surely such a rational, organized program was bound to succeed.

Hardly! And ironically, the man who discovered the missing planet wasn't even looking for it.

DISCOVERY OF CERES

Giuseppe Piazzi, an astronomer at Palermo, Sicily, was preparing an accurate star catalog. The one then in use was full of errors and Piazzi was intending to correct that.

On New Year's Day 1801, he mapped a tiny point of light in the region of the sky he was surveying. When he checked his plottings the next night, he found it was gone. Instead there was a "new star" a little distance away. On January 3 he found a third.

By now Piazzi was sure the "stars" weren't stars at all, but rather one object on the move. He decided he had discovered a new comet and sent his findings to several colleagues—including Johann Bode. Mean-

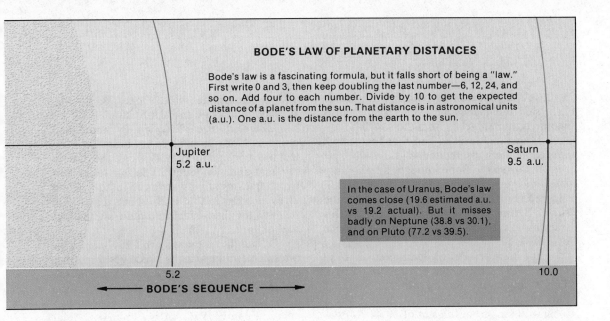

BODE'S LAW OF PLANETARY DISTANCES

Bode's law is a fascinating formula, but it falls short of being a "law." First write 0 and 3, then keep doubling the last number—6, 12, 24, and so on. Add four to each number. Divide by 10 to get the expected distance of a planet from the sun. That distance is in astronomical units (a.u.). One a.u. is the distance from the earth to the sun.

Jupiter
5.2 a.u.

Saturn
9.5 a.u.

In the case of Uranus, Bode's law comes close (19.6 estimated a.u. vs 19.2 actual). But it misses badly on Neptune (38.8 vs 30.1), and on Pluto (77.2 vs 39.5).

5.2

10.0

◄── **BODE'S SEQUENCE** ──►

while, he kept observing his new "comet" until February 11, when bad weather closed in and clouds obscured the sky.

When Bode got the news he checked his charts and calculations and decided Piazzi's discovery was no comet but the sought-for missing planet.

Piazzi named the planet Ceres, after the patron goddess of Sicily. But by now it was lost. He hadn't made enough observations for astronomers of those days to plot its orbit. And Ceres was now too near the sun for further observation.

It fell to a then-obscure young German mathematician named Karl Friedrich Gauss to come up with the breakthrough.

Gauss was a true mathematical genius. He had just developed a new method of calculating the orbits of heavenly bodies using only a tiny amount of data, something no one else at that time had done. Gauss decided the Ceres problem was ideal to test his new method on, and he worked out an orbit for Ceres in October 1801.

He fired off his predictions on where Ceres should be found in the night sky. Baron von Zach himself, one of the instigators of the crash program to find the missing planet, located Ceres with Gauss's predictions on December 7, 1801, and by December 31 had verified it. A few weeks later German astronomer Heinrich Olbers, also using Gauss's numbers, spotted Ceres.

The missing planet—missing twice, in fact—was now found. Its distance from the sun in astronomical units: 2.76, just a tad off the 2.8 predicted by the Titius-Bode Law.

AND THEN THERE WERE TWO . . .

The drama wasn't over yet; in fact, it had just begun. On March 28, 1802, Olbers threw a cosmic monkey wrench into the proceedings by discovering a *second* planet. He named it Pallas. Gauss again worked his mathematical magic and there was no doubt: Pallas, too, was in orbit between Mars and Jupiter.

Then 18 months later, on September 1, 1804, German astronomer Karl L. Harding discovered a third planet, which he named Juno. Three years later, on March 29, 1807, Heinrich Olbers found a fourth planet. It was named Vesta. All four had orbits lying between 2.3 and 2.8 AU's from the sun—as the Titius-Bode Law had predicted for the one missing planet.

These new objects were small, hardly at all planet-sized. Ceres is only 1,000 kilometers (620 miles) in diameter, Pallas 534 kilometers (334 miles), Juno 240 kilometers (150 miles), and Vesta 530 kilometers (330 miles). They are not really planets at all but minor planets, planetoids, or asteroids—"little stars."

BAD NEWS FOR THE "LAW"

How did the Titius-Bode Law fare in all this? Not too badly at first, but by 1846 it was in disrepute after Johann Galle of the Berlin Observatory found Neptune. Neptune lies at

30.06 AU's from the sun, but the Titius-Bode Law said the planet next out from Uranus should be at 38.8 AU's from the sun. The 8 + AU discrepancy was so bad that the "Law" was completely discredited.

In fairness to Bode, though, he probably knew the "law" wasn't a law at all. After all, the decision to divide the distance from the sun to Saturn into 100 parts was quite arbitrary as was the decision to use the sequence of 0, 3, 6, 12, and so on.

But consider Pluto, discovered in 1930 by the U.S. astronomer Clyde Tombaugh. This strange little object, which doesn't fit into any planetary scheme of things, has a mean distance from the sun of 39.44 AU's—almost exactly the 38.8 AU's the long-dismissed Titius-Bode Law claims the planet beyond Uranus should have. Maybe we should take another look at the Titius-Bode Law.

MANY MORE FOUND

Meanwhile, 38 years of fruitless searching went by after the discovery of the fourth asteroid, Vesta. Then in 1845, German astronomer Karl Hencke found a new asteroid he named Astraea. With that, the scramble for asteroids was on again in full force. It became popular for many astronomers in the 19th century, and not a year has gone by since without new ones being found. More than 2,000 are known so far, with wonderful and exotic names like Hebe, Bamberga, Wladilena, Icarus, and Ra-Shalom.

Asteroids are identified by name and number. Until its orbit is confirmed, an object has a designation made up of the discovery year and two letters. The first letter tells which half-month it was found in, the second gives its order in that half-month. Thus 1976 AA was the first object found during the first half of January 1976.

When the asteroid's orbit has been accurately determined, it then receives a number corresponding to its official listing in the catalog of known asteroids: 1976 AA was number 2062. At this point its discoverer can give it a name. 1976 AA became 2062 Aten.

SOME IN FAMILIES

Most asteroids orbit the sun between Mars and Jupiter. They range in size from Ceres, 1,000 kilometers (620 miles) to tiny mountain-size chunks—and probably even smaller. True to their eccentric reputation, though, not all of them inhabit that region. The moons of Mars are probably asteroids captured by the red planet eons ago.

A family of asteroids called the Trojans travel in the orbit of Jupiter. The Apollo-Amor group have weird orbits that carry them inside the orbit of earth. And the enigmatic object Chiron, orbiting between Uranus and Saturn, may be a newly-discovered member of a class of asteroids beyond Saturn.

Astronomers believe that some asteroids have small moons. The drawing at left is based on a recent study that suggests this configuration for the asteroid 2 Pallas. The moon casts a shadow on the surface of Pallas.

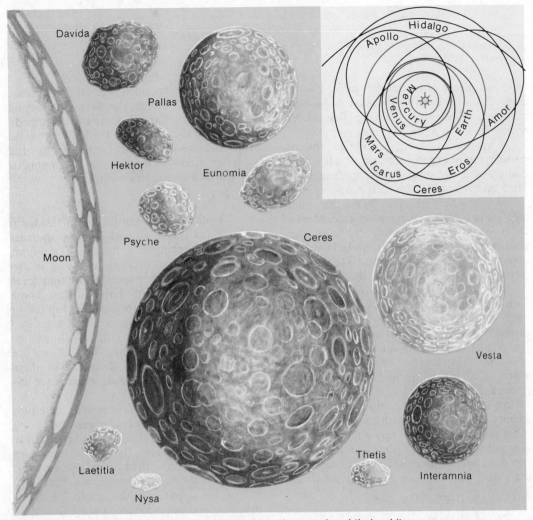

Above: relative sizes of a few asteroids (compared to the moon) and their orbits.

Some 95 per cent of all known asteroids, though, do lie in the main belt and take from two to six years to make a complete orbit. Most of their orbits are not too far from circular and lie pretty much in the plane of the solar system.

Many gaps—ten major ones—exist in the main belt. The gravitational pull of Jupiter sweeps these 10 gaps clear of objects and thus creates 10 definite groups of asteroids, called "Hirayama Families." About one-third of all asteroids in the main belt belong to such groupings.

AN EXPLODED WORLD, OR ONE THAT NEVER WAS?

What are these strange objects, anyway? What are they made of? Do they come in different kinds? Are they the remnants of an ancient planet that exploded? Asteroid-hunters have been asking these questions for a long time, and it's only recently that they've started getting some real answers. True to their past history, asteroids still have some surprises in store for us.

Where do they come from? Heinrich Olbers thought they were the remains of a full-sized planet that once existed between Mars and Jupiter, and which either exploded or was torn apart by Jupiter's gravitational field. This seemed a reasonable theory during Olbers' time. After all, the Titius-Bode Law was still strongly held and it had correctly predicted the distance of Uranus.

But after 1846, when the Law began to be questioned, astronomers wondered about Olbers' theory. Had there ever been a planet there in the first place? Perhaps asteroids were just pieces of matter that never had the chance to form a planet, because of Jupiter's influence. Soon this became the second major theory of asteroid origin.

Theorists suggested yet another: that asteroids resulted from collisions of a few large bodies, and by now there's evidence this third theory may be the correct one.

Astronomers generally agree that asteroids are in a highly fragmented state. Most of them show periodic brightness changes, suggesting they are tumbling, irregularly-shaped objects. Photos of Phobos and Deimos, the asteroidal satellites of Mars, show just such irregular shapes. Studies indicate that 433 Eros is a spindle-shaped rock some 8 by 16 by 32 kilometers (5 by 10 by 20 miles) in dimension, turning end over end.

With this evidence in hand, astronomers now think the asteroid belt originally consisted of about 50 or so large bodies that formed, like the planets, early in the history of the solar system. But Jupiter's meddling gravity started them crashing into one another and breaking up. Only a few of the big original asteroids—like Ceres—remain. The rest have been fragmented over the ages into the slowly cartwheeling rocks we see today.

WHAT ARE THEY MADE OF?

What asteroids are made of is also beginning to come to light—literally. By studying the polarization of the light they reflect and observing how much they reflect (their albedo) in infrared as well as visible light, astronomers have started to unlock the mystery.

Asteroids, say some, fall into two main groups—the low-albedo group and the high-albedo group. The "low-albedo" asteroids are carbonaceous; they seem to be covered with dark carbon compounds and reflect little light. These are the most common. The other group, the "high-albedo" asteroids, seems to be mainly formed of silicon compounds. They reflect more light than the low-albedo group.

It's quite possible some of the early, protoasteroids underwent internal melting like the earth and other large planetary bodies did. They may have differentiated into metallic cores covered by stony-iron

mantles and carbonaceous crusts. When they broke up in collisions, the dark outer layers would shatter off and become the low-albedo asteroids of today, leaving the lighter colored iron- and metal-rich cores behind. Thus the siliceous asteroids may be the fragments of the cores of early giant asteroids.

SOME SO STRANGE

Though most asteroids lie in the main belt, others travel around a bit in unusual orbits. For example, a family of asteroids called the Trojans, occupy a section in Jupiter's orbit. Together with Jupiter they form an equilateral triangle with the sun. These might be asteroids captured by Jupiter or they could be the remnants of the solar system's primordial material, tied to Jupiter for nearly 5,000,000,000 years. Two things are certain at least: several thousand of them exist, and their dark reddish surfaces are unlike other asteroids.

The Apollo-Amor group of asteroids has eccentric paths taking them inside the orbit of the earth on their closest approach to the sun. Like 1 Ceres, the first of the group was discovered and then promptly lost—this time for 41 years. 1862 Apollo was first spotted in 1932, but no orbit could be determined; it was not recovered until 1974. Some 28 Apollo-Amor asteroids are known so far.

The Apollo-Amor objects could be the remains of dead comets. After all, comets and their associated debris are the only other heavenly bodies that cross the earth's orbit (apart from meteorites—which seem to be asteroid fragments anyway). Comet heads and the Apollo-Amor objects both have about the same size—from 1.6 to 16 kilometers (1 to 10 miles) diameter. But they could also be asteroids flung from the innermost part of the belt into eccentric orbits by Jupiter's influence. That area—called the Flora Region after the largest asteroid in the area (8 Flora)—lies near a gravitationally unstable part of the belt.

And then there's Chiron. Discovered by U.S. astronomer Charles Kowal in 1977, Chiron travels from just inside the orbit of Uranus to just inside that of Saturn, a decidedly unusual location for an asteroid. What's more, its orbit is unstable. Because of

© William K. Hartmann

At times some asteroids pass near planets. This is an imaginary view from the surface of an asteroid as it passes the bright polar ice cap of Mars.

Saturn's influence, astronomers can trace Chiron's orbit back into the past and forward into the future only a few million years. Saturn's gravitational pull will eventually throw Chiron into a new, unknown path—perhaps even entirely out of the solar system.

Is Chiron a comet from the Oort Cloud (a gigantic storehouse of comets) that surrounds our solar system? Did it get caught millions of years ago in its gravitational dance with Saturn and Uranus? Is it the first-discovered member of a new asteroid belt? Or is it an interstellar wanderer captured by Saturn? No one really knows.

MOONS, TOO?

The Trojans are exotic, the Apollo-Amor family fascinating, Chiron mysterious. But asteroids have still another surprise in store: satellites. At least some—and perhaps many—asteroids may have companions in orbit around them.

On June 7, 1978, asteroid 532 Herculina occulted a star called SAO 120774. Two observers not only saw the star wink out when Herculina passed in front of it, they saw a second occultation of the star.

A probable explanation is that Herculina has a moon. This moon would be about 45 kilometers (28 miles) in diameter and orbiting about 1,000 kilometers (620 miles) from Herculina; Herculina is about 240 kilometers (150 miles) in diameter.

Then in December 1978, there were reports that 18 Melpomene may have a satellite. And, during 1980 new observation techniques revealed that asteroid Pallas has a moon and that asteroid Victoria may also. It may be that asteroids with moons are not the usual phenomenon they were first thought to be—another indication that, after 180 years, the asteroids are still surprising us □

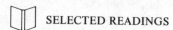 SELECTED READINGS

"Fallen sky" by C. Pellegrino. *Astronomy*, April 1981.

"Study of asteroids coming into vogue" by R. A. Kerr. *Science*, March 20, 1981.

"Sky will fall" by E. R. Shell. *Technology Review*, April 1981.

© John Coffeen/Black Star

On March 22, 1982, the United States' first reusable space vehicle, called the Columbia, was launched for the third time.

THE SPACE SHUTTLE

by Benedict A. Leerburger

WITH the launching of Columbia 1 on April 12, 1981, the United States placed a most unusual vehicle in space. The two-man spacecraft, about the size of a DC-9 jet, accomplished something no other spacecraft had achieved. It returned safely to earth ready to fly again.

The development of a reusable space vehicle, or space shuttle, means that millions of dollars can be saved in future space ventures. Since the primary purpose of the vehicle is to transport people and objects from earth to space and back again, the ability to use one vehicle many times reduces the cost enormously. For both government and private industry the space shuttle provides the opportunity to conduct relatively inexpensive scientific experiments that are not possible on earth.

THE FIRST FLIGHT

The initial launch of Columbia proved that the vehicle and its crew could accomplish a basic mission—orbit the earth, perform scientific experiments, and return safely. Astronauts John W. Young and Robert L. Crippen had little problem in flying the boxcarlike delta-wing craft. Their flight of two and one-half days tested the shuttle's basic components, including the ship's cargo-bay doors.

The shuttle's vast cargo area—a cylindrical compartment 4.6 meters (15 feet) in diameter and 18.3 meters (60 feet) in length—houses scientific equipment to be placed in space and serves as an on-board laboratory. The doors on the cargo bay are designed to be open when the shuttle is in orbit. Special radiators on the inside of the wide doors cool the ship. Failure to open the doors would create a heat problem inside the shuttle. The doors were successfully tested during Columbia's maiden voyage.

THE SECOND FLIGHT

Columbia's second flight was piloted by astronauts Joe H. Engle and Richard H. Truly. It was launched on November 12, 1981 from Cape Canaveral, Florida. After orbiting the earth 36 times, it landed safely 54 hours later at Edwards Air Force Base in California. The mission was scheduled to last five days. One of Columbia's three fuel cells malfunctioned in flight, however, causing the mission to be shortened. The flight of Columbia 2 was considered a success, though, as the astronauts achieved all their major goals, including testing a mechanical robot arm and conducting the first scientific observations from the world's first reusable space vehicle.

The robot "arm" test was considered very important. During future flights this delicate device will be used to pluck satellites from Columbia's cargo hold and place them in a precise orbit. The "arm" will also be used to reach out and grab orbiting satellites for close examination or repair by technicians aboard the shuttle.

SUCCESSFUL EXPERIMENTS AND OBSERVATIONS

The study of thunderstorms was one of the scientific data-gathering chores undertaken by Engle and Truly. Although the abbreviated mission prevented the astronauts from collecting as much data as they wanted, they did photograph several large thunderheads and one lightning flash. There are still many things about thunderstorms that puzzle scientists. No one, for example, yet understands the dynamics of electricity within a thundercloud or what role electrification may play in rain-making. To compound the puzzle, recent satellite observations indicate that there is ten times as much lightning over land as over water. And, another mystery—meteorologists have long thought that clouds and water were necessary to produce lightning, but space scientists have learned that planets without water also produce lightning. Both two- and three-dimensional photographs of thunderstorms and lightning taken during the Columbia 2 voyage may help solve these puzzles.

Columbia 2 also carried special radar equipment that provided information about the relief of the earth's surface. The unique radar device is the first side-looking radar system to fly in space. Other radar systems look down at earth directly, rather than at an angle and cannot provide data about the earth's relief.

The images obtained with Columbia's special radar are photographic-like in quality and can be taken day or night, through clouds and vegetation. The ability to penetrate both cloud cover and vegetation and record detailed relief information will assist in worldwide geologic exploration. Similar radar equipment carried by aircraft discovered a previously unknown network of ancient Mayan irrigation canals built more than 1,000 years ago but hidden by dense forests.

In another experiment—charting the color of the ocean surface—the astronauts gathered twice the data needed by scientists. The test mapped green chlorophyll concentrations in the world's oceans. These concentrations indicate where there is an abundance of plant life and plankton to sustain large fish populations. This information is useful to commercial fisheries as well as oceanographers. The test also indicates where marine life has been destroyed by pollutants.

The Measurement of Pollution from Satellite (MAPS) experiment obtained 32 hours of data. A sensor recorded carbon monoxide pollution in the atmosphere at heights of 7 to 8 kilometers (4.4 to 5 miles) and 10 to 12 kilometers (6.2 to 7.5 miles). The data was analyzed in conjunction with photographs taken of cloud cover and terrain directly below the carbon monoxide.

Another experiment used a multispectral radiometer to photograph the earth's surface using visible red and near-infrared light. The experiment tested an automatic system designed to tell the difference between various physical features—land and water; cloud or snow cover; forest, farm land, or barren ground. The experiment's success means that future earth-surveying satellites will be able to discriminate in their observations, selecting, for example, only corn fields or desert areas to map.

A FEW DISAPPOINTMENTS

Not all of Columbia 2's experiments succeeded. The short duration of the flight prevented botanists from conducting a test with sunflower seeds. They had planned to study the growth of 85 seeds, each in its own cylinder with varying moisture levels, to determine the amount of moisture needed to grow seedlings in a weightless environment. They had also hoped to learn more about plant structure. As plants grow they move in a spiral pattern, a phenomenon known as nutation. No one knows why plants move as they do. Some believe that the twisting is genetically determined, others think that it is caused by gravity. Growing plants in the microgravity environment of space might provide an answer.

Columbia 3 was piloted by two veteran astronauts: commander Jack R. Lousma (left) and pilot C. Gordon Fullerton (right).

THE THIRD FLIGHT

Columbia 3, launched from Cape Canaveral on March 22, 1982, was piloted by astronauts Jack R. Lousma and C. Gordon Fullerton. The eight-day flight completed 128 earth orbits and landed safely at White Sands Missile Range in New Mexico. Like previous missions, the astronauts conducted extensive tests of the Remote Manipulator System, or "arm." In September 1983, Columbia is scheduled to use the arm to lift Spacelab, a huge European-built scientific space laboratory from its cargo bay and place it in orbit. Future astronauts will link with Spacelab and use it as an orbiting work center.

A highlight of the third mission was an experiment on "Insects in Flight Motion Study," devised by an 18-year-old high-

school student, Todd E. Nelson, of Southland Public School in Adams, Minnesota. The experiment tested the effects of zero-gravity on the flight behavior of two insects, the velvet-bean caterpillar moth and the honeybee drone.

Among the other experiments aboard Columbia 3 were a solar flare X-ray test, an induced-atmosphere experiment, and several diagnostic tests to measure the effects of weightlessness on specially prepared blood specimens. Future space experiments will involve testing a process to produce extremely high-purity biological products by electrical separation in space. The process, known as continuous-flow electrophoresis, may lead to space factories that can produce drugs and other materials with a purity never before achieved.

PLANS FOR THE FUTURE

Scientists are now planning future work for the space shuttles. One test, scheduled for 1983, will involve the first manned excursion outside the space shuttle. An astronaut, propelled by a jet-powered backpack, will attempt to rendezvous with an "ailing satellite." This satellite, the Solar Maximum, has been in orbit since 1980 but is now hampered by a defective control module. It is no longer stable enough to be grabbed by the mechanical shuttle "arm," but it does have enough stability for an astronaut to float over to it and manually control it so that the "arm" can be attached.

The present goal of the Space Shuttle Program is to have four shuttles flying 24 missions a year by 1988. Three flights of Columbia are scheduled for 1982. With additional shuttles, five flights are scheduled for 1983, nine in 1984, 13 in 1985, 15 in 1986, and 23 in 1987 □

 SELECTED READINGS

"Space shuttle: a new era in terrestrial remote sensing" by James V. Taranik and Mark Settle. *Science,* November 6, 1981.

"Aboard the space shuttle" by Florence S. Steinberg. *Space World,* November 1981.

"Implications of the shuttle: our business in space" by Jerry Grey. *Technology Review,* October 1981.

Ron Alexander/Stock, Boston

Scientists have new evidence that susceptibility to depressive illness is hereditary.

BEHAVIORAL SCIENCES

BEHAVIORAL SCIENCES
REVIEW OF THE YEAR

Research in the behavioral sciences touched on many areas during 1981, including depression, suicide, senility, and infancy.

Depression. For many years behavioral scientists have had a growing conviction that serious depression was at least partly inherited. Their evidence was, however, only statistical and circumstantial. That may have changed. Scientists at the University of Rochester and University of Toronto report finding the marker of a gene that makes "a major contributor to susceptibility to depressive illness." The gene is located on the sixth chromosome, near the HLA (human leukocyte antigen) site that carries information on the immune system, thus suggesting that certain forms of depression may involve a breakdown in the brain's immune responses. The researchers did a series of complex cross matches on the blood samples of 41 families with more than one person diagnosed as suffering from depression. They found that depressed offspring shared the same HLA genes and inherited the HLA marker from a well, non-depressed parent significantly more often than could be accounted for by chance. The fact that nondepressed parents serve as a carrier of a depression-related gene leads to an important inference—that heredity apparently only dictates a predisposition to a depressive disorder. According to University of Rochester geneticist Lowell R. Weitkamp, "You can have the susceptibility and never show the disease;" actually developing depressive illness seems to depend on "environment." Other researchers, commenting on the apparent HLA link, suggest that the depressed person could possibly produce antibodies that block some chemical action in the brain. Other researchers, including John I. Nurnberger of the National Institute of Mental Health (NIMH) questions these findings, however. NIMH has recently mounted a new project—the first using new gene-splicing technology in behavioral research—to identify the exact gene or genes responsible for manic-depressive illness. A new set of antidepressant drugs are now being tested and may be expected on the market within two or three years.

Suicide. Several interesting findings about suicide emerged during the year. While the overall suicide rate has remained about the same since the 1950's, the proportion of young people taking their own lives has increased. Among 15-to-24 year olds, suicide is now the third leading cause of death. (See also "Teenage Suicide," on page 61.)

In other recent studies of suicide, striking differences in suicide rates for various ethnic groups in the United States were revealed. As they grow older white Americans are increasingly prone to commit suicide, while the suicide rate for blacks and some other minority groups reaches its peak in the 20-to-29 year-old group and then declines. Among middle-aged and elderly Americans the overall suicide rate for whites is three times that for blacks. Why? Dr. Richard Seiden, professor of behavioral sciences at the University of California School of Public Health at Berkeley, suggests that elderly blacks are "survivors," that they feel a "triumph in surviving against adversity." He says that they are also more likely than whites to be a part of an extended family and to have a good deal more participation and purposeful activity—in child rearing for working parents, for example.

Dan J. McCoy/Black Star

Feelings of loneliness, boredom, and loss of status among middle-aged and elderly white Americans contribute to suicide rates that grow higher as people grow older.

Recent research has shown that senility, a condition once believed incurable, is typically the result of a neurochemical abnormality—a deficiency in acetylcholine.

Conklin/Monkmeyer Press Photo

Senility and Old Age. Senility was once thought to be a common, almost inevitable, and incurable result of advanced age. Now research has shown that not all aged people become senile and that senility itself may be treatable. Two biological signs of senility have been known for a while: (1) senile plaques, or cores of abnormal protein, interspersed around nerve cells in the brain, and (2) neurofibrillary tangles, or twisted fibers in the bodies of nerve cells in the brain. These two signs occur especially in those areas of the brain involved in memory and learning. Now a neurochemical abnormality has also been found to characterize senility—a deficiency in acetylcholine, a compound used to transmit signals between brain cells. Research into why this occurs is continuing in many centers throughout the world, but in the meantime attempts are being made to convert the knowledge so far gained into a possible treatment approach. Drugs that increase the amount or activity of acetylcholine and drugs that retard the degradation of acetylcholine alone and in combination have been given to senile patients. The results have been mixed. While there are several encouraging reports of improved memory in treated patients, other results show no improvement or only short-term improvement. Nonetheless, as Kenneth L. Fabid of the Bronx Veterans Administration Hospital in New York City says, it is "a first step along a rational road to treatment."

Studies of Prenatal and Early Life. There was also a good deal of research on prenatal and early life. One aspect concerned the effects of drugs on the developing fetus. The Surgeon General now warns that even small doses of alcohol during pregnancy may harm the fetus and urged pregnant women not to drink at all. Even moderate drinking has been associated with an increased rate of spontaneous abortion and with low birth-weight infants, and heavy drinking is known to cause fetal-alcohol syndrome, a set of symptoms in the newborn, including some facial abnormalities and often emotional and intellectual problems. ■ Prenatal exposure to gonadal (sex) hormones may also later affect the child. Anke Ehrhardt of Columbia University College of Physicians and Surgeons described cases in which boys born to women who had taken estrogen (female hormone) during pregnancy showed less aggressiveness and more nurturing behavior than boys born to women who had not taken the hormone. Though it is hard to characterize human behavior as male or female and it is not known how much of the hormone crossed the placenta to effect the developing fetus, the preliminary findings are interesting and are leading to more research.

And newborns—there're more complicated than we thought. Recent studies have shown that infants are able to see, recognize voices, and respond differently to different people at an extremely early age. Within 35 hours after birth they recognize their own cries and respond to the crying of other infants in a form of "empathy distress." This and a vast amount of other data and improved ways of testing the development of infants is opening a new area of study—infant psychiatry, the diagnosis and treatment of emotional problems unique to children under three years of age. Depression, hyperanxiety, psychosis, and the earliest signs of autism have been detected in babies only a few days old. In research clinics at Yale, the University of Michigan, and the Mental Health Study Center in Adelphi, Maryland, infant psychiatrists are developing new ways to treat the very young. They lead babies through specific exercises, provide proper stimuli, play give-and-take games, and counsel parents—all in hopes of helping the baby and possibly avoiding serious psychological problems in later life.

Barbara Tchabovsky

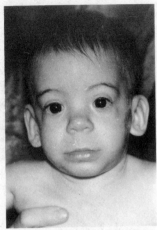

J. W. Hanson

The Surgeon General has declared that pregnant women should not consume alcohol at all. This child's sunken nasal bridge and short nose are symptoms of fetal-alcohol syndrome.

The damaging psychological aftereffects of the atomic bombing of Japan are just now being fully realized. Bomb survivors, like this woman, still suffer bitter emotions.

Kyoko Ureshino

Darlene Hammond/Retna Ltd.

The physical attractiveness of such well-known personalities as actress Sally Field and actor Burt Reynolds may have played a profoundly positive role in their rise to stardom.

THE BEAUTIFUL PEOPLE

by Jane E. Brody

A SUCCESSFUL handsome bachelor enters a crowded cocktail party. His eyes roam the room, filled with animated conversation and the faces of several well-known people in the arts and literature. He settles on an attractive blond across the room, approaches, and strikes up a conversation.

Why has he singled out this woman amid a group of sophisticated intelligent people?

Just because she's attractive? Do looks matter so much to him? Or does he also expect her to be witty, poised, and interesting? Why?

Studies of physical attractiveness show that people do, in fact, judge a book by its cover, often with dramatic effects on those being judged. The findings suggest that expectations based on physical attractiveness can become self-fulfilling prophecies that may strongly influence the course of a person's life.

The studies show that people known (or supposed) to be physically attractive are in-

vested by others with a host of desirable characteristics, such as warmth, poise, sensitivity, kindness, sincerity, and the potential for social, marital, and occupational success. And according to Dr. Ellen Berscheid, professor of psychology at the University of Minnesota, these beliefs about physically attractive people, and the preferential treatment that grows out of them, can have lasting effects on an individual's personality, social life, and educational and career opportunities.

FIRST IMPRESSIONS IMPORTANT

Dr. Berscheid believes that the importance of physical attractiveness is growing. It will continue to grow as increases in geographic mobility, frequent job changes, and divorce subject more people to "one-time" or "few-time" interactions with others, in which they are judged on the basis of first impressions.

The psychologist, who has been studying the effects of physical attractiveness since the mid-1960's, said the findings "give new dimensions to Freud's statement that 'Anatomy is destiny.'" (Freud's proposition referred originally only to physical differences between men and women.) Contrary to democratic notions that "all people are created equal," the findings imply that a person's physical appearance can make a profound difference in his or her life.

"It is clearly a myth that 'Beauty is only skin deep,'" Dr. Berscheid said, adding that both the lay public and U.S. psychologists have long resisted the idea that attractive people are favored. "That our physical appearance should make an important difference in our lives is not a fact that makes most of us very comfortable," she observed.

"Genetic determinism is anathema to Americans, who want to believe everyone is born equal, with an equal chance for a happy life," Dr. Berscheid has remarked. "It's simply not so. The most important factors governing success in life are genetically determined: appearance, intelligence, sex, and height." She cited a continuing study at the University of Minnesota of identical twins who had been reared apart. The study, she says, is showing that "genetically identical children turn out to be very similar even though they grow up in very different environments."

THROUGHOUT LIFE

The preferential treatment of physically attractive people starts right after birth, Dr. Berscheid noted, and continues throughout childhood, adolescence, and into adulthood. These are among the more telling research findings, all of which involved normal-looking people of varying degrees of attractiveness.

Newborn infants who are independently rated as attractive tend to be held, cuddled, and kissed more than unattractive babies, according to preliminary findings by Dr. Judith Langlois of the University of Texas at Austin. On the other hand, mothers of unattractive babies tend to offer them more frequent and varied stimulation, perhaps helping their mental development.

Nursery school children who were rated by adults as physically attractive were found to be more popular with their school friends, in a study by Karen Dion at the University of Minnesota.

College students paired as dates at a "computer dance" preferred others who were physically attractive. The partners' intelligence, social skills, and personality had little to do with the students' reaction to their dates, a Minnesota study by Elaine Hatfield Walster and associates showed. "These results gave the lie to what people had *said* was important to them in previous studies," the researchers concluded.

Another study at Western Illinois University of paired college students who agreed to complete five dates revealed, contrary to expectation, that as the number of dates increased, attractiveness became a more important factor in determining if the partner was liked.

Young adults asked to describe the personalities of people depicted in head-and-shoulder photographs said that those who were physically attractive would be "more sensitive, kind, interesting, strong, poised, modest, sociable, outgoing, exciting, and sexually warm and responsive persons," according to Dr. Dion, who is now at the Uni-

Dr. Berscheid's studies show that beautiful people are inevitably presumed to have desirable traits.
Univ. of Minnesota

© Hazel Hankin/Stock

This good-looking woman has a much greater chance of being hired than a less attractive one.

versity of Toronto. The attractive people were also thought to "capture better jobs, have more successful marriages, and experience happier and more fulfilling lives" than the less attractive. On only one measure, being a better parent, were the attractive not rated as superior.

JUDGED BEST

In a study at the University of Minnesota, men and women whose telephone conversations were recorded were informed that they were talking either to a physically attractive person or to someone who was not attractive. The taped conversations were later evaluated by judges who were unaware of the setup.

"A woman who was talking to a man who believed that she was physically attractive was judged, on the basis of her verbal behavior alone, to be more poised, more sociable, more vivacious, than was a woman who was talking to a man who believed her to be physically unattractive," Dr. Berscheid reported. And the men who thought they were talking to a physically attractive woman were judged by outside observers, again on the basis of their conversations only, to be more sociable, sexually warm, interesting, independent, bold, outgoing, humorous, and socially adept.

As women become more independent socially and economically, Dr. Berscheid sees them placing a greater emphasis on the attractiveness of men, "who are now in the

'meat market' just like women have always been."

Another factor has been the importance women today place on love as a criterion for choosing a mate. In 1967 only 24 per cent of women questioned said they would marry only if they were in love, but a decade later 80 per cent said "being in love" was a necessary condition for marriage.

"When romantic love becomes an important factor in social choice, physical attractiveness becomes important also," Dr. Berscheid told a symposium on the psychological aspects of facial form in 1980. The symposium brought together plastic surgeons, dentists, and others who produce facial changes that often affect patients more powerfully than the functional defects they correct.

Sometimes patients react badly—"with pain and bewilderment"—to significant improvements in their appearance, Dr. Berscheid told the meeting at the University of Michigan. This reaction could result from the realization that we are not just loved for ourselves but for what we look like, she said.

INHIBITS DEVELOPMENT?

Dr. Berscheid believes there is a hazard inherent in denying the impact of physical attractiveness: "Unattractive children who are unpopular may wrongly attribute their lack of popularity to some flaw in their character or personality," she says. Such an error, she believes, could result in lasting and painful scars.

In her own family, Dr. Berscheid says, she was regarded as less attractive than her beautiful sister who, unlike Ellen, was not encouraged in intellectual pursuits. "It was deemed essential for me to go to college, but the emphasis for my sister was placed on her good looks and her native intelligence was never developed," she recalled.

"We can't yet answer the questions most people ask: what is good about being ugly? What is bad about being beautiful? It could be that being beautiful inhibits the development of the person's other potentials. We need to study the effects of attractiveness on the development of other talents and qualities" □

The Vegetarian

Illustrations by Arnold Roth

YOU ARE WHAT YOU EAT

by Edward Sadalla and Jeffrey Burroughs

A PRIZEFIGHTER wolfs down a bloody steak before a title fight. Photographers and reporters are summoned to capture the ferocious spectacle of the contender tearing his dinner apart, steer blood trickling out of the corners of his mouth.

There is plenty of casual evidence that people choose food not only for taste and nourishment but also because it bolsters their self-image and sends strong messages about them to the rest of the world.

The late Bernarr McFadden, a health-food enthusiast whose ardent zeal would be hard to surpass, went skydiving in his 80's and skinny-dipping in the dead of winter. The press was inevitably present for McFadden's incredible geriatric feats, which were fueled, as he reminded one and all, by wheat germ and black-strap molasses.

Human beings are an omnivorous species, able to survive on a wide variety of foods. Nonetheless, the diets that particular individuals or groups actually choose may be quite limited. Even today, many Eskimo eat little but great hunks of meat, yet return home after a day of seal hunting in the numbing cold with enough energy left for a night of partying.

By contrast, George Bernard Shaw, a lifelong and militant vegetarian, continued to write and rail with energy to burn when his white beard was down to his breastbone.

DIET LINKED TO IDENTITY?

Intrigued by the psychological implications of human eating behavior, our team at Arizona State University set out to determine whether food choices are indeed linked to self-image and to the way others regard us.

We divided foods into five categories: *vegetarian, gourmet, health food, fast food,* and *synthetic food.* We asked an initial group of 500 subjects to list the foods they associated with each category. From their lists, we picked 14 specific dishes to typify each category. Vegetarian dishes included broccoli quiche, avocado sandwiches with bean sprouts, and brown rice with snow peas. Typical gourmet foods were fresh oysters, lobster Newburg, Indonesian roast lamb, and caviar.

The Gourmet

The health-food list included granola with dried fruit, wheat germ, yogurt, and carob cake. The synthetic-food category included such high-technology items as Lean Strips (processed bacon), Egg Beaters (processed eggs), Carnation Instant Breakfast, and Cheez Whiz. At the top of the fast-food list were Whoppers and Big Macs, Kentucky Fried Chicken, hot dogs, and submarine sandwiches.

We presented 150 subjects in a second group with a list of typical foods from each category and asked them to think of the traits that described people who would prefer such foods. This procedure resulted in a list of 65 descriptions such as hypochondriac, unworried about health, executive, blue collar, late, punctual, callous, sensitive, worrier, emotionally stable.

READY RESPONSES

Using our lists of specific foods and descriptions, we performed three separate studies to examine the relationship between food preferences and personality. In our first experiment, 75 college students evaluated a hypothetical person with specific dietary preferences by rating that person on each of the 65 items on our list. We were initially surprised at the promptness and confidence with which subjects paired food preferences with descriptions. If a person was said to like bean sprouts, for example, our subjects described him without hesitation as antinuclear power and prosolar energy.

Our subjects not only "knew" which character traits went with what foods but also were in considerable agreement when we asked them to characterize someone with a specific food preference. They saw fast-food lovers as patriotic, pronuclear, conservative, antidrug, and dressed in polyester suits. They saw vegetarians as pacifist, hypochondriacal, drug-using, weight-conscious, liberal, and likely to drive foreign cars.

That first experiment was designed to assess the inferences people make about others based on food preferences. If people prefer foods that communicate an "appropriate" social identity, then the social inferences of those who observe them should show some agreement. Thus observers should be able to "read" the social information present in food preferences, and their reading should show some consensus with that of other observers. The results we obtained provided strong support for that assumption. The question that follows quite naturally from that finding concerns the validity of the observers' inferences.

The Health-Food Fan

SELF-PORTRAITS

In a second experiment, we examined the extent to which inferences made about a person based on his or her eating preferences correspond to that person's self-image. In order to test that, we screened about 2,000 students at Arizona State University and found 352 whose food preferences fell clearly within one of our five categories. We then asked the students to rate themselves—in terms of the identity they project—on traits we had developed in our first experiment. Then we compared their self-descriptions with the stereotypes that others had constructed about people with those food preferences.

The resulting data indicated substantial agreement between stereotypes and self-descriptions for people whose food preferences fell in the health-food, vegetarian, or gourmet categories. We found less agreement for those in the fast-food or synthetic-food categories.

REAL MEASURES?

Those two experiments indicated that a relationship exists between perceived social identity and patterns of food preference. But to what extent are food preferences related to objective measures of personality and lifestyle?

To find out, we undertook a third experiment. We gave another group of subjects a battery of well-validated personality tests. All the tests are designed to assess thought patterns, behavior, or lifestyle variables related to social identity. We had 275 volunteers—students and nonstudents—complete the battery of tests. They then rated their preferences for specific dishes in each food category.

The data we obtained suggested a significant correlation both between food preferences and objective personality tests, and between food preferences and self-ratings of personality: in other words, the foods people prefer can—to some extent—be used to predict their personalities.

DISTINCT PROFILES

The personality portraits related to the food preferences in our sample were quite distinctive. For example, most vegetarians emerged as relatively noncompetitive, with a taste for handicrafts and for difficult, challenging tasks of an intellectual nature. They claimed to be weight-conscious, "sexy," and to use drugs for pleasure.

Health-food enthusiasts projected them-

The Fast-Food Devotee

selves as noncompetitive, intellectual, and mechanically inclined. They were also hypochondriacal, antinuclear, prosolar, likely to use drugs for pleasure, and, by their own admission, "weird" and individualistic.

Gourmets, who admitted to an even higher "fun" drug use than the vegetarians, tended to be atheistic, liberal, and live alone. They also reported feeling that marriage is more vital to happiness than a job. They claimed to enjoy fast living (gambling, nightclubs, and so on) and engage both in glamour sports and in neighborhood athletics. They considered themselves sensual and sophisticated.

To the extent that a fast-food portrait emerged, the preference seems related to a desire to work hard at one's job, a need to win, and the urge to have children. Fast-food people described themselves as religious, conservative, family-oriented, pronuclear, and antidrug. The synthetic-food fans also showed themselves to be conservative and home-oriented as well as practical and competitive.

To the best of our knowledge, our project was the first systematic attempt to link social symbolism and specific food categories, examining the hypothesis that food preferences are part of the complex system of attitudes and behavior that define social identity.

FOOD-BASED BELIEFS

Many undeveloped or unverified theories about food have been advanced over the years. For example: "we are what we eat;" familiar foods represent security; milk and milk-based products have a tranquilizing effect thanks to nursery memories; wine and gourmet cooking are attempts to gain some control over eating.

In his classic anthropological work, *The Golden Bough,* James Frazer wrote extensively of the ritual use of food. He concluded that "among primitive tribes, there is a universal belief that by eating the flesh of a man or an animal, an individual acquires the physical, moral, and intellectual qualities of that man or animal."

The Creeks and Cherokee of North America thought the person who dined on venison would be swifter and smarter than the one who fed on the meat of the clumsy bear, the slow-footed cattle, or the wallowing swine. Similarly, the Zaparo Indians of Ecuador tried to avoid meat from heavy animals such as tapirs and pigs. They preferred

The Synthetic-Food User

birds, monkeys, deer, or fish. And in Central Africa, young men seeking instant courage ate the flesh and hearts of lions, while would-be lovers desiring sexual strength dined on the testicles of goats. Before the Zulu warriors went into battle, they would often eat meat smeared with dried powder made from the flesh of leopards, lions, and elephants in hopes of acquiring the strength and aggressiveness of those creatures.

SYMBOLIC MESSAGES

The magic that primitive hunters and warriors saw in their food is not so different from the symbolic messages contemporary men and women believe their eating patterns convey. Accordingly, we think that our research helps shed light on the problem of why some people choose diets that are nutritionally poor or linked with medical problems. Medical research has begun to suggest that people in the United States as a group tend to overeat and to eat foods too rich in animal fat and sugar. It is possible that such patterns of food preferences stem from the symbolism inherent in certain foods—red meat symbolizing status, success, power, and achievement; sugar-laden foods representing pleasure, self-reward, and playfulness.

Our study, confined to middle-class people in the U.S. who are able to choose what they eat, suggests that the symbolism of food must also be taken into account in trying to get people to change their eating habits. Advertising executives understand this symbolism very well, of course. They concoct innumerable advertising campaigns linking this or that food with success, status, or romance. While the particular personality portraits associated with given food preferences may change with time or geographical region, we assume that some food-identity linkages will be present even if the specific relationship changes.

Our experiments in Arizona make it clear how the diner who orders Indonesian roast lamb and asparagus with hollandaise sauce, washing it down with a vintage bottle of wine, is reinforcing his sense of self—and sending a message about himself to others.

Doing the same is the pretty young woman in bare feet and granny glasses who calls for comfrey tea with clover honey, granola with dried fruit, and carob cake. Likewise feeding a sense of self (as well as his body) and sending out a message is the teenager who shouts for a Big Mac, fries, and a chocolate shake to go □

At the Benhaven School in New Haven, Connecticut, an instructor helps an autistic child develop his ability to understand sign language as a means of fostering language use.

AUTISM: A WORLD APART

by Bruce Bower

THE condition may be noticeable from day one. The newborn child is physically normal, but his attention fades in and out. He is uncomfortable when held. He may cry almost nonstop, or he may seem unusually quiet. At one year of age his main diversion may be looking at his fingers or banging his head against the crib—for hours. Even to his mother, the infant may respond no more warmly than to a piece of string or to a small toy.

These are some of the early symptoms of what has come to be known as childhood autism. It is a rare disorder, afflicting about 5 out of 10,000 children, and is four times more common in boys than girls. It is also a confusing disorder, because its symptoms often resemble other ailments, such as childhood schizophrenia, mental retardation, and phenylketonuria. But it is certainly not new, having been described by physicians as far back as 1809.

EMPTY FORTRESS

Recent research suggests that a new diagnostic tool may be available to help identify types of autism. Donald J. Cohen and his colleagues of the Yale University School of Medicine performed computed tomographic (CAT) brain scans on a group of autistic children and found deficiencies in the left hemisphere of the brain among those children with neurological and central nervous system defects. Children without such problems had normal results on the scans. Treatment can now be more effectively planned for the two groups.

CAT scans may provide a valuable look at the brain functions of autistic children, but the disorder remains stubbornly resistant to efforts aimed at revealing its causes. In the 1950's and 1960's most investigators believed that autism was primarily a social withdrawal by the child, a retreat from parental rejection and emotional iciness into what psychoanalyst Bruno Bettelheim termed an "empty fortress." But it was difficult to demonstrate that autistic children experienced such extreme conditions, and researchers began to question these assumptions in the late 1960's.

At that time research in the field was still analogous to the story of the blind men and the elephant: each blind man felt a different part of the animal and each conveyed the picture of a different creature to his comrades. Likewise, researchers with different perspectives on autism were not reaching a consensus as to what "animal" they were studying. Was it nature or nurture, biological predisposition or parental behavior that was creating such severe problems for a small number of unfortunate children?

INBORN CAUSE

Theories still vary, but researchers now generally agree that autism is caused by biological and inborn factors. No one has solid proof for this, but it is clear that scientists are describing a different elephant than had been imagined. "Today ... parents of autistic children are considered to be like the parents of other handicapped children whose care poses inhuman burdens," says Cohen. "Parents are usually unhappy, worried, angry, discouraged, and exhausted. But they are not, as a group, unconcerned or unloving."

Experimental results obtained by Susan

E. F. Berstein/Peter Arnold

Early theories about the causes of autism stressed parental effects. Therapy often involved substituting real parents with warm, accepting surrogates.

Folstein and Michael Rutter of the Institute of Psychiatry in London suggest that an inherited cognitive abnormality can cause some autistic cases, that brain damage at birth can cause others, and that both factors may work together to trigger the disease. The effect of heredity on autism is uncertain, but the two per cent rate of autism in siblings is 50 times that of the general population. This correlation provides ammunition for theories of an inherited defect, but more research is required. It is also true that wealth and divorce run in families.

Mimi Forsyth/Monkmeyer Press

A devoted therapist reaches out to an autistic youngster in a new special-educational classroom located within a regular elementary school.

© Andrew Skolnick/Benhaven School

At a farm owned by the Benhaven School, an autistic teenager learns horticultural skills in a program set up to provide vocational training to older children and young adults.

The genetic baton is now held by psychiatrist Edward R. Ritvo of the University of California at Los Angeles. He recently founded the UCLA Registry for Genetic Studies of Autism, which is involved in an international investigation of the multiple occurrence of autism in families. So far, more than 200 families have been located, and Ritvo is in the process of verifying the multiple incidence. The National Society for Autistic Children in Washington is helping him find the families. One of Ritvo's main hypotheses is that autistic children may inherit a lack of resistance to a virus that contributes to brain damage before or after birth and causes neurological problems. "We've had an unprecedented response from families so far," says Ritvo. "It seems likely that genetic factors work in conjunction with others, such as biochemical problems, to cause autism."

BIOCHEMICAL PROBLEMS

While Ritvo sees autism as an inherited disease of the brain, Mary Coleman of the Children's Brain Research Clinic in Washington calls it not a disease but a set of three syndromes. "Classical autism" occurs by early infancy and there are no apparent neurological or electroencephalographic (EEG) problems. "Childhood schizophrenia with autistic symptoms" occurs after 30 months of age and additional psychiatric symptoms are present. "Mental retardation with autistic symptoms" occurs when there is evidence of organic brain disease and neurological and EEG abnormalities.

In a 1976 study of 78 autistics and 78 matched controls, Coleman found that 48 per cent of the autistics had biochemical problems. There was either an error in purine metabolism, an error in calcium metabolism, or a decreased level of the neurotransmitter serotonin. (Neurotransmitters are chemicals involved in the transmission of impulses between nerve cells.)

Genetic and biochemical findings have accumulated and slowly evolved, but other research has stimulated far more controversy. Bernard Rimland of the Institute for Child Behavior Research in San Diego has reported significant improvement in 11 of 16 "autistic-type" youngsters after giving them massive doses of vitamin B6 daily. B6 apparently increases serotonin levels, but Coleman says her findings indicate that only 5 per cent of autistics have depleted serotonin supplies. Other researchers also tend to minimize the potential of megavitamin therapy. Rimland remains unfazed and continues his investigations. The most important research breakthrough, he says, will be deciphering the relationship between allergies, especially food allergies, and brain functioning. Megavitamin therapy may counteract allergic reactions in some autistic children.

ROLE OF PREGNANCY

While most investigators concentrate on genetic and biological studies of autistic children themselves, Alan J. Ward, director of the Henry Horner Children's Center in Chicago, is looking at the effects of pregnant women's anxiety and family problems on the development of autism in their children. He has found a significantly higher degree of experienced anxiety in mothers of autistic youngsters as opposed to mothers of a control group of children. Ward is now involved in a project to expand basic prenatal care to Chicago-area mothers and "red-tag" potential problems during pregnancy. "The mother's problems before birth can result in a more vulnerable child . . . one with neurological or developmental handicaps—a child who never really starts to grow," says Ward.

NO SHORTCUTS COMING SOON

As researchers trace the boundaries of autism's causes, the fact remains that the parents of a 3- or 4-year-old autistic child may go from physician to physician in search of a diagnosis. They may find that the child is given such labels as severe mental retardation, schizophrenia, aphasia, atypical personality development, learning disability, or severe emotional disturbance. Each of these diagnoses illuminates one particular facet of the child's problems.

"The universal symptom of autism," says Cohen, "is the inability to relate to people and social situations in a normal way." These children have little or no expressive language and may engage in bizarre verbal behavior, such as the mechanical repetition of words and phrases. Sensory input is difficult for them to integrate and understand. Their behavior is ritualistic, showing no emotional connection to parents or other children.

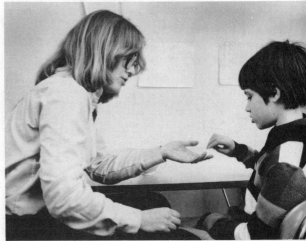

Benhaven School

A teacher instructs an autistic adolescent in a specially-structured room, where picture windows are omitted to minimize all visual distractions.

Yet some of these children have what are known as idiot savant capabilities and are able to perform complex musical, intellectual, or artistic feats, even if they have a subnormal IQ. These capacities are related to functions of the brain's right hemisphere and some investigators suggest a possible left hemisphere deficiency in autistics. This theory is strengthened by the CAT scan findings at Yale that show just such deficiencies in some autistic children.

Although optimistic about the future of their efforts, researchers don't expect the sea to part and provide a shortcut to better understanding. "There are very few academic researchers in autism," says Cohen. "It's a wild field" □

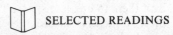 SELECTED READINGS

"Autistic children's responses to structure and to interpersonal demands" by Peter Clark and Michael Rutter. *Journal of Autism and Developmental Disorders,* June 1981.

"Autistic children learn to relax" by Rochelle Albin. *Psychology Today,* April 1980.

"Benhaven: A School That Works for the Autistic" by Stephen Rudley and Cynthia Lynes. *New York,* October 8, 1979.

"Kids with the faraway eyes" by Donald R. Katz. *Rolling Stone,* March 8, 1979.

The Granger Collection

Sigmund Freud, the founder of psychoanalysis, wrote a classic work on slips of the tongue.

FREUDIAN SLIPS

by Robert Geballe

IN the heat of the summer of 1968, the city of Chicago hosted the Democratic National Convention. The United States at that time was embroiled in internal conflict over the war in Vietnam, and the convention was expected to be the focal point of passionate views. Chicago Mayor Richard Daley, defending the possible use of police force to control unruly demonstrators, was speaking to a downtown audience. "The policeman isn't there to create disorder," he said. "He's there to preserve disorder."

Daley's speech mistake was a common one, especially since it occured in a situation of great stress. We all have experienced moments when language—"the gift of the gods"—has seemed more like a booby trap for their amusement. But Mayor Daley was severely chastized for his slip of the tongue. His true feelings were said to have been exposed. Is this the truth? Why do our tongues befoul us at times?

INTO THE UNCONSCIOUS

The classic work on slips of the tongue is that of Sigmund Freud in his book *The Psychopathology of Everyday Life* (1914). In this book, Freud examines forgetfulness, inability to keep resolutions, reading and writing mistakes, and slips of the tongue. These common human foibles were to him, and many a psychiatrist afterwards, flickering lamps illuminating the human unconscious.

Freud suggested that slips of the tongue—or "Freudian slips," as they have since become known—could be the result of one of two things. (1) The two words interchanged "lie very close to each other in the unconscious," and the wrong one is accidentally chosen by the conscious mind. (2) There is some hidden significance in the mistake in word choice, and the slip of the tongue "exposes our innermost thoughts." Freud preferred the latter hypothesis—that mistakes in language are a glimpse into the unconscious. He said, "mistakes in speech often perform the most valuable service" in discovering the thought content of patients. "Nobody wishes to acknowledge a mistake in speaking, due to the resulting shame," he declared. "This points to a 'motivation' in the formation of the disturbance."

David Hartman on "Good Morning, America," . . . "We'll be right back after this word from General Fools."

Freud described some examples:
• Distorting someone's name, when done intentionally, is an insult. It could have the same significance when it occurs "accidentally."
• Introducing yourself to someone you respect by substituting his or her name for yours could be a sign of admiration.
• Choosing a word of opposite meaning could be a betrayal of your true feelings. Freud cites the example of a fellow therapist who told a patient she was "incompetent to take care of her affairs," when he meant to say "competent." He later confided to Freud that he actually thought she would have a hard time.

Freud's ideas on slips of the tongue were constantly attacked, yet he was very clever in defending them. He drew support for his theory from popular behavior. "When a speech blunder occurs in a serious squabble and reverses the meaning of one of the disputants, it puts him at a disadvantage which his adversary seldom fails to utilize. This clearly shows that although people are unwilling to accept my theory, they nevertheless interpret speech blunders in a manner similar to mine."

Harry von Zell announcing the winner of the 1928 Presidential election ... "Ladies and Gentlemen, the President of the United States—Hoobert Heever!"

Freud's explanation of slips of the tongue held popular attention for several decades. But as the study of language grew in the 20th century, a new and more critical look was taken at this commonplace occurrence. The science of linguistics attempts to describe human language. Slips of the tongue help linguists define the rules by which language is organized.

PHONEMES AND MORPHEMES

Modern linguistic theory states that language is composed of discrete units. The basic units of sound are called "phonemes". They are combined to form the larger units of language—"morphemes," as well as phrases, and sentences. The linguist studies how the units are combined and in that way tries to uncover the rules of language.

Freudian slips, since they can occur at any of these levels, offer a chance to learn something about how all aspects of language are organized. But tongue slips are a difficult subject for scientific study. They seem to occur randomly, and not very often when one is conscious of one's speech, as would be the case in a linguist's laboratory. Collecting a compendium of slips of the tongue is thus no small project. Dr. Victoria Fromkin, of the University of California at Los Angeles, spent five years collecting over 6,000 examples of spontaneous speech mistakes.

Fromkin first looked at the basic tenet of linguistics—that language is composed of individual phonemes. Acoustic analysis shows that in normal speech it is usually impossible to indicate where one word ends and the next one begins. Syllables of words, and words themselves, are not pronounced as isolated, individual events. But what takes place before a sound is actually spoken? Does the brain organize language in phonemes? Fromkin's analysis of phonemic speech mistakes indicates this is so. For example, mistakes like "Yew Nork" for "New York" and "taddle tennis" for "paddle tennis" indicate that discrete units do exist at some earlier point in speech generation.

Ed Sullivan, closing his show after doing a public-service announcement on tuberculosis ... "Good night, everyone, and help stamp out T.V."

If phonemes do exist as discrete units in the brain, then are there internal rules for their combination into sensical sounds? Freudian slips also shed some light on this. Certain mistakes are "outlawed" in a language, because the resulting sequence of phonemes never occurs in that language. The phrase "planting the tulips" is never transposed into "tlanting the pulips" because the phoneme 'tl' never occurs at the beginning of an English word.

LIRDBIKE

We also make mistakes in how we combine morphemes, the next step up the linguistic ladder. A morpheme is the basic unit of meaning in a language. The word "birdlike" is composed of two morphemes, "bird" and "like." Each has a distinct meaning, and each is composed of several phonemes. Are there internal rules for combining morphemes to form meaningful words? Once again, Fromkin's work indicates this is indeed so. She cites many mistakes involving morphemes: "motionly" for "motionless," "bloodent" for "bloody," "groupment" for "grouping." These wrong combinations of morphemes can only be explained if we learn individual morphemes as separate units, and then learn the rules for combining them.

Richard M. Nixon, acknowledging an introduction by Governor Dan Evans, during the Watergate hearings, 1974 ... "Thank you, Governor Evidence."

Freudian slips have also illuminated the most complex level of speech—the structure of sentences. Are sentences formed by stringing words together one by one, like putting beads on a necklace? Fromkin says instead that we choose entire phrases. There are two major reasons for this speculation:

1. The intonation of a phrase remains the same even when the phrase is transposed. Phrases have a certain rhythm and melody, and this is specified by the entire phrase, not by the individual words in the phrase. The disordered sentence "He put the salami and basket in the cheese" would have the same sound as "He put the salami and cheese in the basket."

2. When words in a sentence are transposed, they are almost always transposed with words of the same grammatical category; nouns for nouns, verbs for verbs, adjectives for adjectives. For example, the sentence "I think it is reasonable to measure with care" would be transposed into "I think it is careful to measure with reason" rather than "I think it is care to measure with reasonable." We seem to have some sort of internal monitor that requires that even our disordered sentences conform with grammatical rules.

William A. Spooner, dean of New College, Oxford, for whom the term "spoonerism" is named ... "queer old dean" for "dear old Queen."

The theories of linguists like Fromkin help us to predict what types of tongue slips will occur, but do not bring us any closer to answering our basic question—why do we make mistakes in speech? Here possibly another branch of science can help. Neurolinguistics attempts to understand which areas of the brain are responsible for our ability to speak, and how language is organized in those areas. When a speech difficulty can consistently be correlated with damage to a certain area of the brain, then we can start to gain an understanding of the role that part of the brain plays in speech. For example, damage to the arcuate fasciculus, a bundle of nerve fibers that connects the frontal and posterior parts of the cortex, causes substitution of phonemes to occur. These patients say "mahther" for mother, or "dayshus" for dishes. Damage to Wernicke's area (in the temporal lobe) or to Broca's area (in the frontal lobe) produces naming substitutions—"sofa" for chair, "wife" for mother. Mistakes like this indicate that the patient has understood the meaning of what he or she wants to say, but chooses the wrong word.

Work done by two University of Washington researchers, Dr. Catherine Mateer and Dr. George Ojemann, supports these findings. Working with patients undergoing brain surgery, they found that errors in naming occur mostly when the activity of nerve cells in Broca's and Wernicke's areas are inhibited, and that errors in grammar occur when widely scattered parts of the cortex are inhibited.

Governor John Connally discussing Spiro Agnew's legal problems ... "I hope that Spiro Agnew will be completely exonerated and found guilty of all the charges against him."

The explanations for slips of the tongue run from neurological to psychological, but nothing seems sufficient to cover our momentary embarrassment. Perhaps it is best to remember as our cheeks redden, that as great a gift as language is, it is only as perfect as its users □

📖 SELECTED READING

"Slips of the Tongue" by Victoria A. Fromkin. *Scientific American*, December 1973.

© Stuart Rosner/Stock

HASSLES

by Richard S. Lazarus

MODERN research on the effects of stress has concentrated on the dramatic events of life: the death of a spouse or a friend, divorce, marriage, retirement, or being fired. This research has largely ignored the effect of the minor but more frequent daily events that might be best described as hassles. Hassles, as I define them, are the irritating, frustrating, or distressing incidents that occur in our everyday interactions with the environment. They can take the form of disagreements, disappointments, accidents, or unpleasant surprises. They range from getting stuck in a traffic jam to losing a wallet; from an argument with a relative to a conflict with a classmate or co-worker.

I recently completed a year-long study of the effects of daily hassles with a group of my colleagues at the University of California at Berkeley. We discovered that daily hassles are more closely linked to, and may have a greater effect on, our moods and our health than the major misfortunes of life.

THE LIFE EVENTS APPROACH

Our work marks a significant shift in stress research. Most previous work in the field has operated under the premise that all major life changes—whether positive or negative—produce stress and that the more a person endures, the greater the potential for physical and mental illness. Our study raises serious doubts about that premise.

The preoccupation with major life events began in the mid-1960's with the pioneering work of Thomas Holmes and Richard Rahe at the University of Washington. Using interviews and health histories of several thousand people, Holmes and Rahe found a statistically significant relationship between the major events in their lives and their physical condition within the next year or two. The effect seemed to be cumulative: the more life changes, the greater the likelihood of a later illness. This finding applied both to positive events like marriage or pro-

An unexpected hassle, like getting stuck in snow, may seem to be just a petty problem. But it can have a serious impact on people under stress.

Hassles from frequent fighting among married couples can cause negative physical and psychological changes that may result in illness.

motion, and to negative events like divorce or getting fired.

Holmes and Rahe developed a 43-item checklist of "recent life events." They gave each item a numerical value in "life-change units" based on its estimated impact as a stressor. Death of a spouse, for example, they rated at 100 units; death of a close friend, at 37; and a minor violation of the law, at 11. People who have accumulated more than 300 life-change units in the previous two years are supposedly more likely than others to suffer serious health problems.

In recent years, however, the life events approach to stress research has come under increasing criticism on a number of different grounds.

HOW HARD DO THEY HIT?

The impact of hassles on our physical and mental health depends to a great extent on their frequency, duration, and intensity. A person's response to a given hassle depends on a variety of other factors: personality, coping style, other resources, and how the person's day has gone. When someone is under pressure, petty problems that otherwise might be ignored—a broken shoelace, for example—can have a much greater effect than if they had occurred at less anxious times.

For that reason, the particular hassles cited by the people we surveyed are less important than their overall intensity and the individual reactions to them. We suspect that some of the impact of hassles stems from their personal meaning and significance, or from a person's ineptness in coping with certain interpersonal difficulties.

The kind of hassles that affect a person's overall psychological economy have several possible sources. Major life events, in addition to their obvious or immediate impact, can create continuing hassles—a kind of "ripple effect." Divorce, for example, might force a man inexperienced at such tasks to make his own meals, do the laundry, or clean the house. It might force a woman to handle household finances or repair a leaky faucet for the first time.

Some hassles may recur because of a permanent but not always harmonious relationship in marriage or at work, such as sexual incompatibility with a spouse or personality conflict with a co-worker. Other hassles may occur not as a result of any major life change or permanent relationship, but from a momentary situation—an unexpected phone call, an uninvited guest, or a flat tire.

"As a matter of fact, the small monthly payment ISN'T ALL. There are large weekly payments that go with it."

Sidney Harris

UPLIFTS: EMOTIONAL BUFFERS?

Assessing the effect of daily hassles led us to consider the effect of uplifts, their positive psychological counterparts. These include pleasant, happy, or satisfying experiences like hearing good news, getting a good

This mother's ability to cope with hassles brought on by her children is just one factor that determines how much she will be affected by the negative stressors she must face.

© Sybil Shelton/Peter Arnold

Bert Miller/Black Star

Being delayed in a major traffic jam is a daily source of frustration for many people. This kind of frequent, intense hassle is a prime causative agent of poor overall health.

night's rest, and solving a difficult problem. Just as negative stressors or hassles can cause physical and psychological changes that may result in illness, we think that uplifts may serve as emotional buffers against the same disorders.

There are several ways in which uplifts may help people cope with daily hassles. They may serve as breathers, sustainers, or restorers when psychological resources have been run down during stressful periods. They may help us recover from the effects of harm or loss. They may act as psychological protection against the effects of hassles or major life changes.

A NEW STUDY

A group of us compiled a list of daily hassles and uplifts by citing common annoyances and pleasures that occur at work, among family and friends, or in other contexts. We got additional suggestions from

patients enrolled in a regional group health insurance program. Then we converted our list into a hassles questionnaire. The questionnaire does not have a fixed or final form, for there are undoubtedly many common examples that could or should be on our list. The list itself may not be appropriate for certain groups, such as young parents or the elderly.

We selected our research sample of 100 people (48 men and 52 women), ages 45 to 64, from a much larger survey population in Alameda County, California. Our subjects were mainly white, middle-aged, middle-class, and Protestant, with above-average incomes and education. Most were married (86 per cent), and relatively stable in employment history and residence. While we know that our sample is not representative of the general population, at this preliminary stage of our research we wanted to test our notions on a relatively small and homogeneous

Dr. T. H. Holmes and his colleagues devised this scale of impacts to gauge the amount of stress associated with various life situations.

University of Washington Medical School

THE SOCIAL READJUSTMENT RATING SCALE

LIFE EVENT	IMPACT VALUE
1. Death of spouse	100
2. Divorce	73
3. Marital separation	65
4. Jail term	63
5. Death of close family member	63
6. Personal injury or illness	53
7. Marriage	50
8. Fired at work	47
9. Marital reconciliation	45
10. Retirement	45
11. Change in health of family member	44
12. Pregnancy	40
13. Sex difficulties	39
14. Gain of new family member	39
15. Business readjustment	39
16. Change in financial state	38
17. Death of close friend	37
18. Change to different line of work	36
19. Change in number of arguments with spouse	35
20. Mortgage over $10,000	31
21. Foreclosure of mortgage or loan	30
22. Change in responsibilities at work	29
23. Son or daughter leaving home	29
24. Trouble with in-laws	29
25. Outstanding personal achievement	28
26. Wife begin or stop work	26
27. Begin or end school	26
28. Change in living conditions	25
29. Revision of personal habits	24
30. Trouble with boss	23
31. Change in work hours or conditions	20
32. Change in residence	20
33. Change in schools	20
34. Change in recreation	19
35. Change in church activities	19
36. Change in social activities	18
37. Mortgage or loan less than $10,000	17
38. Change in sleeping habits	16
39. Change in number of family get-togethers	15
40. Change in eating habits	15
41. Vacation	13
42. Christmas	12
43. Minor violations of the law	11

group. We hope to study more diverse groups in the future.

Participants in the study filled out a variety of questionnaires over the course of a year. (The questionnaires measured physical and mental health, and mood fluctuations.) At the beginning and end of the year, they filled out a 24-item life events scale comparable to the Holmes-Rahe scale. Each month the subjects kept a log of their emotions for four consecutive days. They also filled out a 117-item hassle checklist and a 135-item uplift checklist. They marked the items that had occurred that month, and rated the frequency and severity of the items on a 3-point scale.

RESEARCH RESULTS

As we expected, hassles turned out to be much better predictors of psychological and physical health than life events. The more frequent and intense the hassles people reported, the poorer their overall mental and physical health. We found no significant relationship between life events that occurred during the study and the health of the participants at its end. We did find, however, a moderate relationship between life events that occurred during the two and a half years *before* the study and people's health at the end. In short, we found that major events do have some long-term effects, but in the short term, hassles seem to have a much stronger impact on mental and physical health.

Our results do not mean to deny the very real impact of major setbacks. Clearly, the death of a loved one or a divorce can cause great emotional pain, and when such events are compounded, they can increase a person's susceptibility to illness.

That the effects major life events do have may occur through the daily hassles they provoke is also suggested by our findings. Suppose that a middle-aged man learns that his brother, who lived in a distant city, has died. He may grieve at the loss, but his daily life will be disturbed little, if at all. Should his business partner die, however, he would not only feel the emotional loss but might also have to cope with numerous hassles in adjusting to his partner's absence. In the latter case, he would presumably be a

The Top Ten Hassles and Uplifts

What are the most common sources of pleasures and hassles in life? It all depends on who you are.

When my colleagues and I asked 100 white, middle-class, middle-aged men and women to keep track of their hassles and uplifts over a one-year period, we got one set of candidates for the Top Ten annoyances and joys. When we asked a group of college students, we got another. Canadian health professionals gave us still another list. Each group had certain hassles and uplifts common to its station in life.

The 10 most frequent hassles and uplifts in the middle-aged group were, in order of frequency:

HASSLES

1. Concern about weight
2. Health of a family member
3. Rising prices of common goods
4. Home maintenance
5. Too many things to do
6. Misplacing or losing things
7. Yard work or outside home maintenance
8. Property, investment, or taxes
9. Crime
10. Physical appearance

UPLIFTS

1. Relating well with your spouse or lover
2. Relating well with friends
3. Completing a task
4. Feeling healthy
5. Getting enough sleep
6. Eating out
7. Meeting responsibilities
8. Visiting, phoning, or writing someone
9. Spending time with family
10. Home pleasing to you

People differ widely in the problems and pleasures typical of their lives. Only three hassle items—and not a single uplift—rated among the top 10 for all three groups. The big three were: misplacing or losing things, physical appearance, and too many things to do.

As for pleasures, the only two shared by young and middle-aged alike were completing a task and having good times with friends.

more likely candidate for physical or psychological illness.

When we added the information from the mood scales and daily logs of emotions to the data on hassles, we found that particularly for men, the more hassles and the more negative emotions, the worse a person's subsequent health. Our results strongly suggest that hassles trigger unpleasant emotions, which, in turn or in combination, have an adverse effect on health.

Contrary to our expectation, uplifts did not seem to have much buffer effect on the impact of hassles in this study. In fact, for women, uplifts seemed to have a negative effect on emotions and on psychological health.

At such an early stage in our research, we have no explanation that we can support with data for these surprising findings. In future studies we will continue to search for the positive functions that we still believe uplifts play in a person's psychological economy.

In summary, our own results are a mix of hassles and uplifts. But we do feel we have demonstrated that the small defeats and troubles of our daily lives may cause as much harm as the great ones □

Tension mounts as police officers and priests try to keep a troubled teenager from shooting himself. The men finally convinced the boy to put down the gun and surrender.

TEENAGE SUICIDE

by Frederick C. Klein

THE suburbs just north of Chicago are among the richest in the United States. Their wealth is reflected in their large and stylish homes, well-kept parks, and schools whose facilities and academic reputations are the envy of their neighborhoods.

But according to health professionals in the area, some of the towns have another distinction they would much rather do without: one of the nation's highest youth-suicide tolls.

Dr. Mary Giffin, a child psychiatrist who practices in the area, and several associates, looked into the circumstances of 23 suicides, and numerous suicide attempts, that occurred among teenagers there from mid-1978 to mid-1981. The figure is far out of proportion to the region's population, she says.

Dr. Griffin finds the suicide count puzzling as well as dreadful. "We have looked at this carefully, but we haven't been able to identify a 'typical' suicide profile. Many of the children were high achievers and socially adept, not the sort you usually associate with the act," she says. "We can only conclude that we are raising children who have very fragile personalities, kids who can be devastated by the slightest setback."

"ORDINARY PEOPLE"

Mounting youth suicide rates in well-off areas all around the United States are the ultimate manifestations of a complex subject that has been receiving increased attention of late: the pitfalls of growing up affluent.

The focus stems in part from the fact that John Warnock Hinckley Jr., the 25-year-old accused of shooting President Reagan, is an oil executive's son who grew up in comfort in a Dallas suburb. It also has come from the popular and critical acclaim accorded the movie *Ordinary People,* whose theme was the emotional poverty of a well-to-do family.

Less dramatic but more important, it comes from a growing pile of statistics and reports that show alcohol and drug use, out-of-wedlock pregnancies, crime, and membership in bizarre religious cults to be on the rise among the children of the middle and upper-middle classes.

In an emotional scene from the movie "Ordinary People," Donald Sutherland talks to his distraught son, Timothy Hutton, who thinks of taking his own life.

Paramount Pictures

Psychiatrists, psychologists, social workers, police juvenile officers, and others who work among the young say there is nothing new about well-off youngsters "going wrong." Nor is it claimed that the problems of the affluent young match those of their poorer contemporaries; if anything, the difficulties of the prosperous tend to be magnified because they are most likely to reach the eye of professionals.

SUCCESS AS A DETRIMENT

But experts say that this shouldn't detract from their seriousness. "The material success of parents can be a detriment to child-raising if it comes at the expense of time that should be spent with their children," says Lee Salk, a New York clinical psychologist and author of several books on parenthood. "Children can tell fairly young what their parents consider important. If they see that everything comes ahead of them, there's likely to be trouble ahead."

The inattentiveness of busy parents is the factor most often cited as contributing to behavior problems in their children, but the full picture is a good deal more complicated, others say. According to Dr. Bennett L. Leventhal, director of the Child Psychiatric Clinic at the University of Chicago medical school, it begins with the assumptions about parenthood that some well-educated, well-off people make.

"A lot of them minimize the burden of being a parent. They think that because they're doing all right, their kids just naturally will do all right, too," he says. "They also tend to approach their children on an intellectual level that's more appropriate for

adults. Their kids develop extraordinary verbal skill very young, but this can serve to mask their true, child's level of understanding."

VALUES AND GOALS

Dr. Leventhal adds that some parents are unsure of their own values, so are unable to offer their children any goals beyond material success. "The kids perceive their parents' expectations that they'll succeed, but not much else," he says. "Too often, they grow up lacking the internal controls they need to keep on course."

Aggravating the difficulties that some young children face are regimens of music, dance and language lessons, and participation in organized competitive sports, that many observers have come to lump under the label of "overprogramming." The activities are designed to develop youthful talents, but they also can serve to accustom children to a hectic pace and often increase their anxieties about success.

Pressures mount further in the high schools of the suburbs that house families of ambitious executives and professionals. There, large numbers of bright and highly motivated students test themselves against curricula studded with "accelerated" and college-level courses.

"The competition gets awfully fierce," says Russell Sullivan, a psychologist attached to the public schools of Lower Merion Township, an affluent area near Philadelphia. "For a lot of our kids, good grades aren't enough, they have to be the best. Obviously, they can't all make it. It's hardest on kids with average or even slightly above average abilities. They are made to feel dumb even though they aren't."

Competitiveness in upper-crust high schools extends beyond the classrooms and into extracurricular activities. Laura Aronberg, a recent college graduate who attended New Trier East High School in the wealthy Chicago suburb of Winnetka, recalls being "amazed" in college at meeting "kids who were involved in all sorts of high-school activities—volleyball, cheerleading, debate, you name it." She explains: "At New Trier, there was so much competition for places on teams and things that you pretty much had to pick one activity and give it everything you had."

NEED TO UNWIND

Not surprisingly, the children of the affluent often need to "unwind" during their leisure hours, and many do it the way their parents do: with alcohol and drugs. Surveys show that alcohol use has become almost universal among people 16 to 18, and that more than one-half of those in their late teens use marijuana.

Most past studies showed that teenagers from poor or blue-collar families were more likely to drink or smoke marijuana than those of the middle class, and that use of more-potent drugs was largely confined to lower-income groups. However, recent studies indicate that better-off kids are catching up.

In 1980, for instance, the University of Michigan Survey Research Center's annual national poll of high-school seniors showed that drinking among seniors who were college-bound, a rough measure of middle-class status, stood at 88 per cent. That percentage was almost the same as the figure for seniors who didn't plan to attend college. Rates of increase for marijuana use were about the same for both groups, but the use of cocaine rose among the college-bound while leveling off for the others.

Parents in the executive enclaves around big cities report that drinking is a common part of teen parties in their areas. "It's very simple: if you don't serve beer or wine, you don't have parties," says the mother of a teen-aged girl in one suburb of New York.

GAP CLOSING

Much the same situation is evident in patterns of sexual activity. Surveys by Johns Hopkins University of teen-aged women in U.S. metropolitan areas showed that the biggest increases in early sexual intercourse and out-of-wedlock pregnancies between 1971 and 1979 came among whites. Pre-marital pregnancy among whites aged 15 to 19 more than doubled to 13.5 per cent in that period, while the rate for blacks, while higher at 30 per cent, was up by only one-fifth. John Kantner, one of the principal researchers in the study, says his data doesn't show wide differences between income groups among whites.

"A lot of the girls we see have sex with their boyfriends out of a desire for intimacy they don't find at home," says Sandra Wade, director of North Shore Youth Health Services, an agency that gives birth-control counseling to teen-agers in Chicago's north-

Fierce academic competition and parental expectations of success create pressures that contribute to high suicide rates among affluent youths.
© Ed Lettau/PR

ern suburbs. "They tell us in effect that the sex is incidental to being close to someone."

She adds: "Our kids get pregnant out of ignorance, just like poor girls. They don't think what they hear in sex-education class applies to them."

Crime by teen-agers in the suburbs isn't nearly the problem it is in the inner cities, but it is probably understated in official statistics. "When a rich kid gets caught for a minor offense, he's likely to be reprimanded and released to his parents," says Diane Grieder, a probation officer in suburban Bergen County, New Jersey, near New York City. "A poor kid who does the same thing goes to reform school."

"You name the crime, we've got it here," says James McCarley, chief of police in Plano, Texas, a bedroom suburb of Dallas. He notes that many of the teen-agers his men arrest for burglary, theft, and other economic crimes come from "families where money isn't tight," so he theorizes they do it out of boredom or to get attention. "The attention part comes through when we call the parents to come get their kids," he says. "A lot of times, they aren't around for whole weekends. They've gone off and left their kids alone."

TRUSTING, SEEKING KIDS

Some authorities on the behavior of young people say that the crisis for many comes when they leave home for college. "That's when they find out that life isn't as safe or as predictable as they thought," says Dr. John G. Clark Jr., a Boston psychiatrist who is on the faculty of Harvard medical school. "It's also when some of them are first forced to confront their limitations, which can be a painful experience."

Dr. Clark has studied and written about cult membership among the young, and he says that children of the well-to-do are especially vulnerable to the appeals of so-called religious groups with strong dogmas and charismatic leaders.

"About half the kids who join cults are what we call 'seekers,' people with troubled histories who are looking for causes that might give structure to their lives, but the other half have no such background," he says. "They are trusting kids whose minds have been opened by their parents to the play of ideas. The cults take advantage of their naivete and openness to hook them. They can't do that nearly as easily with streetwise kids who know a con when they see one."

Dr. Clark estimates that cult membership in the United States has climbed to more than 3,000,000. It is a development that he calls "frightening." He warns that "the mind-changing process involved in cult conversions can seriously alter a person's mental and physical makeup with long-term implications we're only beginning to learn."

LACK OF DIRECTION

It is in the early adult years, too, that increases in suicide have been most marked. Between 1968 and 1978, the suicide rate nationally rose by about 17 per cent, but for white males aged 20 to 24 the increase was 86 per cent—the highest of any group—and for white males 15 to 19 it was 66 per cent.

Suicide was the second leading cause of death in 1978 among white men aged 15 to 24, ranking only behind accidents.

The reasons given for this rise cut across class and racial lines. They include high unemployment, increases in family breakups, and the declining influence of religion as a stabilizing force in U.S. life. But some experts also attribute it to a more general malaise that particularly affects the young.

"Most parents cheered when the great youth rebellion of the late 1960's and early 1970's failed, but maybe they shouldn't have. It at least gave dissatisfied youngsters a legitimate outlet for their grievances," says Dr. Norman R. Bernstein, a professor of child psychiatry at the University of Illinois' medical school in Chicago. "Kids I see today are more private and self-indulgent than they were then. A lot of them don't particularly want to follow in their parents' footsteps, but they see no real alternatives. There's been a loss of optimism, a lack of direction" □

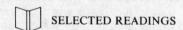 SELECTED READINGS

"Too weary to go on" by John Langone. *Discover*, November 1981.

© Bill Meng/New York Zoological Society

An experimental embryo transplant from a rare wild ox to a domestic cow resulted in a successful birth. Such transplants may enhance the survival of some endangered species.

BIOLOGY

REVIEW OF THE YEAR

Charlie Nye/Eugene Register-Guard

George Streisinger led a team of University of Oregon biologists in successfully raising hundreds of zebra fish that are genetically identical. Some of the clones, however, have physical abnormalities.

Advances in genetics, cloning, and the application of genetic engineering techniques to the production of useful products continued to dominate much of the news in biology during 1981. Animals were also in the news—good news in hopes for a vanishing wild species and bad news in the destruction caused by a pest fly. Fraud in research was also a topic of debate.

Genetics. Scientists succeeded in raising hundreds of genetically-identical zebra fish. University of Oregon researchers, led by George Streisinger, used sperm incapable of providing genetic material but capable of stimulating the egg to develop. They prevent the product—the stimulated egg—from dividing until the egg's genetic material has doubled, providing a full set of identical paired chromosomes. After that the egg is allowed to divide and develop. When the process is repeated with eggs from these adults, all their offspring are identical. The scientists report finding some physically abnormal fish within the identically-reared clones, indicating that the abnormalities must result from something other than hereditary makeup alone.

Scientists succeeded in transferring genes from one animal to another, from one plant to another, and from a bacteria to a plant. Cornell University workers transferred 17 bacterial genes necessary for nitrogen fixation into a yeast, but they haven't gotten the genes to work yet. Nitrogen fixation is the process that enables an organism to use nitrogen from the air instead of depending on symbiotic bacteria, fertilizers, or soil-based nitrogen. ■ A bacteria was used to transfer a gene between plants. University of Wisconsin researchers used a bacterium to transfer a gene that manufactures a seed protein from a French bean to a sunflower plant. They have not as yet detected the protein in the sunflower. ■ Ohio University researchers have had more luck. They reported a successful transfer of a gene between animals—specifically, from a rabbit into a mouse. They injected a gene that manufactures a blood protein into newly fertilized mouse eggs. Not only did the adult mice produce the rabbit protein, but their offspring did as well. The technique may prove useful in improving agricultural yield, as a way to transfer defective human genes into laboratory animals for study, or as a way to figure out how a gene is turned on—that is, made to produce its product.

Intense research has continued on interferon as a possible treatment for some kinds of cancer and virus infections. It is an antivirus substance produced by the human body.

Courtesy of Genentech Inc.

More about the genetics of viruses was unearthed during the year. Scientists at several institutions described finding pieces of genetic material in human chromosomes identical to that of a virus that causes leukemia in animals. ■ And Naomi Kitamura and coworkers at the State University of New York at Stony Brook described the exact order of the 7,433 subunits of the genetic material of the polio virus. The procedure may enable the manufacture of non-infectious pieces of virus as a vaccine, or allow scientists to figure out how to disrupt the virus's activity.

The first vaccine made using genetic engineering was reported by independent groups in the United States and Germany. Genes that produce a protein from the foot-and-mouth virus were inserted in bacteria. The bacteria then pump out many copies of the protein, which, in turn, can be injected into animals to produce immunity against the whole virus. Foot-and-mouth virus causes a nonfatal, highly infectious disease in over 30 species of animals. The annual cost of wasted meat is in the billions of dollars. The new vaccine may help eradicate this costly animal disease from the world.

Genetic engineering may also be used to create a hepatitis-B vaccine. Scientists at the University of California at San Francisco spliced a gene for a hepatitis-B virus protein into a yeast. The yeast produced not only the intact protein but also a complex structure similar to a particle capable of immunization that is found in people with hepatitis B. The particle from humans was successfully used to vaccinate people against hepatitis B, which affects some 500,000,000 people and results in liver damage. Yeast-produced immunizing particles would greatly facilitate vaccine production.

Meanwhile, genetic engineering may soon really be a "true industrial process." A gene machine—a machine that constructs synthetic genes—was marketed by Bio Logical, a small Toronto firm during the year. (See "Review of the Year—Technology" on page 320.)

Animals. For the first time, a common domestic animal gave birth to a member of an endangered species. The event occurred at the Bronx Zoo in New York City in August after New York Zoological Society researchers transplanted a seven-day-old embryo from a gaur, a rare Asian ox, into a Holstein cow. The event gave researchers hope that the procedure will work with other endangered species. (See page 65 for a photo of the gaur.) ■ University of Pennsylvania researchers reported success with another breeding technique—in-vitro fertilization. They combined egg and sperm from a cow and bull and then implanted the embryo in a cow. This was the first time in-vitro fertilization had been done in cows.

An "unendangered" species made news too: the Mediterranean fruit fly threatened California's most fertile fields. In the summer of 1981, after initial hesitation, the fields were sprayed with the pesticide Malathion. Though there was no evidence of Medflies by the end of the year, officials fear a new infestation in the spring of 1982. (See "The Fly in our Fruit" on page 80.)

Fraud. Fraud in research was the topic of heated debate among scientists and the subject of several U.S. Congressional hearings in 1981. At one hearing, Dr. John Long, formerly of Harvard University, confessed that he fudged data included in a paper he authored on Hodgkin's disease. Later in the year a young graduate student at Cornell University whose work had led to a new theory on viruses and cancer, resigned after his superiors came to believe that he falsified his data. ■ In the area of applied research four officials of Industrial Bio-Test (IBT) Laboratories, one of the largest drug-and-pesticide testing laboratories in the United States, were indicted after the U.S. Food and Drug Administration and the Environmental Protection Agency found that many of the test results IBT had submitted to them were invalid. Some of the pesticides approved as a result of IBT tests have now been pulled off the market. ■ And in a curious twist on fraud: scientists are taking a second look at the work of William Summerlin. Back in 1974 Summerlin admitted painting black patches on white mice to make it look as if a skin graft had been successful. Now the handful of scientists who continued work in the field say that though Summerlin may have faked his results, his theory—namely, that skin grafts are more likely to take if the skin is given a little time in a culture dish before grafting—looks good. (See "Science Frauds" on page 264.)

Joanne Silberner

Woods Hole Oceanographic Institution

Marine biologists discovered giant tubeworms living near warm-water vents in the ocean floor. This photo was taken by the submersible *Alvin* at 2,800 meters (9,000 feet).

Studies have shown that mud-living, magnetic bacteria can distinguish north from south, and can sense the earth's magnetic field via iron-rich structures in their bodies.

Courtesy of R. B. Frankel, R. Blakemore, D. L. Balkwill, and D. Maratea

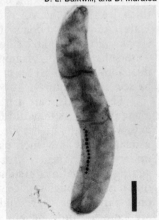

Far below the ever-frozen surface of Lake Hoare in Antarctica, blue-green algae carpet the lake floor and live just as they did in the Precambrian era.

LIFE AT THE END OF THE EARTH

by Patrick Young

THE day is going well. Researchers from Virginia Polytechnic Institute (VPI) and State University have pierced the permanently frozen surface of Antarctica's Lake Hoare. They are using a large copper coil with hot antifreeze coursing through its tubing to melt through the 5.5-meter (18-foot)-thick ice. Now the voice of biologist-diver Dale Andersen booms through a loud speaker. From the lake's floor in dark, frigid waters that verge on turning to ice, Andersen describes the rich carpet of blue-green algae he sees before him.

The scientists are here to see how the algae live just as they did 600,000,000 years ago, without any higher life-forms. They also want to know how such plant life can exist under a permanently frozen lake surface, getting only a tiny fraction of the sunlight that passes through the ice, and even that for only part of the year. And other biologists are here to study lichens living inside the rocks, a recently discovered niche that suggests to some scientists that the Viking landers on Mars may have looked for life in the wrong place.

WINDOW TO THE PAST

Brilliant Austral-summer sunshine floods Taylor Valley, part of a small and rare ice-cap-free region called the Dry Valleys. Standing in the dazzling light, aquatic ecologist George M. Simmons Jr. holds up a sample of blue-green algae retrieved only minutes before and seeks to explain what lures him to this frozen oasis in the world's coldest desert.

Beneath him nature has created a living "window to the past, an analogue to an ancient ecosystem," he says. "Here you can look back in time 600,000,000 years and see how an ecosystem functioned without higher life. This lake is almost a remnant of the past—almost like finding a dinosaur."

Blue-green algae—the name is a misnomer; they can assume all kinds of colors—straddle the evolutionary ladder between bacteria and green, or "higher," algae. Their cell structure resembles that of bacteria, but they possess that distinguishing capability of green plants—oxygen-producing photosynthesis.

These organisms are among the oldest and most ubiquitous of earth's life-forms. And they have changed little through their 3,500,000,000 years of existence. For nearly 3,000,000,000 years, they dominated the world's waters, thriving in dense mats like those that stretch from shore to shore along the bottom of Lake Hoare. But the appearance of higher organisms some 600,000,000 years ago ended their reign, as such evolving creatures as worms, mollusks, crabs, and shrimp broke apart the algae's thickly matted filaments and dominated the habitat.

UNIQUE LABORATORY

Thus the discovery in 1978 by Simmons and his VPI colleague, botanist Bruce C. Parker, of an ancient life-form living its Precambrian life-style provided a unique biological laboratory. It also raised some intriguing questions. How, for example, could these algae-plants that depend on sunlight for photosynthesis and life—survive and thrive in a place where no sun shines at least four months of the year?

That is what draws Simmons and others back each year to the Dry Valleys, their search for answers that can be sought nowhere else. The area is a treasure trove for scientists trying to fathom the geologic and glacial history of earth's fifth largest continent and the tenacious ability of life to exist in extraordinarily harsh environments. The Dry Valleys may also explain the weathering processes of Mars, and the puzzling chemical composition of the Martian soil discovered by the Viking landers in 1976.

In a frozen land where the ice cover averages more than 1.6 kilometers (1 mile) in depth, where mountains have lain encased in blue ice for millions of years, the Dry Valleys are a rare sight, barren and brown. Here and there an ice-covered lake lies amid their glacial moraines, and their flanks harbor an oc-

casional alpine glacier moving very slowly down from the mountains above. Snowfall is meager. Rain has never been recorded. An average air temperature for one of the valleys has been found to be about −18° Celsius (0° Fahrenheit), and at times hurricane-force winds suddenly sweep down from the high plateau of the East Antarctic Ice Sheet.

For years, the mountains rising above the valley floors were believed devoid of life. But life had found a foothold inside porous rocks. Unique lichens lived there, shielded from Antarctica's harshest elements and the eyes of the few scientists who passed by. These rock denizens, with their distinctive colored layering, were finally discovered by microbiologist E. Imre Friedmann of Florida State University in 1976.

A researcher helps his co-worker put on an insulated mitt as the diver prepares to plunge into the dark, icy water to collect algal samples.
Gordon Love

Patrick Young

Lake Vanda in Wright Valley may not seem unusual as viewed from its ice-covered surface. But the more than 60-meter (200-foot)-deep lake is 25° C (77° F) at bottom.

GOLD MINE VALLEYS

This region of mountains, high plateaus, and valleys—principally Taylor, Wright, and Victoria valleys—covers about 2,600 square kilometers (1,000 square miles) sandwiched between the western edge of the Ross Sea and the Transantarctic Mountains. It is only a helicopter hop from McMurdo Station, the main Antarctic base of the National Science Foundation, which now runs the U.S. Antarctic program.

"These valleys have turned out to be gold mines for understanding the continent's glacial history," says geologist George H. Denton of the University of Maine at Orono.

There were no Dry Valleys 25,000,000 years ago. The land lay buried under an expanding East Antarctic Ice Sheet that had overrun the Transantarctics. Heat rising from the earth's crust and friction melted the underside of the ice. Over millions of years, the water beneath the glacier eroded weakened bedrock, creating valleys as later glaciers would carve the fjords of Norway.

By 7,000,000 years ago the ice sheet had retreated to its present size and mountain-building activity had thrust the Transantarctics higher. These two processes greatly reduced the flow of ice into the region. Winds blowing down from the ice sheet wore down the glacial remains, filling the valleys.

"The winds acted almost like blotters, soaking up the ice and snow," explains Denton. "The amount of ice lost exceeded the amount of ice that could pour through the valleys. So they became dry about 4,000,000 years ago. If the ice sheet should become smaller or the mountains higher, then there would be other dry valleys created."

LAKES ALL DIFFERENT

The lakes and ponds of the Dry Valleys are a perplexing lot with a diversity rarely matched in such a small area. "You would expect lakes in the same region to have more similarities than differences," Simmons says. "But that is not true in the Dry Valleys. Lakes lying side by side might as well be on the other side of the world with regard to their water chemistry."

Hoare is a freshwater lake with a temperature of 0° Celsius (32° Fahrenheit). Bonney, another Taylor Valley lake, is fresh at its surface and 12 times saltier on its bottom than seawater. The shallow Don Juan Pond in Wright Valley is so salty it never freezes, making it unique among Antarctic lakes. A few ponds are frozen solid.

In the Antarctic summer of 1977–78, Simmons and Parker began a survey to assess the water chemistry of ten lakes, and to study the limited life that existed within their waters. A year later, during their first scuba explorations of the lakes, the VPI team discovered the Precambrianlike growth of Lake Hoare's blue-green algae. Since then, Simmons and Parker have focused much of their work on the algae.

Blue-green algae are hardy plants, adept at growing in extreme and hostile environments. Their existence in the Dry Valley lakes has been known for years. Each summer, the edges of the lakes melt a short distance around the shore, leaving the permanent ice encircled briefly by a moat. Specimens of the algae had been collected from these waters. But it wasn't until the VPI researchers used equipment to melt through the lake ice that algae were found growing all across the lake floor. With no higher creatures to disrupt their complex structures, the algae were thriving much as Precambrian algae had done throughout much of the world.

For a scientist, entering this watery realm is like passing through a time warp. "All of a sudden you get this feeling that you are down in a deep ocean looking at life as it was 600,000,000 years ago," says Gordon Love, a VPI graduate student.

PLANTS WITHOUT SUNLIGHT

Lake Hoare's year-round ice is an extraordinarily effective sun block. Only about one per cent of the light that strikes the ice surface penetrates to the water beneath. Algae growing at a depth of 25 meters (82 feet) must make do with only about 0.1 per cent of the surface light. Yet somehow the algae harness that small amount of sunlight, using it as a source of energy for photosynthesis. They convert water and carbon dioxide into the organic compounds they need to live.

The discovery of the luxurious algal mats posed the question of how plants that rely on photosynthesis survive when the sun retreats below the horizon for one-third of the year. Simmons and Parker have studied the algae in the laboratory and offer a theory.

During photosynthesis, the algae produce and excrete some short-chain carbon compounds, particularly one called glycollate. These compounds stay in the water and, when the sun disappears in winter, the algae use them as an energy source.

The system works this way: glycollate has to be produced, Simmons says. "And when we spike the algae growing in the laboratory with the compounds we expect to be produced, they take them up like a hungry man going through hamburgers."

VPI researchers are now continuing attempts to measure glycollate production and to conduct special experiments on what influences its formation and use.

AND WITHOUT OXYGEN

The algae and other microorganisms in Lake Hoare do not live by normal photosynthesis and its by-products alone. VPI divers

Just below the surface of the sandstone rocks at left live hardy plants called lichens that have adapted a unique way of surviving in Antarctica.
© E. I. Friedmann

The multicolored bands seen in these samples of sandstone reveal rock-dwelling lichens that receive most of their nutrients from minerals.

© E. I. Friedmann

have found an anaerobic zone—a small basin within the lake where the waters contain no free oxygen. Hydrogen sulfide is released by bacteria, and possibly by the algal mats, living in the water and sediments of the lake floor.

Under anaerobic conditions photosynthetic bacteria, as well as blue-green algae, use hydrogen sulfide instead of water in their photosynthetic process and produce sulfur as a by-product instead of oxygen. This is the same process that the earliest photosynthetic microorganisms used before there was free oxygen in the environment.

Anaerobic photosynthesis is common in such places as the bottom water of lakes in warmer climes. But the process has not been studied well in the Antarctic. Now, Simmons says, the question is whether the algae lived in the basin before it turned anaerobic and somehow adapted to an oxygen-free life.

In 1979 the VPI team concentrated on four Dry Valley lakes: Hoare, Bonney, Vanda, and Fryxell. Algal mats grow in all four. In Lake Bonney, the mats were found thriving in waters two to three times saltier than the oceans. At Lake Vanda, divers found mats at 30 meters (100 feet) and dredged more samples from as deep as 55 meters (180 feet). They also found the algae in all four lakes are apparently forming stromatolites, a type of fossil. Comparing the Antarctic stromatolites with older fossils might reveal some of the environmental conditions that existed far back in time.

Simmons is unconcerned about how the algae found their way to the Dry Valleys; it is enough that they are there. "If someone told me these blue-green algae are the direct descendants of cells that used to live in swamps that existed when Antarctica was part of Gondwanaland, I could believe it," he says. (Early in earth's history Africa, South America, and Australia formed a huge super-continent known as Gondwanaland.)

Imre Friedmann is no more certain how lichens appeared high above the valley floors, though he can now explain how they move from one rock to populate others.

SHELTER INSIDE THE ROCKS

Lichens—small plants formed by the symbiotic association of a fungus and an alga—have been known in parts of Antarctica since the beginning of the 20th century. But these were traditional lichens, attached to the surfaces of rocks and easily recognized; they were not incognito species disguising their structure.

The discovery of the rock-dwelling lichens was no accident, yet it held its own surprises. In the early 1960's, Friedmann was teaching at Hebrew University in Jerusalem. He and his microbiologist wife, Roseli, discovered the first example of life inside rocks. It was a blue-green alga that flourished within porous rock in the Negev Desert. The find proved to be the first of many.

"It turned out that wherever light-colored, porous rocks that also transmit light are present, there is a good likelihood there will be organisms under the crust," Friedmann says. "They are common in virtually all the desert areas of the world. We found them later in America, Africa, and Australia."

During the 1960's and 1970's, scientists working on the experiments the Viking spacecraft would carry to Mars chose the Dry Valleys as the place on earth most similar to the Martian surface, and therefore worthy of concentrated study. Friedmann, by then on the Florida State faculty, suspected that the coldest of earth's deserts might also contain rocks harboring algae. In 1973, he asked Wolf Vishniac, a University of Rochester biologist bound for the Dry Valleys, to bring back some sandstone rocks for him.

Vishniac died in the Antarctic that year, killed in a fall. Later Friedmann received from his widow a bag filled with rocks Vishniac had collected before his death. Inside one, Friedmann found a blue-green alga very similar to the ones that inhabit the rocks of hot deserts.

Friedmann finally went to the Antarctic in 1976 under a National Science Foundation grant. One December morning a Navy helicopter landed him and a graduate student high in the Asgard Range separating Taylor and Wright valleys to search for rock-dwelling life. He still recalls that day with relish.

"We rushed to the first big boulder and cracked it with a geology pick," he says. "And there it was, the absolute first one we hit. In the hot deserts, it is always a brownish or greenish layer. And this was a three-colored layer—very unusual."

LIFE IN DELICATE BALANCE

Friedmann's surprise came when he learned what accounts for the rock's odd coloration. The blue-green alga in the rock back in his laboratory was a rarity. Most of the life in the Dry Valley rocks consists of lichens. With the aid of several colleagues, including lichenologist Mason Hale of the Smithsonian Institution's Museum of Natural History, Friedmann has studied these rock flora extensively, on site and in the laboratory.

The organisms grow only under the north side of rocks—the side that gets direct sunlight and faces away from the bitter

Gordon Love

Dale Anderson, a biologist from Virginia, looks on as a melter slowly makes its way through the 5.5-meter (18-foot)-thick ice covering Lake Hoare.

winds blowing down from the South Pole. In summer, air temperature may be minus ten degrees Celsius, or just in the teens Fahrenheit, but just under a rock's sunlit surface, temperatures can reach a cozy 10° Celsius (50° Fahrenheit). Sunlight, penetrating the porous sandstones as deep as one centimeter (0.5 inch), provides the energy that is needed for photosynthesis.

"In the Dry Valleys, the surfaces of rocks are so cold and inhospitable that no organism can survive on the outside," Friedmann says. "These lichens, instead of adapting to these inhospitable climate conditions, found a way to go underground, to go inside the rock where a better climate exists.

"They are living in very delicate balance. They have warm temperatures, light, and they get water from snow melt. The water is sucked in by the porous rock, which serves as a reservoir for the organisms inside. Most nutrients are present in the rock as minerals.

"But where do the organisms get nitrogen? We thought at first they must be nitrogen fixers, able to take nitrogen from the air. But they aren't. Rather, they get nitrogen from the snow. The snow has certain amounts of nitrates in it. There is just enough in the melting snow so that nitrogen is not a problem."

Classifying the Dry Valley lichens has proved difficult. For one thing, their structure is unusual. Rather than forming the normal, compact, coherent lichen body, the lichens' fungal filaments wind through the rock's tiny air spaces and twist around its mineral crystals. For another, the Dry Valley lichens do not exhibit the normal sexual stages of lichens, on the basis of which lichens are recognized and classified.

The lichens living inside the rock are a new type. "Nothing like them exists in the world." Dr. Friedmann says. Yet, the chemical substances they produce are similar to those of other lichens. So far, Hale has identified five chemically different lichens living in the Dry Valley region.

In winter, the lichens simply shut down and await the warmth of another spring's sun. "One of their important adaptations is that they can stop and go easily, which other organisms can't do as fast," Friedmann says.

And at times some move on to new homes, uprooted perhaps by the chemicals they excrete in living.

"Some chemical activity, which we do not understand yet, causes the rock crust to flake off and the lichen is exposed," Friedmann explains. "Particles of the lichen are blown off by the wind. Once such a small piece gets into the proper place, it can invade and colonize a new rock. The remaining lichens grow deeper down when the crust falls off."

INFORMATION BANK

The existence of the Dry Valley lichens has buoyed the hopes of some that simple life might dwell hidden somewhere on Mars. The Viking landers found no evidence of life. But they did find terrain remarkably similar to parts of the Dry Valleys. Photographs returned by Viking 2 look as if they were taken near Don Juan Pond in Antarctica.

Soil samples analyzed on the surface by Viking experiments puzzled scientists, for they suggested a land enriched with sulfur and chlorine. Exotic rock compositions were suggested to explain the findings. But the high-sulfur, high-chlorine content may be nothing more than a by-product of cold-climate weathering.

Geochemist Everett K. Gibson of the National Aeronautics and Space Administration's Johnson Space Center in Houston finds the concentrations of sulfur and water-soluble chlorides in the Dry Valley soils to be almost identical to the Martian concentrations measured by the Viking 1 and 2 landers.

"We see from our Dry Valley studies that soil enhancements can occur because of the weathering processes that occur in dry, cold deserts, and you don't need exotic rock compositions," Gibson says. "You can produce the concentrations seen by Viking by such things as daily freeze-thaw cycles, seasonal temperature variations, the very low moisture that is there, low relative humidities, and the wind velocities that allow the surface to be sculptured.

"By using the Dry Valleys to interpret Mars data, we can now begin to get a firm handle on the weathering processes that are at work on Mars. This will give us a real understanding of what we should look for the next time we go there."

It is for new understandings like these that scientists go south every year. "Antarctica is like an information bank," says George Simmons. "You go down there and work in the weirdest, wildest places and put knowledge in the bank: and later on you have questions about what happens elsewhere in the world—or even in other worlds. And you find that what you've learned there becomes worth its weight in gold" □

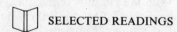 SELECTED READINGS

"Cyanobacteria—blue-green algae: their evolution and relationship to other photosynthetic organisms" by D. W. Krogmann. *BioScience*, February 1981.

"Antarctica: freeze-dried desert" by C. Petit. *Science Digest,* May 1981.

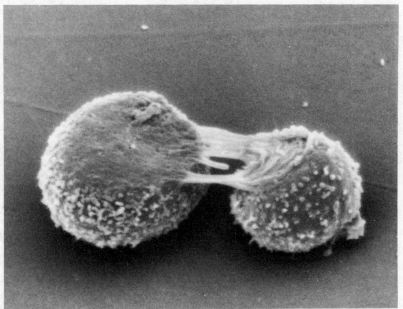

An antibody-making cell was fused with a cancer cell to form this hybrid-oma, or hybrid cell, which divides to form clones.

MONOCLONAL ANTIBODIES

by Jerry E. Bishop

IMAGINE for a moment a new cancer treatment using the principle of the guided missile. A sub-microscopic "missile," when injected into the body, could selectively seek out cancer cells, ignoring all the normal cells. The tiny missile could carry a radioactive "beacon" to reveal where cancer cells are hidden. Or it could carry a "warhead" of an anti-cancer drug to destroy the cancer cells on the spot.

Such a powerful anti-cancer weapon isn't yet available. But some new advances in the laboratory suggest that it is in the realm of possibility.

Scientists are making remarkable strides in developing what are known as "monoclonal antibodies." These are invisible bits of protein manufactured by animal and human cells grown in the test tube. Each type of antibody—and there are hundreds of them—has the incredible ability to "recognize" and latch onto a specific target. The target can be any piece of living matter down to and including a single biological molecule. In theory, a monoclonal antibody can be made that would pick out a flea in a haystack, or the eye of the flea in a haystack, or even a speck in the eye of the flea.

PROJECTED USES

An anti-cancer guided missile is only one of hundreds of potential uses that excited scientists are envisioning for monoclonal antibodies. Other projected uses:

• Laboratory tests of unprecedented accuracy for diagnosing diseases.

• Treatments for such hitherto incurable scourges as malaria and rabies.

• A means of preventing the rejection of transplanted kidneys and other organs.

• Methods of identifying unknown drugs and chemicals in the body, and perhaps treating drug overdoses.

• New ways of spotting contaminants in foods and the environment.

• And new industrial techniques for leaching valuable chemicals out of complex solutions.

A fledgling industry has sprung up around monoclonal antibodies to serve the needs of scientists who are using them to investigate the secrets of the living cell. Antibodies that can zero in on such targets as various types of white-blood cells, distinguish between strains of viruses and bacteria, or identify human hormones are sold by Becton, Dickinson & Company, Johnson & Johnson, New England Nuclear Corporation, and Bethesda Research Laboratories, among others.

"The research interest in monoclonals is enormous," says Bernard A. Shoor, a vice president of Becton Dickinson.

Mr. Shoor and others caution that despite the high scientific interest, it is far too early to know whether the antibodies will live up to their advance billing as commercial products. Exotic uses in human beings may or may not work out, they say. Such caution, however, hasn't prevented investors, speculators, and venture capitalists from endowing monoclonal antibodies with some of the same glamour they attach to gene-splicing and genetic engineering. Already a flock of small venture-capital firms, and several gene-splicing companies have become involved in developing monoclonal antibodies.

ARMY AGAINST INVADERS

All mammals, including human beings, produce antibodies as the cornerstone of immunity to disease. Whenever the body is invaded by some "foreign" material, such as a virus or a bacterium, the immune system counterattacks with antibodies. The antibodies, which are protein molecules, latch onto the invader and render it harmless until scavenger cells can sweep it up and get rid of it.

Once an army of antibodies has been activated against a particular invader, the antibodies continue to circulate for years afterward on standby. This is why a person, after a feverish bout with a mumps virus, for instance, remains immune to mumps for years.

The immunity phenomenon is one of the most "specific" reactions in nature. An antibody produced against a mumps virus will attack the mumps virus and nothing else. Because there are millions of substances in nature that a person's body would consider "foreign," the immune system can turn out millions of different kinds of antibodies, each kind "specific" for only one substance.

The immune system recognizes a foreign substance by reading molecular "fingerprints" called antigens, which are carried on the surfaces of all biological matter. When the body senses a foreign antigen, an antibody is launched against that antigen.

THE WHOLE ALPHABET

By injecting antigens such as mumps or measles viruses into test animals, scientists can recover antibodies in the blood against the antigens. But no matter how pure an antigen the researchers inject into a test subject, they get back an alphabet soup of different antibodies. Because they can't separate one

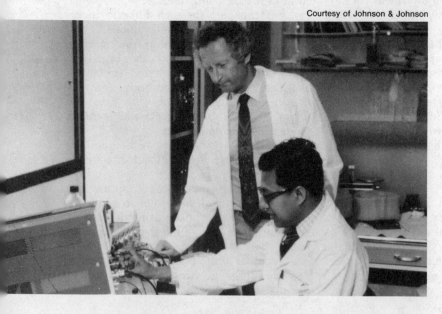

Dr. Gideon Goldstein, who directs Johnson & Johnson's development of hybridoma technology, looks on as Dr. Tapan Audhya, an immunological researcher, conducts tests using monoclonal antibodies.

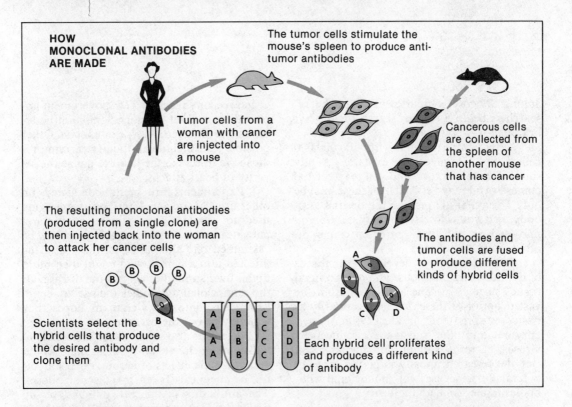

HOW MONOCLONAL ANTIBODIES ARE MADE

Tumor cells from a woman with cancer are injected into a mouse

The tumor cells stimulate the mouse's spleen to produce anti-tumor antibodies

Cancerous cells are collected from the spleen of another mouse that has cancer

The resulting monoclonal antibodies (produced from a single clone) are then injected back into the woman to attack her cancer cells

The antibodies and tumor cells are fused to produce different kinds of hybrid cells

Scientists select the hybrid cells that produce the desired antibody and clone them

Each hybrid cell proliferates and produces a different kind of antibody

kind of antibody from another, scientists haven't been able to fully exploit antibodies.

This has been a major roadblock to the medical use of antibodies. But now scientists say monoclonal antibodies are the isolated antibodies they have long been seeking. New techniques now allow scientists, in effect, to reach into the alphabet soup and pluck out and grow one letter—one kind of antibody—in a test tube.

In the body, the tiny white blood cells that manufacture antibodies lie in such tissues as the spleen, displaying a molecular sample of their antibody "product." When an antigen drifts along that fits the antibody sample, the white cell starts dividing, creating a clump or clone of identical copies of itself. The clones then churn out a stream of antibodies.

Researchers tried to grow these clones in a test tube to obtain a ready source of pure antibodies. But such cells failed to reproduce outside the body. The breakthrough came in 1975 when Georges Kohler and Cesar Milstein of the Medical Research Council in Cambridge, England, forced the antibody-making cells to fuse with cancer cells. The result is a hybrid cell that grows like a tumor in the test tube and is known as a hybridoma. Hybridomas can produce an antibody by the

liter. Because these antibodies come from a single clone of hybrid cells, they are called monoclonal antibodies.

MAKING ANTIBODY CLONES

"Everyone in the world is making hybridomas," says Hillary Koprowski of Philadelphia's Wistar Institute. The scientists' goal is to build up a vast library of hybridomas, each one making an antibody specific for one of the millions of antigens found in the biological world.

Ulrich Hammerling, a young Scandinavian at New York's Memorial Sloan-Kettering Cancer Center, is using monoclonal antibodies to see whether certain antigens are clues to an animal's susceptibility or resistance to disease.

In his laboratory, amid a sparkling clutter of glassware, microscopes, stainless-steel cabinets, and flashing electronic counters, are the tools of the hybridoma trade: a cage of hairless, or "nude," mice and square plastic trays divided into scores of tiny compartments. The researchers take an antigen against which they want a monoclonal antibody and inject it into a mouse. Later, the animal's spleen is removed, and the spleen cells are mixed with the special cancer cells for fusion. The mixed cells are distributed among the tray compartments, and the researchers begin a tedious search for the hybridoma.

"You may start off with 100,000,000 cells," Dr. Hammerling explains. "Only some of these will fuse, and you may get 100 clones or you may get 1,000. Of these, maybe only 1 per cent are making the desired antibody, and you'll lose some of these. So you may end up with only 20 or so clones or, often, none," he says.

Researchers have developed thousands of hybridomas from mouse and other animal tissues since 1976. The antibodies from the vast majority of these are used primarily as basic research tools to identify hormones, enzymes, and other substances produced by viruses, bacteria, animal, and human cells. But the research already is giving hints of potentially wide uses for monoclonal antibodies in medicine and industry.

FOR DIAGNOSIS AND TREATMENT

Within the next few years, the new techniques should produce a flock of new, commercially available diagnostic tests, replacing current tests using animal-serum antibodies. Johnson & Johnson's Ortho Diagnostics di-

A laboratory technician prepares a measles virus antigen for injection into mice. The antibodies the mice make against the antigen will be recovered.
Courtesy of Bethesda Research Laboratories, Inc.

vision recently received U.S. government approval to market a monoclonal antibody-based test for a certain type of anemia. Other possible tests include antibodies carrying radioactive tracers to the heart to gauge the severity of heart attacks.

Experiments are being conducted on other uses. Monoclonal antibodies are being used to pinpoint the antigens on malaria parasites. If these antigens could be "skimmed off" the parasites, they could be injected into a person who could then build up his own antibodies against the disease. Or the monoclonal antibodies themselves could be injected into the victim, in hopes they would wipe out the parasites.

Scientists also say it might be possible to make monoclonal antibodies that would neutralize the effects of heroin, other narcotics, or chemicals taken in poisonous doses. The antibodies could seek out and tie up molecules of the chemical, enabling the body to get rid of it.

The antibodies could also aid in purification and manufacturing of such substances as interferon, the highly publicized protein being tested against cancer and virus infections. Human cells or genetically engineered bacteria produce interferon as part of a complex mixture of 1,000 other proteins. Recent research into a monoclonal antibody that will attach itself only to interferon could make it a simple matter to extract the substance from other proteins.

CANCER SEARCH

Meanwhile, scores of scientists are using the antibodies to search for the long-elusive unique cancer antigens that could bring a new treatment for the disease within sight. "We and others now have sifted through hundreds of thousands of antibodies looking for the perfect diagnostic reagent," says Ronald Levy of Stanford Medical School. "So far, no one has found an antibody that can tell absolutely between leukemia cells and normal cells," Dr. Levy adds. But the research is helping doctors to distinguish between different types of leukemia and in some cases is helping to guide treatment.

Ultimately, scientists would like to find an antibody that would react only with a cancer cell. This antibody could be tagged with an anti-cancer drug and injected into the body. The antibody would go to the cancer cell and destroy it without damaging nearby normal cells.

AND NOW TO HUMANS

But even after scientists have found the unique cancer antigens and their corresponding monoclonal antibodies, another problem will remain. So far, most hybridomas have been made from mouse tissues and therefore make mouse antibodies. But the human body considers such antibodies foreign and ironically will make antibodies against them. In March 1982, however, Dr. Levy and his associates successfully used monoclonal antibodies made with mice to achieve a long-lasting remission of an uncommon kind of cancer in a 67-year-old man with an advanced case of the disease.

Monoclonal antibodies made from human sources would be very useful but are harder to obtain. In recent months, however, scientists have managed to make human hybridomas under special circumstances. Henry Kaplan and his associates at Stanford University took white blood cells from a patient who, for medical reasons, was injected with a chemical called DNCB just before his spleen was removed. The white blood cells making antibodies against DNCB were isolated, extracted, and fused with malignant spleen cells from a cancer patient. The result was an all-human hybridoma making monoclonal antibodies against DNCB.

About the same time, in Philadelphia, Carlo M. Croce and his associates at the Wistar Institute were treating a 19-year-old woman suffering from encephalitis caused by a measles-virus infection of the brain. The researchers took a sample of her blood, extracted the white blood cells that were producing large amounts of anti-measles antibodies, and fused them with human cancer cells to make a hybridoma. The hybridoma then began making monoclonal antibodies against the measles virus.

Since then, Dr. Croce says, the Wistar group has made many hybridomas by the same method from patients suffering from myasthenia gravis, a certain type of diabetes,

Courtesy of Bethesda Research Laboratories, Inc.

Antibody-producing spleen cells mixed with special cancer cells are distributed into these tiny tray compartments for fusion to form hybridomas.

and a disease called Greaves disease. These are thought to be "autoimmune" diseases, in which a person erroneously makes antibodies against his own tissues. It is thought, for example, that some diabetic patients make antibodies that destroy the cells that make insulin, thus causing their diabetes. The hybridomas make monoclonal autoantibodies that presumably cause the patients' diseases. If, in the next step, the researchers can make monoclonal antibodies against the autoantibodies, they might have a new means of treating these autoimmune diseases □

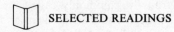 SELECTED READINGS

"Antibodies: getting their genes together" by J. L. Marx. *Science,* May 28, 1981.

"Cells that search and destroy" by W. Froelich. *Family Health,* March 1981.

"Experiment that had to succeed" by R. Lewin. *Science,* May 15, 1981.

"New method helps attack cancer cells" by Harold M. Schmeck Jr. *The New York Times,* August 31, 1981.

© Tom McHugh/PR

A scientist sprays an insecticide mixed with a protein bait on the base of a fruit tree and the ground around it to destroy Medfly pupae that have burrowed into the soil.

THE FLY IN OUR FRUIT

by Lisa Yount

IN mid-July 1981, residents of northern California's Santa Clara Valley searched the night sky for a sight that many of them found alarming: helicopters spraying sticky droplets of insecticide and protein bait over their houses and yards. Just a few weeks later in Tampa, Florida, a similar attack was launched from the ground, followed by an airborne assault. The people and equipment in these two incidents—and in outbreaks later—were troops in an all-out war on one of the world's most devasting insect pests.

The "enemy" was the Mediterranean fruit fly, commonly called the Medfly. The battleground was the heartland of the U.S.'s multi-billion dollar fruit-growing industry. Despite all the commotion and the resulting headlines, infestations of the pest are hardly new. In the United States, the insects, which are smaller than houseflies, had previously cropped up in California, Texas, Hawaii, and Florida. Elsewhere, they are major problems from Israel to Peru, Australia to Spain.

In spite of quarantines, sterilization campaigns, spraying, and other weapons to beat them back, they have moved to new feeding grounds worldwide. Their cream colored larvae, or maggots, destroy the insides of more than 250 kinds of fruits and vegetables, including apples, apricots, most citrus, coffee berries, mangoes, nectarines, peaches, plums, and tomatoes. Their "migrations" go back to the early 1800's.

TINY REPRODUCTIVE GIANTS

As flies go, the formidable monster causing all this trouble is rather pretty. The brown bands on its two clear, drooping wings suggest abstract art, which may be why its family was once called the "picture-winged" fly. Its yellowish abdomen shows iridescent overtones in some lights.

The Medfly makes up in reproductive powers what it lacks in size. In hot areas, such as Hawaii, it can go through 12 or 13 generations a year. The hotter the temperature, the faster it reproduces. Before the adult Medfly can mate, however, it must eat, and its diet is exotic. It feeds on honeydew, a sweet deposit secreted by aphids, mealy bugs, and scale insects. Studies of honeydew by Kenneth Hagen, a fruit fly specialist at the University of California at Berkeley, led to the development of a protein bait that is mixed with insecticide in the spray most commonly used to control Medflies. The bait, resembling honeydew, attracts the flies.

LIFE CYCLE

About a week after they become mature, male Medflies gather in groups on host fruits or on leaves nearby. Females are attracted by the male's scent and characteristic buzz. After mating, the female looks for a fruit that is just beginning to ripen. She uses her sharp-pointed ovipositor, or egg-laying apparatus, to puncture the skin of the fruit. She then lays a half-dozen to a dozen whitish, glistening eggs in the resulting hole. A single Medfly female in the wild can lay up to 500 eggs during her adult reproductive lifetime of about one month.

The eggs hatch after a day or two into larvae, and these soft-bodied grubs feed on the fruit. The fruit falls off prematurely and rots. After a week or two, the mature larvae—now about 8 millimeters (0.3 inch) long—crawl out. Each one burrows into the soil and forms a brown, seedlike pupa. After about nine days, it emerges as a fly to begin the cycle again.

THROUGHOUT THE WORLD

The Mefly probably originated in West Africa, where it was reported in the early 1800's, but it quickly spread. In 1842 it was found in Spain, and from there it traveled across Europe to the Mediterranean basin. It was discovered in Australia in the 1890's and South America in 1901. It got to Hawaii, probably on a ship from Australia, about 1910. Today, it is found in most tropical and subtropical regions of the world, where it joins some close relatives, including the Oriental fruit fly, the olive fly, and the melon fly, in decimating fruit. In August 1981, California's Medfly problems were compounded by a small infestation of Oriental fruit flies.

For all its journeying, the Medfly is not a natural traveler. It can fly only about one and one-half kilometers (one mile) or so under its own power. Human beings are responsible for its worldwide distribution. In the old days, the carriers were usually sailors. Today, they are more apt to be tourists. The Medfly larvae that began the Santa Clara Valley outbreak, for example, probably came in fruit brought from Central America.

LIVE WITH IT OR BATTLE?

Countries that have the Medfly respond to it in different ways. Italy, Greece, and most other Mediterranean nations simply live with the pest. It is too widespread for them to do anything else. Some report up to 100 per cent infestation of soft fruits and a few vegetables. Israel, on the other hand, is a fierce fighter in the "fly wars." The Israelis cannot eradicate the Medfly, because they are surrounded by countries in which it is widespread. But their citrus crop, which they export to Europe, is one of their biggest money-makers.

Since the mid-1960's, the Israelis have regularly sprayed the same insecticide-plus-

These male Medflies, made sterile in a laboratory, were released to breed with wild females. Their mating will produce only infertile eggs.

© Tom Evans/PR

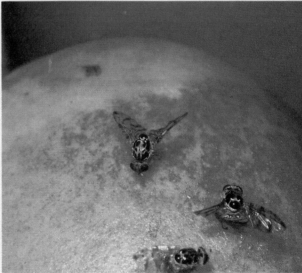

bait used in California to kill adult flies. They apply it from the air any time a Medfly is found near the orange groves. They also fumigate their fruit before exporting it to kill larvae or eggs. Normally, fruit with dead maggots inside is visibly damaged and never gets to the consumer. But in France, tweezers are often issued with fruit desserts in restaurants—to pick out the grubs.

Like Israel, Australia works hard to keep its Medfly problems under control. Today, the fly is confined to the southwest corner of the country. Medfly outbreaks occur almost yearly around Adelaide, the capital of South Australia, when people bring infested fruit from Western Australia. So far, however, the fly has been eradicated each time it has appeared.

Part of Adelaide's success is due to early warnings of outbreaks through a "housewife alert system." The city's residents have been trained to recognize the fly and report it immediately. The vigilant Adelaide housewives are said to be more effective than conventional traps in detecting Medflies.

WEAPONS

Wherever they are fighting, soldiers in the Medfly wars have much the same weapons to draw on. The first of these, in areas where the fly is not present all the time, is early detection. Lacking Australia's sharp-eyed housewives; most countries put out small traps. A Medfly trap looks like a little pup tent made of cardboard. Attracted by a sex lure, flies enter the device and are captured by sticky material on its floor.

Once a Medfly outbreak is detected, one or several attack methods can be used. Usually, an insecticide is applied to the ground to kill pupae and emerging flies. Other methods include stripping of host fruits, release of sterile flies, biological control by means of parasites, and the insecticide-plus-bait spray. The insecticide usually used is called malathion. All these methods, except for parasites, have been used in California.

A small Medfly outbreak can often be eradicated by the release of sterile flies. The flies, mostly males, are sterilized by radiation in a laboratory and then released into the wild population. Ideally, enough are set free to outnumber the wild flies by about 100 to one. Wild females mate with the sterile males and produce infertile eggs, thus interrupting the breeding cycle.

Worldwide, malathion is the most popular and effective tool for combating large Medfly outbreaks. Not only scientists but also the people in the sprayed areas usually seem to regard it as both necessary and relatively safe. In California, though, its use was opposed by a number of people—including Governor Jerry Brown—who feared that it could cause birth defects or illness in people. Because the insects are drawn to the spray by the bait, only relatively small amounts of insecticide need to be used.

Using parasites offers a different solution. Tiny wasps, they lay their eggs in the eggs or larvae of the fly. Parasites can reduce a fly population, Kenneth Hagen says, but they cannot eradicate it. He points out that if a parasite wiped out its host species, it would destroy itself as well. The parasite control method has been used extensively in Hawaii, where the Medfly population is well-established.

NOW WAIT . . . AND WATCH

If eradication fails, Californians, like other Medfly fighters, will have to fumigate their fruit. It is an expensive, nasty job. Fumigation chambers are expensive to build and run, and fumigant gases also shorten the shelf life of fruit. Fumigation is strictly a rearguard action in the Medfly battle.

The results of California's "fly wars" remain uncertain. But whatever the outcome, Californians can be sure that veterans of Medfly battles elsewhere will be watching—with the pesky insects buzzing around their ears ☐

SELECTED READINGS

"March of the Medfly" by M. Reese and others. *Newsweek*, July 27, 1981.

"Malathion threat debunked" by J. Marx. *Science*, July 31, 1981.

"1981 Medfly battle" by R. Rodale. *Organic Gardening*, September 1981.

"Use and nonuse of insects" [biological control of insects] by T. R. Odhrambro. *Bulletin of the Atomic Scientists*, August 1981.

Courtesy of the Chocolate Manufacturers Association of the USA

CHOCOLATE GROWS ON TREES

by Allen Young

THERE are very few people who do not like chocolate in some form or other: chocolate bars, chocolate mousse, chocolate ice cream, hot chocolate, crème de cacao. The source of this welcome delight is the seeds or "beans" of the cacao tree, *Theobroma cacao*. Native to tropical America, the trees have been cultivated for more than 4,000 years.

Both the ancient Mayans and Aztecs of Central America revered the fermented beverage *chocolatl* as a libation to their gods. When the Mayans migrated northward through Central America, they carried cacao beans, spreading the cultivation of cacao as far north as the Yucatán by 700 A.D. The Aztecs believed that the beans were blessed by the god Quetzalcoatl, and believed that the god had brought the seeds from the Gar-

den of Life and given them to humanity.

The exalted drink chocolatl was prepared by drying the cacao beans in the sun, roasting them in earthen pots, and then crushing them between stones, as if milling maize. This cocoa paste was mixed with spices and molded into small cakes for storage. The drink was made by pulverizing the dried cakes and mixing them with water.

From its pre-Columbian origins in the American tropics, the cultivation of cacao spread rapidly to the African continent as a result of the Spanish conquest and the subsequent frenzied interest in chocolate in other European nations. The first chocolate company in North America was the Walter Baker Company, founded in 1780, in Massachusetts.

The delicate cacao flowers grow directly out of the tree's branches and trunk on tiny, leafless stems. Miniscule midges pollinate the flowers.

© Kjell B. Sandved/PR

POPULAR AROUND THE WORLD

Today, chocolate is a household word around the globe. The world's annual consumption is estimated at more than 1,000,000 tons. The United States and Europe together consume about 70 per cent of the annual production. On a per capita basis, the Swiss have the highest consumption, at about 22 pounds per year; the English are next at 15 pounds a year, the Germans at 14, the Belgians, Swedes, and Austrians collectively at 12, and the Americans at 10.

There are not enough cacao beans to meet the world's demand for chocolate. The demand is so intense that attempts have been made to produce an artificial or synthetic chocolate, but with little success. There is simply no known substitute for the distinct flavor of real chocolate, as anyone with a "sweet tooth" would admit.

THE CACAO TREE

Cacao plantations abound in the wet, tropical regions of the world, within 20 degrees of the equator. They are most abundant in Central and South America, Africa, and Malaysia. The trees attain a height of 10 to 15 feet and must be shaded. Young plantations generally have banana trees for shade, but these are eventually replaced by permanent tall trees, such as rubber (*Hevea brasiliensis*).

Each year the cacao tree produces muskmelonlike pods that are 4 to 12 inches long when mature. The ripe pods may be green, yellow, red, or purple, depending largely on the variety. Each pod contains 20 to 60 reddish brown beans embedded in a sticky white pulp, usually arranged in five rows. Each bean is roughly the size of an almond. From 7 to 14 pods produce one pound of dry beans, and anywhere from 200 to 3,000 pounds of dry beans are produced per acre.

Some pods are produced throughout the year in most cacao-growing regions, but the main harvest begins at the end of the wet season and extends for two or three months. Monkeys and large rodents may break open some of the pods to feed on the moisture-laden, sweet white tissue surrounding the seeds, but they drop the seeds, untouched, for raw cacao beans are very bitter.

HARVESTING AND PROCESSING

Harvesting and processing the beans are laborious tasks. First, the ripe pods are plucked by hand from the trees, thrown into bins attached to tractors or oxen, and brought to drying areas, where the pods are split open and the beans extracted. The sticky pulp covering the beans is removed by mixing them with sawdust in large sacks and then sifting them through coarse screens to remove excess sawdust. The fine coat of sawdust mixed with the pulpy film makes it much easier to clean each bean manually. The naked beans, deep red and smooth, are dried in the sun on large trays. The fermentation that takes place gives the beans the characteristic chocolate flavor and smell. The release of certain essential oils within the fermenting seed leaves is responsible for this transformation.

When thoroughly dried, the beans are shipped to chocolate factories in burlap sacks. At the factory, the beans are further cleaned, then roasted and ground into a pastelike substance called chocolate liquor. Anyone fortunate enough to live near a chocolate factory has experienced the pleasure of intense chocolate aromas carried by the breezes.

A cacao bean is about 53 per cent cocoa butter, or fat. Pressing out the fat from the chocolate liquor produces dry cocoa. Commercial chocolate is made by adding specified amounts of cocoa butter and other ingredients to the cocoa. Since the Spaniards' discovery of the chocolate drink of the ancient peoples of Central and South America, chocolate refinement has focused largely on the defatting process and on the addition of other substances to produce beverages, candies, and baking products.

TWO STIMULANTS

Much of the unique flavor of natural chocolate comes from two prominent stimulants, theobromine and caffeine, as well as from the fat in the cacao beans. Because theobromine, the major stimulant found in cacao beans, stimulates muscles rather than nerve cells, the consumption of large amounts of chocolate does not result in "coffee nerves."

One ounce of pure cocoa contains about 50 milligrams of stimulants. The old wives' tale that chocolate soothes a broken heart may not be so farfetched, as researchers recently discovered that cocoa contains sizable amounts of phenylethylamine, an amphetaminelike substance produced by human brain cells during emotional episodes.

MANY VARIETIES

A long history of cultivation and experimentation has produced many different varieties of *Theobroma cacao,* with names like 'Pound-7' and 'UF-26.' Most commercially available chocolate is actually a blend of several varieties, just as coffee may be a blend of different coffee beans.

Basically there are two kinds of cacao beans, the Criollos and the Forasteros, and each has a distinctive flavor and color. Criollo cacao is grown primarily in Central and South America and is considered to be the finest cacao because of its exquisite flavor. Criollos are used to add aromatic, nutty, and floral nuances to chocolate. But Criollos are harder to grow than the more robust Forasteros and thus the supply is limited. Forastero cacao is the base chocolate of the world's candy bars and other forms of commercial chocolate. The African 'Accra' and

These ripe cacao pods are ready to be harvested. The chocolate-bearing beans inside are embedded in a sweet, white pulp.

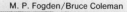
M. P. Fogden/Bruce Coleman

Bruce Coleman

In a chocolate factory in Argentina, a worker mixes up a big batch of the confection. Each year, over 1,000,000 tons of chocolate are consumed.

Brazilian 'Bahia' are the two main Forastero cacaos grown in the world today. To this base chocolate, selected Criollos are added to produce various quality grades of chocolate.

UNSTABLE PRODUCTION

In 1979 Ghana alone produced about 45 per cent of the total cacao-bean crop, followed by Nigeria, the Ivory Coast, and Brazil. Tropical Asia is also becoming a major cacao producer. Until the early 1900's South America was the major producer of cacao, but today the West African nations produce about three times as many raw cacao beans as any other region. Such a shift in production is not uncommon. There are many examples of introduced species doing exceptionally well in their new environments. Dandelions and gypsy moths do better in North America than in their native Europe.

As a rule, introduced species do well when they leave their natural enemies behind.

Nevertheless, there is concern about the world's production of cacao beans, since the supply is very uncertain from year to year. And the demand for chocolate shows no signs of slowing. Cocoa futures are extremely volatile, subject to the vagaries not only of the environment but also of political events. Governments of cacao-growing nations often change with little or no notice, sometimes reducing the flow of beans to the major consumer nations. One or more years of low production can suddenly be followed by several years of high production, thus causing a shift in the supply and cost of raw beans to chocolate brokers and manufacturers. For example, the 1980–81 growing season was the fifth year in a row of oversupply of cacao beans, with the 1981 surplus exceeding 75,000 metric tons.

TREE WITH FEW PODS

While there is little that can be done to assure political stability in cacao-producing regions, a great deal of research is being directed toward increasing the production of the cacao trees themselves.

The cacao tree is a classic example of cauliflory, the production of flowers on leafless stems, including the larger branches and even the trunk of a tree. This is a botanical phenomenon seldom seen in the flora of temperate zones. The flower buds of cacao trees simply push through the thin bark. A cacao tree laden with flowers popping out of the trunk and larger branches, with few or no flowers in the canopy, is a startling sight.

Individual cacao trees have thousands of flowers annually, but very few pods. A typical tree produces about 10,000 flowers during a single year, but only about 30 ripe pods. The single most important factor in successful fruit set is pollination, and pollination frequency is dramatically low in cacao plantations. It is tempting to try to hand-pollinate the flowers to increase the fruit set, but hand pollination of cacao is labor-intensive.

The "bees in the orchard" approach, so successful with apple trees, will not work because bees do not pollinate cacao. Many kinds of insects routinely turn up at cacao flowers, apparently attracted by the promise of food from microscopic nectaries lining the inner surfaces of the petals. Few of these insects are able to make contact with the female reproductive organ, the stigma, to deposit pollen, however. Nature has not made it easy. Each cacao flower bears five helmet-shaped petals, each one enclosing a small pocket of male pollen-discharging anthers. A tall, rod-like stigma is at the center, but it is surrounded by a barrier of five equally long filamentous staminodes that hinder access to it.

TINY MIDGE POLLINATORS

The most effective pollinators of the pink and white cacao flowers are tiny midges, two to three millimeters long, of the family Ceratopogonidae. A female midge lands on one of the staminodes (sterile stamens), crawls down it, and crosses over to a petal sac. There she brushes against the anthers, causing several pollen grains to stick to bristles on her body. After presumably feeding on nectar, the midge flies off and lands on another flower. While moving down the staminodes, she deposits a ball of pollen grains on the stigma. If enough pollen grains are deposited, pollination takes place. The pollination of self-incompatible strains of cacao requires that midges transport pollen to different trees. If the match is not correct, fertilization is only partial, the embryo dies, and no pod develops.

Since pollination appears to be a limiting factor in the number of pods produced on a cacao tree, it is worthwhile to examine what happens when the number of midges is increased. A relatively small-bodied insect with a thin cuticle, the midge is susceptible to death from desiccation. Its natural habitat includes the lower strata of lowland tropical wet forests, where the shade cover promotes high air humidity and where breeding sites—various kinds of rotting organic debris—are abundant.

Cacao-growing regions with a long annual dry season, such as Ghana's, impose special problems on pollinating midge populations, since dry spells cause midge populations to decline, while enhancing flower production on plantations. The resulting asynchrony between peak flower abundance and midge abundance results in low pollination.

My studies in Costa Rica, funded by the American Cocoa Research Institute, have involved the deliberate "garbaging up" of selected plantations with piles of various kinds of rotting debris attractive to midges as breeding sites. By comparing the abundance of midges in these modified sites with their abundance in natural leaf litter under cacao trees, I have discovered that midge populations can be increased significantly by using slices of stems from banana plants as breeding sites. Preliminary results also indicate an increased number of pods on cacao trees where there is an increased midge population.

PLANTATION OR CACAO FOREST

These encouraging results suggest that a cacao plantation resembling a natural forest is a better environment for pollination. A cacao tree removed from the wild and grown in a monoculture or simple polyculture is usually cut off from its natural breeding system. Robert Hunter, a tropical agronomist, operates cacao plantations in northeastern Costa Rica, where he is experimenting with various wild tree species as canopies for cacao. His work reveals that some timber trees do very well with cacao, and it also illustrates how various economically important tree species can be grown together, thus conserving natural forest cover in surrounding areas. The "cacao forest" approach used in Ghana, in which natural forest is thinned for planting cacao, is an important step in providing the high-humidity conditions and shade necessary for a healthy, productive plantation.

There is a need for continued study of how cacao fits into the plantation environment, as compared to its relationship with the tree species in its wild habitat. Only by studying the entire community in which the cacao tree lives can we maximize the likelihood of adequate supplies of cacao beans from year to year. Meanwhile, the chocolate lovers of the world must rely for their sweet treat on the interaction of cacao trees with a formidable host of factors ☐

THE 1981 NOBEL PRIZE IN PHYSIOLOGY OR MEDICINE

by Barbara Tchabovsky

Wide World

Roger Wolcott Sperry was awarded a Nobel Prize for his work on split-brain research.

THE 1981 Nobel Prize in Physiology or Medicine was awarded to three researchers for work leading to a better understanding of the organization and function of the human brain. One half of the award was given to Roger Wolcott Sperry of the California Institute of Technology for his demonstration that the right and left hemispheres of the brain have different and sometimes independent functions. The other half of the award was shared by David Hunter Hubel and Torsten Nils Wiesel of Harvard University for their studies of how the brain processes visual information.

This work has led to a major revision of ideas of brain function. It has already had some practical applications—specifically in the understanding and treatment of certain reading, writing, and visual difficulties—and is so fundamental that it has opened up new avenues of research that may well lead to an understanding of many complex brain disorders that have long baffled science. The research also touches on the controversial issue that there may be innate differences between the brains of females and males. Such biological differences—and not cultural and social conditioning—could be responsible for some observed behavioral differences between men and women. Ongoing investigations of the functions of the brain hemispheres may help explain why boys and girls respond differently to similar situations and show variations in such things as early speech ability, gross and fine motor performance, and an understanding of spatial relationships.

SPLIT-BRAIN STUDIES

Sperry began split-brain experiments in 1954 on animals in which the fibers between the brain hemispheres had been cut. During the 1960's and early 1970's he continued his research on humans in which the nerve connections between the left and right hemispheres of the brain had been severed to halt severe epileptic seizures for which all other treatments had failed. In both series of studies he demonstrated that each hemisphere has its own preferred functions, is largely independent in regard to learning and retention, and can be oblivious to what the other hemisphere is learning when the connections between the two are severed. He then started mapping various areas of the brain and their functions.

In the words of the Karolinska Institute, which awards the Nobel Prizes he "brilliantly succeeded in extracting the secrets from both hemispheres of the brain and demonstrating that they are highly specialized and also that many higher functions are centered in the right hemisphere." The Nobel committee further stated that through Sperry's research science has learned that "the right hemisphere is clearly superior to the left in many respects, especially regarding the capacity for concrete thinking, spatial consciousness, and comprehension of complex relationships." The right hemisphere is also believed to be the focus of musical and artistic ability. The isolated left hemisphere is believed to be concerned with abstract thinking, symbolic relationships, and logical analysis of details, particularly temporal relationships. "It can speak, write, and make mathematical calculations," said the committee.

According to Herbert Pardes, director of the National Institute of Mental Health which has funded Sperry's research for more than 20 years, Sperry's demonstrations that the left hemisphere contains the primary speech capacity while the right is involved in short-term memory are paramount to understanding brain function both in normal and abnormal states such as autism and Alzheimer's disease." Pardes further states that Sperry's continuing research on mental concentration will probably "have implications for the understanding of such illnesses as schizophrenia and depressions."

HOW THE BRAIN SEES

Hubel and Wiesel have concentrated on the visual system in the brain. They used anesthetized cats and monkeys in experiments aimed at determining the specific functions of individual cells in the brain's visual cortex. Electrodes in the visual cortex detected the firing of individual nerve cells as animals looked at a screen illuminated with variously oriented lines and patterns. The researchers found that the cells respond not just to where the light hits the retina of the eye but also to different elements of shape and position. A hierarchy of nerve cells—termed "simple," "complex," and "hypercomplex" by the two Nobel laureates—react in various ways to the original stimulus. They then translate the

pattern of light, dark, and color received by the eyes into a coherent picture for the brain.

These studies of the "building blocks of perception" showed that visual perception is much more complicated than had been previously thought. The primary visual cortex of the brain is now the most thoroughly mapped area of the brain in terms of cell function and organization.

Wiesel and Hubel also showed that the normal function of cells involved in vision require stimulation in the early stages of development. This led to a better understanding of two congenital visual defects—strabismus and a certain form of cataract—and to a recognition of the importance of very early treatment of these disorders.

Work related to the pioneering efforts of Wiesel and Hubel has also shown that one species' vision of the world may differ from that of another. In a well-known experiment MIT researcher Jerome Lettvin showed that a frog could starve to death though surrounded by freshly killed insects on which it normally feeds. The frog would not grab for

Sperry's studies brilliantly demonstrated that the right and left hemispheres of the brain have highly specialized, and sometimes independent, functions.

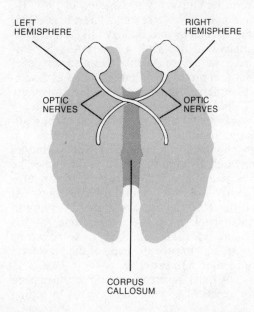

LEFT HEMISPHERE

RIGHT HEMISPHERE

OPTIC NERVES

OPTIC NERVES

CORPUS CALLOSUM

Laureates David Hubel and Torsten Wiesel of Harvard University did pioneering research on how the brain processes visual information.

something motionless, its brain responding primarily to movement and not to shape, size, or color.

Roger Wolcott Sperry was born August 20, 1913, in Hartford, Connecticut. He received a master's degree in psychology from Oberlin College and a doctorate in zoology from the University of Chicago in 1941. He then pursued his research interest in combining psychology and biology at Harvard University and the Yerkes Laboratory for Primate Biology in Atlanta. He also served as assistant professor of anatomy and as associate professor of psychology at the University of Chicago.

In 1954 he joined the faculty of the California Institute of Technology as Professor of Psychobiology and began his Nobel-winning research. In addition to split-brain studies, he has made important contributions to neurobiology and experimental psychobiology. At all times he has pursued a goal of trying to understand the conscious processes of the human brain. His total body of work can be considered to provide many of the objectives of modern neuroscience.

A quiet, reserved man, Sperry has been the recipient of numerous awards including the Albert Lasker Medical Research Award and the Warren Medal of the Society of Experimental Psychologists.

David Hunter Hubel was born in Windsor, Ontario, Canada, in 1926. He received his bachelor's of science in 1947 and his medical degree in 1951 from McGill University in Montreal. As a postdoctoral fellow at Johns Hopkins University, he met Wiesel and began their research collaboration.

He moved to Harvard University Medical School in 1959 and served in several faculty positions before becoming George Packer Berry professor of neurobiology in 1968.

Torsten Nils Wiesel was born on June 3, 1924, in Uppsala, Sweden, and remains a Swedish citizen though he has worked in the United States for virtually all his career. After earning his medical degree at the Karolinska Institute in Sweden, he served as instructor in physiology there for a year.

In 1955 he went to Johns Hopkins University as a postdoctoral fellow and began his collaboration with Hubel. They moved to Harvard four years later. Wiesel is now Robert Winthrop Professor of neurobiology at Harvard □

IBM

With its optional printer and text management software, this IBM personal computer becomes an individualized word-processing center. The system has many other useful applications.

COMPUTERS & MATHEMATICS

COMPUTERS & MATHEMATICS
REVIEW OF THE YEAR

During 1981 researchers continued their efforts to bring people and computers closer, to expand the computer's uses, and to turn the computer into a familiar tool for nonscientists. A new program to deal with "math anxiety" was also developed during the year.

Computer Data-Bank Systems. Programmers have been designing data-base management systems to organize electronic data-bank files for all kinds of people and their needs and for all kinds of computers. Data-base management systems were once available only for the largest computers. Today, though, there are systems for even the smallest computers, including desk-top models. And, at the same time, computers are becoming more and more adept at handling requests given in plain English. One newly developed computerized data-bank system is LEXIS. Using LEXIS, supplied by Mead Data Central, lawyers can call a computer and tell it verbally to check a point of law for them. LEXIS doesn't simply scan a list of index terms; it is programmed to search for any word or combination of words that occurs in the full text of legal material stored in its memory. It thus provides quick reference to a wide range of legal data.

Computers in the Arts. By programming a computer called the Writer's Workbench with advice on elements of style and with rules of grammar, Bell Laboratories in New Jersey hoped to design a system that would polish and perfect the user's prose. The machine's value as a literary critic is, however, questionable. When it was fed these lines from Dickens:

"It was the best of times, it was the worst of times, it was the age of wisdom, it was the age of foolishness . . ."

the machine reduced the sentence to:

"The times were the best and worst, wise and foolish."

And there's computer music. A digital synthesizer is an instrument designed to do the work of an entire orchestra. Sound currents are measured thousands of times per second and the measurements stored by the digital synthesizer as a series of numbers. Because of microprocessors, these music machines can now perform the calculations necessary to reproduce sound instantaneously. Using carefully measured on/off pulses of electricity, digital synthesizers can mimic and combine instrumental or natural sounds. These computers can also create new sounds and new combinations of sounds that are impossible to produce any other way. A musician sits at a keyboard, punches a button for the instrument he or she wishes to mimic, and then begins to play. The machines can be programmed to respond to the speed and force with which the keys are pressed. As a result, the new music machines can be played with expression. The synthesizers are becoming more and more common in broadcast commercials and film soundtracks. Many professional musicians fear that the public will accept the computer's imitation of real musicians and lose the ability to distinguish a real orchestra from a computer copy. (See "Computer Music" on page 104.)

Musicians can instantaneously reproduce the sound of any instrument in an orchestra by playing the keyboard of an amazing computer instrument called a digital synthesizer.

Dr. Duffy, of Harvard Medical School, uses a computer called BEAM (Brain Electrical Activity Mapping) to study color images of patterns of brain activity.

Computers in Science and Medicine. Since the mid-1920's physicians have been able to record the electrical activity of an enormous range of brain cells using an electroencephalograph. Now, researchers have a computer called BEAM, for Brain Electrical Activity Mapping, that allows them to sort that electrical activity by wavelength and frequency and then to record the various types of signals in contrasting color on a map of the brain. Researchers at Harvard Medical School are comparing BEAM images of healthy individuals with BEAM images of subjects suffering from various mental disorders. They hope to identify the patterns of brain activity that characterize each mental disorder. Eventually, psychiatrists may be able to diagnose their patients by simply glancing at a computer map of their brains.

Hospital computers are doing much more than storing medical records and processing bills. Some systems, like PROMIS, use stored data on patients to help doctors evaluate the risks and benefits of various treatments. Other systems actually diagnose cases. One new computer system, developed by Duke University researchers, stores data on the illness and outcome of a large number of patients with heart disease. Many characteristics of the patient's illness are described. Using these characteristics, new patients can be matched to similar patients seen previously, and likely responses to different therapies can be accurately estimated.

Computers and the Handicapped. Computers are also being used to help the handicapped. The Veterans Administration Medical Center in Palo Alto, California, is looking into possible uses for computerized video games in hospitals. Since video games are designed to challenge memory, hand-and-eye coordination, and logic, they may provide important stimulation for the victims of strokes and other serious forms of brain damage. ■ Researchers at the Smith-Kettlewell Institute of Visual Science in San Francisco are working on a seeing-eye computer. If they are successful a miniature television camera will rest on the shoulders of the blind. The camera will produce images of nearby objects and then the computer will name the objects for the blind person. ■ The deaf may also be getting help. The lip positions that produce very different pairs of sounds in the English language sometimes look almost exactly alike— and that makes lip reading difficult. Now NASA is working along with the Research Triangle Institute of North Carolina to develop a special pair of glasses that will allow the deaf to "see" sounds. A computer will be programmed to pick up "look-alike" sounds and to flash a symbol for the sound across the lens of the glasses. The researchers are struggling to make the glasses small enough to wear comfortably.

Teaching Mathematics. The latest attempt to deal with "math anxiety" is the HM (Harvard University and Milton Academy) Math Study Skills Program. The guide can't replace math textbooks but it can put students on the road toward mathematical understanding. The guide covers skills students need—before they even begin to learn algebra—listening as a mathematical skill; problem solving; understanding the language of mathematics; learning from homework; formulas; preparing for and taking a math test; and, of course, estimation. Most of us were never taught to estimate in the classroom. But today teachers recognize the importance of this skill. The ability to estimate helps in coping with standardized multiple choice tests, and may, in a society heavily dependent on computers, provide the best protection against any absurd error in paychecks, bills, or bank balances.

Jeanne O'Neill

Smith-Kettlewell Medical Research Institute of San Francisco

A seeing-eye computer being developed by researchers at the Smith-Kettlewell Institute of Visual Science in California would allow blind people to achieve much greater mobility.

The IBM system seen here was developed for Japan and Taiwan to make the Chinese written language of 50,000 characters compatible with a conventional computer keyboard.

© Dan McCoy/Rainbow

The ever-growing popularity of computer games has caused a dramatic rise in the number of arcades that are springing up across the country, like this one in Massachusetts.

COMPUTER GAMES

by Paul Trachtman

"IT'S easy to get isolated and become a hermit with computers," a young games programmer named Dave had told me the night before. We were in his den, with starfields exploding on the screen of his desk-top Atari 800, and the world ending in a shower of nuclear warheads on the upright Missile Command module in the corner, its computer patiently playing against itself in the absence of a human opponent. Now, the morning after, we are entering the hermitage.

The sun that once ripened apricots is rising over California's "Silicon Valley," an area south of San Francisco Bay where computer plants now thrive in industrial parks. Inside the engineering headquarters of Atari, the world's first manufacturer of coin-operated video games, Dave finds a computer printout waiting for him on his desk. His office space is a paneled cell, as fit for contemplation as the cells of medieval hermits, with a small chalk board on one wall. He studies the printout to see whether the corrections he requested have been added to his program, a still sketchy set of instructions for a new game he is working on. Then he has his first brainstorm of the morning, grabs pencil and paper, and begins writing:

"Multi monster sequence. Every other wave: no friend. For each attack IF timer equals 4 THEN 'too slow,' exit monster mode. After monster is zapped, IF timer is 4 THEN reinitialize monster mode."

"Is that programming language?" I ask. "Oh no," he says. "It's plain English."

I have a feeling that I've been zapped.

TRANSPARENT TECHNOLOGY

To most of us outside the computer culture, its initiates seem to live in a world so alien that they might as well be medieval hermits, or in some other time warp of their own. They appear in a popular campus poster as "nerds," whose heads are the only thing about them not screwed on backwards. But Dave is hardly a nerd. If anything, he is still the mischievous kid with tousled blond hair who liked physics and chemistry in high school but didn't like the titration experiments. "I liked to make the bombs and flares and stuff," he says. Only now he is making them into electronic fantasies, and is far happier than in the days when he worked developing computerized check-out systems for supermarkets.

He is working now at designing coin-operated video games, among people who see technology itself as a game. "We're making technology essentially transparent," one Atarian says. "We're making it friendly," says another. "That has not been the point of view of the big-business systems, or the military computer business, and it gives us an advantage in going into the electronic home that will emerge in the Eighties."

Arcade video games have made Atari a major new player in the entertainment empire. A 1980 market research survey by Atari showed that 86 per cent of the U.S. population between the ages of 13 and 20 has played some arcade video games, and estimated that people in the United States are spending $2,500,000,000 a year on them. They have spread so rapidly that they have taken the culture by surprise. Not even the players seem to know quite what to make of them, or why they are so appealing. Kids whose attention span approaches zero in schools spend long hours at apparently repetitive tasks on these machines, improving their skills. The players frequently describe themselves as addicts and junkies. Massachusetts Institute of Technology (MIT) sociologist Sherry Turkle reports that some business executives she has interviewed in the game arcades compare the experience of playing these games to transcendental meditation.

© Dan McCoy/Rainbow

David Theurer, a creative engineer who designed the video game "Missle Command," studies a computer printout of instructions for a new game.

FRIENDLY COMPUTERS

Inside the engineering labs and offices at Atari there is a similar air of excitement and inspiration. Everyone here seems to feel that computers are going to play a much friendlier role in our lives than most people ever expected. The image of the large, centralized computers that make impersonal organizations even more impersonal, that insist on their own billing errors, and whose superior mentalities seem best suited to writing junk mail, are not the kinds of computers Atarians have in mind. And their perceptions seem to be based on their own experiences. "People aren't going to be able to be scared of computers very much longer," one young games programmer assures me.

Dave takes me a short distance down a corridor lined with numbered lab doors. Behind them are the video games of the future, in various stages of development from a few blips and squiggles on video monitors

© Dan McCoy/Rainbow

Atari engineers and programmers anxiously wait their turns at a video game under development. Meanwhile, an associate zaps "monsters" that appear on the video screen.

hooked up to rows of printed circuit boards, to advanced mock-ups in cardboard skins, with display panels that blaze into action when anyone hits the start button. Most of the time, someone has. Dave pulls his chair up to a video tube next to a computer, types in a few instructions, and begins to play his new game. He begins by intently twisting a control knob and hitting the fire button, avoiding electric bolts and zapping monsters, no longer talking to me, and unaware of the pack of other programmers and engineers gathering at his back to wait a turn at the game. Some of them haven't had breakfast yet.

They are doing what other people are putting millions of coins a day into video-game machines to do in arcades around the world. "I have a terrible time going home some nights and telling my wife that I've worked for a living," one of the pack admits. "For me," says another, "a tough day is trying to find those two little bugs in my game, so I spend hours playing it. Sometimes, of course, you have to spend hours pushing a pencil. And for most people here, pushing a pencil is the most aggravating thing they could do."

Other labs are springing to life now, as more programmers and engineers say hello to their computers and ask what is on their simulated minds. Pushing open a door, I step into an unearthly greenhouse sprouting wires that climb the walls like clematis vines. An engineer who looks more like the gardener is hunched almost into a video tube, his shirt-tails mentally flying as the computer bests him.

Across the lab, a programmer in blue bib overalls is scratching a bird's nest of hair and swearing at his computer. On a shelf in front of him, a little vehicle has just gone haywire on the graphics display monitor. He types out a new instruction, pushes a control button, and watches intently. "It disappeared!" he sputters. "I know I didn't blow it up, so something else blew up! Like the program!"

The gardener comes over to commiserate. "Is it breaking down?" he asks. "It hasn't become sane yet!" the programmer moans. "I have yet to convince it to speak anything that's even a semblance of reality!"

One door down, things are working better. A wavy-haired woman in rosy velour and jeans spins a control ball with long slender fingers to move images around the screen. Dona may go down in the annals of computer science as the programmer who turned animations of centipedes and spiders into objects of female fantasy. "I'm convinced my game is a woman's game," she says, with a soft Arkansas laugh. "It's a nice game. It's very straightforward."

Like Dave, who yearned to work for Atari from the moment he saw the original Pong game in a bar, Dona was drawn to Atari by playing games in an arcade. She was working at General Motors' programming a microprocessor to govern such things as idle speed, spark advance, and cruise control in the 1981 Cadillac. But GM's assembly-line approach to programming was frustrating.

So she escaped to a nearby arcade at lunchtime, out of boredom: "I knew about the Silicon Valley, everybody talked about it, but I read somewhere about Atari being up here and it just dawned on me: 'They make these games. What they do every day is what I do every day, but look what they get out of it. I get Cadillacs and they get these!' "

A PAL THAT DOESN'T GET MAD

What is it about these games? When Asteroids was still in the lab, on its way to becoming Atari's most popular game ever, a programmer named Lyle was the force who helped make it work. "I was also," he admits, "the original Asteroids junkie. By junkie I mean I would go into the lab after work at five or six in the evening and start playing Asteroids, and when I would finally snap out of my trance it would be eleven at night, and I'd say, one more game, and when I snapped out again, it was two in the morning, and I knew I was in trouble. If I counted what it would have cost me in quarters, I would have spent several thousand dollars playing Asteroids."

A strange thing is going on here. These people are being changed by the computers they work with. They love the machines, bugs and all. It's not just the games, nor the engineering personality's desire for logic and order that makes these computers so stimulating: it's their size. They've become small enough to be individuals. These programmers are no longer working with systems. They are working with friends. They are on such intimate terms that they swear at them, hit them, even laugh with them. What is strangest, though, is that they seem to bear

no resemblance to those human cyborgs science-fiction writers warned we would become once the computers got hold of us. Instead, these people seem to be having a good time.

Trying to explain, Dona talks about her microprocessor with a romantic passion that men don't always inspire. "In the Valley, almost everybody has something to do with computers, and some people think I'm just frittering my life away here," she says without a blush. "A lot of them work on IBM 370's and that kind of thing, and they can't fathom what it is to have the whole little thing to yourself!"

What's really going on here? Before coming to Atari I had asked Isaac Asimov, a pioneer in science fiction, why he thought these games were so attractive. "Kids like the

A "logic" expert in an Atari chip design lab checks every circuit by hand before miniaturizing and engraving the diagram onto a tiny chip (far right).

John McDermott/Rainbow

With a creative mind and a bit of electronics ingenuity, Nolan Bushnell built the first video game,
which changed the history of the computer.

computer because it plays back," he said.
"You can play with it, but it is completely
under your control, it's a pal, a friend, but it
doesn't get mad, it doesn't say 'I won't play,'
and it doesn't break the rules. What kid
wouldn't want that?"

That sense of being in control seems to
be something Atari programmers enjoy as
much as the players. Indeed, there are cognitive psychologists like James McConnell at
the University of Michigan who think our
most basic drive is an urge to get the environment under control.

McConnell describes behavior in terms
of feedback terminology: "The nice thing
about using computers is that you can establish control over your inputs, which allows
you then to control your outputs." In other
words, if you control the challenge or re-
ward, you can improve your performance.

McConnell's language is remarkably
similar to what one of Atari's electronics engineers said to me, as he was explaining how
a game works: "Essentially we have a microprocessor and input-output devices. All these
games are, is process control. You take some
kinds of inputs and you generate some kinds
of outputs, and it's a feedback system, and
the player is in the loop of the feedback, and
while he's giving the feedback to the game,
we hope he's getting some kind of enjoyment
out of it."

HOW IT ALL BEGAN

Which is how it all began, in the mind of
Nolan Bushnell. Bushnell is the man who
figured out how to get us to love the computer, and who started Atari to do it.

He first got the idea of video arcade
games as an undergraduate at the University
of Utah. He played Spacewar games on the
engineering lab computers at night and supported himself by working at an amusement
park in the summertime. At the park he realized what an attraction the engineering lab
computer games would be. "But when you
divide 25 cents into an eight-million-dollar
computer, there ain't no way," he says, "so I
sort of filed that concept in the back of my
mind."

In only a few years, however, the price
of minicomputers came down so far that
Bushnell, with a bit of electronics ingenuity,
almost had the hardware for an arcade game
worked out, using one minicomputer hooked
to several television terminals. The minicomputer was not quite powerful enough, so
Bushnell added more computer circuits to
the terminals to keep track of specific things,
and he kept making the terminals' hardware
smarter. Then he had a 25-cent idea. "I said,
'Hey, maybe I can do it all in hardware, and
have a stand-alone terminal. And the minute
that happened I worked it out, and the eco-
nomics were overwhelming. That was really
how the first video game started."

That 25-cent idea changed the history of
the computer, but no one knew it at the time.
The legend is that Bushnell built the first
game, Pong, in his garage. Actually, he
moved his daughter out of her bedroom to
build it, and it wasn't Pong. The first was a
game called Computer Space, a flying saucer
and rocket ship dogfight with turn, thrust,
and fire buttons, in a fiberglass cabinet. Only
2,000 Computer Space games were made,
but it was enough of a success to encourage
Bushnell to build his next game, Pong, which
became so popular and so widely distributed
that almost everyone could get his hands on
the hardware.

The games were marketed through the
traditional distributors of pinball machines
and still are, except that they now make up

about 80 per cent of the business in many places. Many distributors at first showed no interest, and most thought the games would make a brief splash, then disappear from the market. The distributors still don't know quite what happened, or why. Despite an initial appearance in places where pinball was played, which led many people to see these games simply as a new sort of electronic pinball, the computer games are as different from pinball as the iron horse was from the horse.

Pinball is essentially a game in which the player matches mechanical skills with a machine. It is the natural plaything of the industrial revolution, in which machines created a mechanical advantage over human labor. The computer games are the first playthings of an information revolution, games in which the player matches wits with an intelligent machine.

The computer game called Pac Man, shown here ablaze in action, is considered to be one of the best on the market by video-game enthusiasts everywhere.

© Dan McCoy/Rainbow

NEW WAY OF THINKING

Computer games may also turn out to be more than that. With the continuing decrease in the cost of the hardware, the games have become much more sophisticated. In order to play some of these games, many players develop styles of thinking and seeing that they do not ordinarily use.

Out in the arcades now, MIT sociologist Sherry Turkle has been watching the players. "I think they are learning a lot of spatial thinking, a lot of geometrical thinking," she says. "What I see is an experience that great athletes have, where they can allow their bodies to think for them. The games are giving that experience to larger numbers of people. With good players their fingers are doing the thinking." The games are also teaching a lot of people that computers can be playful.

At the Claremont Graduate School in a Los Angeles suburb, psychologist Robert S. Gable suspects that the players he sees in the arcades may be thinking with faculties even more surprising than their fingers. "The game players are intellectual and social mutants," he says. He sees their play as a form of learning that may be more suited to the computer-based society that is emerging than the linear education now available in schools and books. "The arcade machines are skillful teachers," Gable says, "with more variety and individuality than many human teachers."

His words are echoed by Michigan's James McConnell. "Go into one of the arcades and watch the students there play," McConnell advises. "They're being challenged in strange sorts of ways, and they're vocal and emotional about it. And then go to the library, and watch the kids sitting in a row, and they aren't smiling and they aren't enjoying anything. If they did, if one of them got an insight from reading a book and stood up and yelled 'Eureka!' they'd throw him right out of the place."

Are those psychologists saying the arcades are the new schools for survival? Is it somehow more valuable to learn Missile Command than to learn English?

To know that, you may have to hit hyperspace. Hyperspace is a concept intro-

© Dan McCoy/Rainbow

Steven Jobs, coinventor of the Apple computer, confers with a product manager. Jobs made computers more accessible on a personal scale.

duced in early science fiction and used in some of the first computer video games. In hyperspace you disappear from your current frame of reference and reappear in the same world but in a different dimension of space or time, or at least at different coordinates on the screen. It is not a perfect concept. There's a chance you will blow up on reentry. But sometimes it's worth trying.

Hyperspace. And reenter in the weather-beaten barracks office of U.S. Army Major Dave Robinson, a trim armored cavalry officer who, as he gets up from his desk, looks as if he might shoot right through his own flat-cut hair. Major Robinson's assignment is to explore the effectiveness of a modified Atari arcade game in gunnery instruction. Yes, now the military is studying the potential value of arcade games as training aids. "I am not a programmer or design technician," Robinson says. "I'm an armored cavalry officer and damned proud of it. But I've got a gut feeling that you can take these machines and put them in every company-sized unit in the army and get a lot of training value out of it."

Dr. Thomas Longridge, at the Human Resources Laboratory at Williams Air Force Base near Phoenix, is using an aircraft carrier landing game for research on pilot judgment. He sees the array of information that players of some arcade games cope with as requiring skills like the rapid information processing performed by fighter pilots with video displays in their cockpits. And he thinks the games—like the multibillion dollar computer cockpit simulators long used in pilot training—may train people in a kind of "multiplex," many-channeled thinking.

PLAYING OR LEARNING?

The distinction between computer games and computer simulators is blurring here, and in many other places where small, inexpensive microcomputers are taking over tasks that required huge mainframe computers a few years ago. Home computers have more versatility than most people know what to do with. One Atari engineer calls them "solutions in search of a problem." Already they have begun to make the distinction between playing and learning a little hard to draw. An example of this is a home computer game that simulates the political economy of an ancient kingdom:

You have a ten-year reign as the king and you have so much grain, so many people, and so much land. You can buy or sell land for grain but you can't plant more land than you have people to work at farming it. If you don't feed your people enough, they start to die. If they die, you can't plant as much grain anymore, and you may get into a downward spiral. But if you plant too much and store it, rats eat some of it, and people start coming from other villages to join you. Simulations like this first appeared on the university computers of the 1960's, along with games like Spacewar. Now kids are playing them at home.

Even more imaginative and powerful kinds of simulations are becoming available. A physicist who is working with Atari developing holography for a home game—combining the laser optics of holograms, those three-dimensional images of pure light, with the electronics of the computer chip—mentions an idea he thought was pure fantasy.

"I think you could teach special relativity with video games," he told me. "You can build any set of physical laws into that universe, and you can alter the parameters so that they are more apparent than they are in normal life; so on the screen you make the speed of light be ten miles an hour, put in some gravity, make it a game, and kids will start learning special relativity . . ."

I didn't know it then, but that game already exists. In the Artificial Intelligence Laboratory at MIT, Seymour Papert developed an orbital game of just this sort where the player controls an object on a screen that obeys the laws of physics in space. The results were dramatic. People—those with training in physics and those with none—began for the first time to have a feel for relativity, to incorporate it into their intuition of the world.

The computer language called Logo that Papert developed and used to create this game was marketed in the summer of 1981 by Texas Instruments for use on its home computers. Papert is now advising Logo Computer Systems, a new company which is developing versions of the language for other home computers and for use in schools. Similarly powerful simulations, using a computer language called Smalltalk, have been developed at the Xerox Palo Alto Research Center. There children have been animating Saturday morning cartoons instead of watching them, designing music, and playing with electronic paint brushes. Alan Kay, who directed this research, predicts that home computers that allow kids to do this sort of thing will be on the market, at no higher cost than the current ones, before 1990. And they will be no larger than a typical school notebook.

NEW AGE ALREADY HERE

Such predictions have been made before and failed to materialize, but it is clear that the microcomputer has got out of the arcade. "The friendly computer is not something that's going to happen," Isaac Asimov points out, "it *is* happening. It's all around us, the games, appliances, the word-processor instead of the typewriter. It's the new age, and it is here."

If the new age is anywhere, it may be in the spare, modern office of Steven Jobs, who with his partner Stephen Wozniak invented the Apple computer.

Steve and his partner "Woz" may be remembered as the two college dropouts who

Atari

In an Atari workshop in Sunnyvale, California, a technician in the coin-operated video games manufacturing department assembles a component for a new game.

Apple

Home computers give youngsters access to an artificial technology, which allows them to use their imaginations and learn in an innovative way.

change Steve Jobs has in mind can already be seen at places like MIT, where an office-of-the-future project includes a computer you can communicate with by touching its screen, or talking to it in plain English, or even simply by pointing at it with your finger and directing it to move an image from one part of the screen to another.

It may be a while before you can wag your finger at a personal computer and get an intelligent response. But it seems certain that these machines will continue to surprise us. Dr. Robert E. Kahn, at the U.S. Defense Department's Advanced Research Projects Agency, is convinced that we're going to see "some very powerful and intelligent systems show up" in the next few years.

"In the next decade, we'll see a lot of what I call garage-shop computer engineering, and maybe even a little science," he says. "It's getting to the point now where you can go to your local supermarket and if you can't buy a floppy disk now, then tomorrow you'll be able to, and for $19.95 you can get a bag of logic, and some powerful chips. I think we're going to see a world of innovation come out of young kids, high school kids, and pre-teens of all kinds, who are just given access to technology, with creative minds and no constraints. And talk about cultural effect—I think people may be incredibly surprised at how clever some of these young people can be. While they may not have a good basic knowledge of the outside world, they will be dealing with an artificial technology where they can construct anything that they can imagine. And they've got great imaginations."

brought the computer down to earth. "Most people's view of it is still 1984ish," he says, "and yet the way it's really happening is closer to whole-wheat bread! Instead of leading to centralized intelligence, centralized decision-making and personal unenrichment, it's started happening on a personal scale." If the computer is becoming decentralized, cheap and more accessible to the individual, Steve and Woz had a lot to do with all that.

In 1976 Steve and Woz decided to make their own computer because they couldn't afford to buy one. "I was working at Atari at the time and Woz worked at Hewlett-Packard designing calculators," Steve recalls. The Apple was not the first personal computer, but it was the first popular one because it hooked up to a television set, something Steve learned from Atari.

Steve sees the concept of games taking on new meaning as the computer evolves to meet us on our terms. "The challenge," he says, "is to spend more of the intelligence in the box to make the computer adapt to the way people do things rather than what we do now, which is to force people to adapt to the way computers do things." The sort of

MICROWORLDS

After watching kids at MIT's Artificial Intelligence Lab, Seymour Papert has a similar view. "I don't think there's anything wrong with arcade games," he says, "except that you have to play *that* one. I think in terms of creating a computation environment in which you not only have access to unlimited numbers of games but where you can make them yourself. And then the word 'game' takes on a different meaning. I think what it is all about is getting into 'microworlds,' simulated environments which

Elizabeth Marshall/Gamma-Liaison

Instead of staring at a television for entertainment, a group of young boys gather before
a large movie screen to take turns at sharpening their skills in electronic sports.

are exciting because you can manipulate them. I think we don't fully understand what makes that sort of manipulation so powerfully attractive."

Are the Atarians in their cells really the monks of these microworlds? Not long before he built the first Apple computer, while he still worked at Atari, Steve Jobs went to India. Having grown up in the Silicon Valley, he says, he was amazed to find that Western rational thought is not an innate human characteristic. When he came back, he says, he couldn't help observing that the best computer people he knows "are probably the closest thing I have met in America to Zen monks."

"The computer," he says "is one of the pinnacles of Western rational thought. Semiconductors bring together physics, electronics, chemistry, and mathematics all into one thing. But computers bring together all that, plus they bring logic into it, and philosophy, information theory, all that. So to me, anyway, the computer represents the culmination of all Western rational thought into an artifact.

"And the people working on these computers possess a passion about the discovery and creation of something. It's not even the creation—they *know* it's there, and it's sort of what Michelangelo expressed when he was sculpting: he would look at a big rock and say, 'My statue is inside there and I just have to get it out.' It's a passion that I have only seen matched in people pursuing what they consider to be the truth of their existence. It's the same purity of spirit I have experienced in monks. These people feel that it is going to be the one most incredible revolution in our lifetimes. It's going to dwarf everything else. We are on the cliff" □

SELECTED READINGS

"Electronic games: here's what makes them work" by W. H. Buchsbaum and R. Mauro. *Science Digest,* July 1979.

"Electronic game race" by R. Blumenthal. *The New York Times Magazine,* December 14, 1980.

How to Win at Pac-Man®. Editors of Consumer Guide. Pocket Books, 1982.

"Games people program" by E. R. Shell. *Technology Review,* November/December 1980.

"How electronic games grew up" by B. Rice. *Psychology Today,* November 1979.

Jim Harrison/MIT Experimental Music Studio

Barry Vercoe, director of the MIT Experimental Music Studio, composes and then edits a
graphic score by playing notes into a computer as violinist Marcus Thompson looks on.

COMPUTER MUSIC

by Kevin Jones

THE notion of a composer struggling to produce a masterpiece by candlelight—armed
with a quill pen and out-of-tune piano—is
long gone. Among the tools of many a musician today are a light pen, a graphics screen,
a powerful computer system, and a familiar-
ity with such computer jargon as "program-
mable read-only memory," or PROM.

Many composers are now using computers to aid composition. World renowned
composer and conductor Pierre Boulez now
heads the music research center IRCAM in
Paris where composers are investigating the
potential of sophisticated computer music
systems. Boulez is convinced that the computer is an integral and necessary part of
musical development. In common with almost every human activity in the developed
world, music is benefiting from the computer
revolution, and its effects could soon have a
larger impact than the phonograph record
and tape recorder on everybody's experience
of music.

NOT JUST ELECTRONIC MUSIC

But how do we define computer music?
To begin with, it is not the same as electronic
music. It may sometimes sound like electronic music, and electronic music may be
produced with a computer's assistance. But
the term "electronic music" usually applies
to sounds produced electronically on tape recorders, analog synthesizers, or organs, all of
which have been around for some time.
Computer music is a much more recent development. Only since about 1979 or 1980
has it begun to descend from the ivory towers
of research studios and institutes to become a
part of the general fabric of musical techniques.

The sounds of computer music are at
least as diverse as any other variety of music:
it may sound like Bach, Schoenberg, Abba,
African drumming, or clanging sheets of
metal. Or it may include completely new and
so far unimagined sounds. The computer,
coupled with devices that generate sound,

may be an ultra-sophisticated musical instrument, or it could help musicians to compose or manipulate sounds. Most composers and researchers who have used a computer have done so for its capacity to mimic conventional musical instruments. At the other extreme, a few have used it in a rather different way. They eavesdrop on the computer's basic operations to represent electronic processes as sounds (although this often produces noises). The most creative uses of the computer probably lie somewhere in the middle, where the sounds produced are novel, but are sufficiently familiar for our ears to be able to appreciate them.

EARLY ATTEMPTS

The first documented experiments in computer music began as long ago as 1956 at the University of Illinois on an old Illiac computer. Lejoren Hiller and Leonard Isaacson programmed simple rules of harmony and counterpoint—chord structures and the relationship between musical "voices" played simultaneously—to produce coded scores. These scores could then be transcribed into staves, bars and notes, to be played on conventional instruments. At that stage, the computer could not generate sounds directly. But during the 1960's, Max Matthews and his team at Bell Telephone Laboratories developed a sophisticated program to synthesize sound directly. This program and its variants—MUSIC 1 to MUSIC 5—have been the models for most sound synthesis programs since.

Matthews wrote MUSIC 5 in the computer language FORTRAN so that composers could manipulate the program on a mainframe or powerful minicomputer. In this form it instructs computers all over the world. However, composers have found that this is an inefficient way to run the program. To produce one second of sound, a computer programmed with MUSIC 5 in FORTRAN often needs 100 seconds to process the information that describes the sound. For this reason, computer musicians have written new versions of MUSIC 5, and its slightly different companion MUSIC 4, in machine code. Machine codes are "languages" that the computer understands better than "high level languages" such as FORTRAN, which people understand more easily. By writing the program directly in machine code, the composer saves processing time.

These codes may merit the status of languages and include MUSIC 360 for an IBM 360 computer and MUSIC 11 for a Digital Equipment PDP 11, both developed by Barry Vercoe of the Massachusetts Institute of Technology (MIT). MUSIC 10 is a more sophisticated language, designed for a PDP 10 machine. It is running at IRCAM, which has been working with composers at Stanford University in California where research in computer music is a part of the university's artificial-intelligence project.

CULMINATION OF RECORDING TECHNIQUES

All of the MUSIC programs model the operations of sound generators. These are: oscillators, electronic devices that produce pure tones (which are sine-waves); devices that share the sound, or give it its "timbre"; and the sound filters and mixers that are available in conventional synthesizers and electronic music studios. But the programs juggle these operations precisely and in a highly complex manner. The musician is able to combine the components of sound in as complex a fashion as he needs to define the many instruments that a computer can represent. During the 1970's, John Chowning of Stanford University pioneered the use of frequency-modulation techniques in computer music that have advanced the process. So having created a group of "instruments," a composer can proceed to define a "score," with pitch, duration, and volume.

Programming a computer to produce the sounds of conventional instruments can be seen as the culmination of advances in recording techniques. There are two basic recording techniques: analog recording and digital recording. Both depend first of all on the performance of a musician—say, a trumpeter. The trumpet sets up vibrations in the air. Recording equipment then picks up these vibrations and converts them into a pattern of changes in electric voltage.

Very simply, the analog recording system stores the pattern of these changes in voltage on magnetic tape. When a listener replays the tape through an amplifier, the changes in voltage make the cone of a loud-speaker vibrate to reproduce the vibrations that the trumpet originally created. What the listener hears is very close to the original sound.

Digital recording adds several complex steps to the process. The pattern of voltage changes that represents the original sound is fed to a device called an analog-to-digital converter. This converter samples the values of voltages in the pattern at frequent intervals—say 30,000 times per second. The result is a sequence of values, a digital representation of the original sound. A computer collects these values and stores them on tape or disc. During playback, a digital-to-analog converter changes the numbers back into voltages. The listener then replays the music as he would an analog recording. The digital recording process improves the quality of recorded music.

The higher the rate at which the analog-to-digital recorder samples voltages, the greater the range of frequencies that the system can handle. For instance, a sampling rate of 20,000 times per second will handle frequencies up to 8 kiloHertz (kilocycles per second). If the frequency is higher than that, the computer cannot perform accurately. The best digital systems currently sample at a rate of 50,000 times per second.

A computer fitted with devices that can generate a digital version of musical sounds, or which can draw digital information from a store of such information, bypasses the early stages of digital recording.

SAMPLING SOUNDS

More recent developments in the version of MUSIC 5 at IRCAM now allow computer musicians to sample natural sounds, convert them into digital form, and then analyze and manipulate them. Any sound—whether cornet, drum, clarinet, or bassoon—consists of, or can be treated as, a combination of simple oscillations of different frequency. In a complex sound, such as that of a bell, the ear can often perceive these different frequency components, or "partials," with a little concentration. British composer

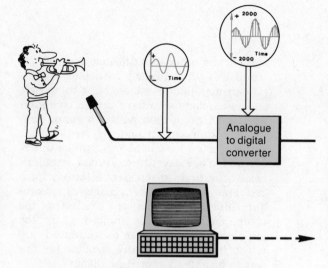

Jonathan Harvey achieved an intriguing effect by recording the sound of Winchester Cathedral's tenor bell and separating the component partials. He then replaced each of the component sounds of the bell with the very pure sound of a boy's voice, appropriately pitched and scaled, and put the whole lot back together again.

HYBRID MINICOMPUTER SYSTEMS

Versatile though they are, these programs can run only on large computers, and use a lot of expensive processing time. Few composers have access to large machines, and those that have find the ration of time available hopelessly inadequate. Very often long sequences of composition need to be run overnight and, allowing for errors, machine failures and other difficulties, it can take a composer a week of work from conceiving a sound to hearing it.

To improve the process, engineers have now produced hybrid systems in which a minicomputer controls separate sound generators. In these systems, the musician has fewer sound generators to play with but has the advantage of the computer's sophisticated control. And because the computer needs to handle fewer data, its response is almost instantaneous—that is, it responds "in real time." It is rather like having two dozen pairs of hands to play an organ or to twist the knobs on a synthesizer.

Other European studios, including the Institute of Sonology at the University of Utrecht in Holland and the Electronic Music Studios in Stockholm, Sweden, have used

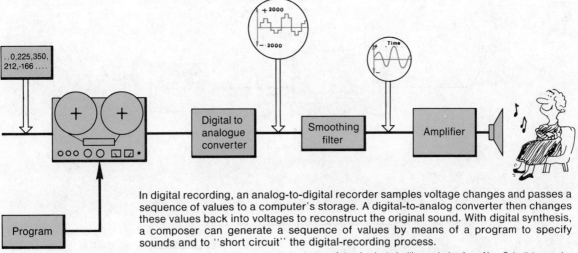

In digital recording, an analog-to-digital recorder samples voltage changes and passes a sequence of values to a computer's storage. A digital-to-analog converter then changes these values back into voltages to reconstruct the original sound. With digital synthesis, a composer can generate a sequence of values by means of a program to specify sounds and to "short circuit" the digital-recording process.

Artwork adapted with permission from *New Scientist* magazine

PDP 15 minicomputers linked to banks of oscillators and other devices. At Pisa in Italy composers share time on a mainframe computer linked to external sound generators. This works well in off-peak periods but when the system is trying to accommodate a lot of users it can become confused, and curious snippets of sound emerge in a very capricious fashion.

Today, as computer technology continues to develop, powerful microcomputers linked to specialist oscillators have given rise to a range of comparatively cheap digital synthesizers. These vary from the "concert" Fairlight and Synclavier instruments, to the "domestic" Mountain hardware and Alf synthesizers available for the small Apple computer. Their design makes such packages useful both to the amateur musician, who can program the computer to do much of the work of composing, and to the experienced user who can program more sophisticated and complex structures.

ANY IMAGINABLE SOUND?

Some claim—boldly—that computer-music systems can create "any imaginable sound." Perhaps in theory this may be true but in practice many of the musicians who program the computers have an inadequate knowledge of acoustics and a limited imagination, constraints that are too easily overlooked. For a long time sophisticated computer-music systems have produced an embarrassingly thin trickle of good music. Although musicians have gained a lot of useful knowledge about acoustics with each fresh attempt to synthesize the sound of a familiar instrument such as a violin, that is not the most creative of jobs for a computer. And how does anyone conceive a sound they have never heard?

Another problem with sophisticated computer-music systems is that the machine needs a detailed specification of a sound. Thousands of instructions may be required to specify a very short sequence of sounds. In order to avoid static, boring or clinically consistent "electronic" sounds, the user needs to specify each small nuance of sound that an instrumentalist's training would lead him to control almost unconsciously.

Composers often adopt a certain random element in computer music to introduce variation with the minimum of effort, a technique that usually works quite successfully. The word "random" should, incidentally, not imply the idea of uncontrollable chance creating chaos. Controlled randomness can be used to great artistic effect. The term "stochastic" is often preferred over "random" to avoid misconception, and to highlight the idea that the composer is aiming at some goal. By applying stochastic techniques a composer can, if he or she wishes, turn the processes of composing and performing upside down: he or she could control volume and timbre, for example, and leave the choice of pitch to the machine.

The Greek composer Yannis Xenakis was the first composer to use the computer to organize sounds along abstract, non-traditional lines to create otherwise unobtainable new sounds and textures. He began by gen-

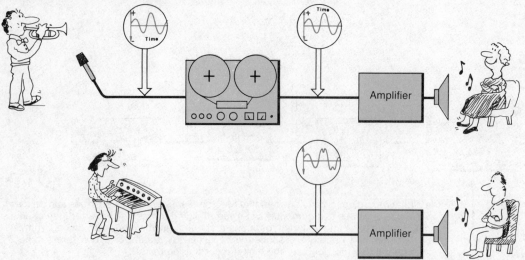

Artwork adapted with permission from *New Scientist* magazine

In analog recording, a microphone picks up sound which is converted into changes in voltage. The pattern of changes is stored on magnetic tape, then replayed. This reproduces the sound quite accurately. An electronic organ creates voltage changes from scratch to simulate natural sounds—but they sound electronic.

erating scores to be played on conventional instruments. One called *ST48,* is for orchestra and another, *ST4,* is for string quartet; both were composed in 1962. More recently, he has designed and constructed a sophisticated computer music system that can interpret and then play a score for which he has drawn, with a light pen, the limits of pitch and time on a graphics pad. Xenakis has had good results in his own compositions, and has also adapted it to successful projects with groups of blind children.

TO BE OUR OWN COMPOSERS

It is in trying to instill creativity into a system that the composer is likely to find most interest. Already there are one or two systems in which the computer continuously prompts and guides the composer, or delivers a selection of sounds from which he can select the ones he wants. At MIT, Curtis Roads is developing an "intelligent composer's assistant," which the composer can program with his own and others' preferences and techniques, so that the "assistant" will make its own unprompted decisions, akin to the composer's wishes, while a score is being written. This is part of a wider project in artificial intelligence and music directed by Marvin Minsky, a leading figure in the study of robots and artificial intelligence. He has recognized the potential importance of music in revealing the workings of people's creative thought, and is supporting this research.

What of the next 25 years? Many musicians are afraid that computer music might do them out of a job, but that should never happen. The same fears arose when phonograph records first appeared, and they proved ill-founded. The music industry grew to become possibly the largest in the world, and music becomes available to wider audiences all the time. Computer music should exist peaceably, side-by-side with conventional music and can even provide new opportunities for musicians.

Within a few years we could all have computer-based, pianolike instruments in our homes and digital music machines linked to vast, central databanks of music. We should be able to dial whatever we want to hear. Instead of phonograph records we could buy tiny boxes, which contain information to control sophisticated digital synthesizers and which could store many hours of music. We could change the sound, while we were listening: speed it up or slow it down; highlight particular instruments and take out others; adjust the acoustic balance; or whatever we wish. Most exciting, perhaps, is that we can all be composers with our "intelligent composer's assistant" providing us with all the technical background we need. And if we are feeling not particularly creative, or just lazy, we can always leave the computer to get on with the job □

RUBIK'S CUBE

by Fred Warshofsky

• In London's Waterloo Station, a man sat twisting a brightly colored plastic cube. Soon a crowd gathered to watch. When the man got on board his train, half the people in the waiting room followed—only to leap off as it started moving, when they realized they were on the wrong train.

• At a Chinese restaurant in Lagos, Nigeria, a young couple sat at a table fiddling with a multi-colored cube. The owner came over, observed, then made a bet: he would solve the puzzle by the time they finished eating, or dinner would be on the house. Three hours, a dinner for two, and several drinks later, the restaurateur had to admit defeat.

• A high-school football game in Connecticut was delayed when one player failed to take the field with the rest of the team. He was found in the locker room, playing with a cube.

All over the world, millions of people are hypnotized by what may be the most maddening and compelling puzzle ever invented. Marketed in the United States as Rubik's Cube, or Magic Cube, it is about the size of a squared tennis ball. Each of its six faces is a different color, and each face is divided into nine squares. A remarkable inner mechanism allows sections of the cube to be rotated independently, either horizontally or vertically.

The cube sells for about $6. In its pristine condition, each face is a solid color. The "cubist" gives it a few random twists and the faces become varied mixes of red, yellow, orange, white, green, and blue squares. The object is to restore the cube to its original state, with each face again a single color. It sounds simple, yet is incredibly complex.

FROM MIND TO MARKET

The cube was invented by Ernö Rubik, who holds degrees in architectural engineering and interior design, and teaches at the Academy of Applied Arts in Budapest,

Ian Cook/PEOPLE WEEKLY © 1981 Time Inc.

Fourteen-year-old Patrick Bossert of England was one of the first to crack the cube's secret. He wrote the book, *You Can Do the Cube.*

Hungary. A small, slender man with an elfin smile, he has a lively mind that darts and flashes across the fields of three-dimensional geometry, mechanics, color, and form like a bee darting from flower to flower.

In the summer of 1974, while thinking about the laws of geometry, Rubik began playing with the idea of a three-dimensional object that could rotate about three axes. "I kept turning the object over and over in my mind," he told me, "and then I realized it was a sort of puzzle, a game."

The challenge now was to turn the theoretical construction floating in his head into something real. His problem: to devise a mechanism capable of converting all of the complicated movements into simple twists and turns that would change the arrangement of squares on the faces of an actual cube.

When finally he had a working model in hand, he gave a few twists—and then confronted possibly his greatest challenge: solving the puzzle. There were an almost infinite number of color patterns. After weeks of twisting and trying to fathom the spatial relationships involved, Rubik at last succeeded in maneuvering the different sections of the cube back to their starting points.

He wrote up the details of the cube's construction and obtained a patent in 1975. In communist Hungary, as elsewhere, entrepreneurs looking for new products to manufacture do not always fall out of the paprika shaker. But Rubik interested a small toy-manufacturing co-operative, Politechnika, in his invention. They eventually overcame the objections of Triál, the state toy distributor, that it was too difficult and complicated for mass appeal.

Cube's inventor, 38-year-old Ernö Rubik, is a professor of architecture in Budapest, Hungary.

Gamma-Liaison

ALL THE RAGE

The original production run of 5,000 was shipped to stores in Hungary just before Christmas, 1977. Within days they had sold out, and another 7,000 cubes were rushed off the production line.

Subsequently a notice appeared in a Budapest newspaper announcing the first meeting of a Rubik's Cube Club. More than 2,000 people showed up. Almost all wanted tips on solving the puzzle.

The cube became the rage throughout Hungary. And cubes in the hands of Hungarians traveling abroad began to attract attention. In 1978, a Hungarian professor of mathematics, Tamás Varga, took several with him to the International Congress of Mathematicians in Helsinki, Finland. David Singmaster, an American who teaches in London, was transfixed and persuaded Varga to give him one. "Back in England, I sent him off a book not available in Hungary and said, 'All my friends are fascinated and would like cubes.' He sent me a dozen. They were snapped up."

Singmaster later devised a set of notations for the faces of the cube and started writing instructions for restoring the cube to its original configuration. The result was a 66-page booklet that has sold 10,000 copies and is now in its fifth edition. The American mathematics teacher has since become chief guru to the world's millions of cubists.

UPBEAT SALES

Sales of the cube continue to soar. More than 4,000,000 have been bought worldwide, and sales are limited only by production. In Hungary, the Politechnika plant (employing over 500 people) runs 24 hours a day, seven days a week, to meet the demand. In the United States, Hong Kong and the Caribbean, by arrangement with Konsumex, one of Hungary's import/export agencies, the Ideal Toy Corporation manufactures 1,500,000 cubes a month, and still cannot keep up with demand. Cubes are also being manufactured by Logical Games, Inc., of Haymarket, Virginia, which introduced the puzzle to the United States under the name Magic Cube in 1979.

"Voyager Two to Houston . . . Voyager Two to Houston . . . we're encountering a unique asteroid formation!"

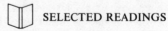

Baginski/Playboy

SUPER SOLVERS

Without help, it may take a new cubist months of fiddling before he can restore the cube to its original configuration. Even skilled mathematicians may need up to two weeks to get back to "Cube One." The actual number of possible combinations that can be tried is staggering: 43,252,003,274,489,856,-000.

Just how fast can the maddening puzzle be solved? Jerôme Jean-Charles, a 25-year-old French sportswriter, can get back to Cube One in 32 seconds on average. Sixteen-year-old Nicolas Hammond of Nottingham, England, says he can do it in 40 seconds. Dedicated enthusiasts from other countries claim times almost as impressive. In December 1981, Ideal Toy held a national competition to determine the fastest cubist in the United States. The winner was Minh Thai with a record time of 26 seconds.

BEYOND BASICS

Rubik never claimed any direct educational properties for the cube, but mathematicians quickly discovered them. "Quite a number of interesting phenomena of group theory (an abstract form of algebra) have been found in the cube," reports Singmaster. "And the group action on the eight corners is related to the group theory of quarks in particle physics."

In the United States, interested cubists on a number of college campuses exchange information on new cube moves and record times for solving the basic cube problem. They also devise new designs—colorful geometric patterns—to be realized on the cube.

Where will it all end? Perhaps David Singmaster's experience contains a warning. "I gave a cube to a friend," he reports, "and a friend in the next flat rang me several days later to say the first friend had gone mad from the cube—and please, could he have 20 more" □

SELECTED READINGS

"Metamagical Themas" by Douglas R. Hofstadter. *Scientific American,* March 1981.

The Simple Solution to Rubik's Cube by James G. Nourse. Bantam, 1981.

Notes on Rubik's Magic Cube by Dave Singmaster. Enslow Publishers, 1981.

Mastering Rubik's Cube by Don Taylor. Holt, Rinehart and Winston, 1981.

Named for the world-famous gambling casino in Monaco, the Monte Carlo method is a mathematical technique that uses random numbers to teach concepts in probability.

THE MONTE CARLO METHOD

by Kenneth J. Travers and Kenneth G. Gray

THE Tripl-Bubl Gum Company decides to promote its gum by wrapping each stick with the photo of one of six rock music stars. Assuming that there are equal numbers of photos of each of the six stars and that when you buy a stick of gum your chances of getting any of the six photos are the same, about how many sticks of gum would you expect to have to buy to get all six photos?

This problem is typical of a large group that, although simple, are difficult to solve. The problem can be more easily solved, however, by using a mathematical technique known as the "Monte Carlo" method, developed by an American mathematician, Stanislaw Ulam.

Monte Carlo is a method that uses random numbers to solve a problem. And what are random numbers? They are numbers that occur "without rhyme or reason;" that is, strictly by chance. For example, the numbers that turn up when a pair of dice are thrown are random numbers.

The bubble-gum problem can be solved by using a six-sided die. (A die is one of the dice; two dies make up a pair of dice.) If each side is taken to represent one of the six photos, a roll of the die is interpreted as purchasing a stick of gum and finding which photo was obtained (Figure 1).

Figure 1.

In table 1, we have assigned names to all six rock stars and recorded our first three "purchases." Suppose, for example, that a student rolls a 6, another 6, and then a 5.

These tosses would represent purchasing three sticks of bubble gum and getting photos of rock stars Stinger and Wally.

We continue our "shopping trip" by rolling the die until a complete set of photos is obtained (that is, until all six sides of the die have been rolled). When this occurs, one shopping trip, or "trial," has been completed, and the number of rolls of the die (sticks of gum purchased) is recorded.

In order to keep track of dice rolls, we need some kind of notation. A simple approach is to write down the results of each roll. For example, the sequence of digits 2325 means that we rolled a die four times and got a 2, a 3, another 2, and then a 5. A slash (/) can be used to denote the end of a completed trial (shopping trip).

Let's suppose, therefore, that the following list of random numbers represents the outcomes of forty-eight rolls of a die, which were required to complete three trials (read the rows left to right).

```
66533   45332   2461/4  22231   26431
26434   35/541  12165   62116   163/
```

The results of these rolls have been recorded in table 2.

You may wish to prepare your own tally and compare it with this table. The first set of all six outcomes was obtained in fourteen rolls of the die, a second set was obtained in eighteen rolls, and a third in sixteen rolls.

STEPS TO THE METHOD

Let's outline the steps that we followed in solving this problem using the Monte Carlo method. These five steps, with only

TABLE 1
Outcomes of Three Rolls of a Die

Outcome (Photo Obtained)	Number of Rolls of Die (Number of Sticks of Gum Purchased)
1 = Billy	
2 = Suzie	
3 = Rocky	
4 = Sid	
5 = Wally	/
6 = Stinger	/ /

slight change, can be used in solving a wide variety of problems.

1. Model. We first had to find a model that could be used to represent purchasing a stick of bubble gum and seeing which photo we got. We used the familiar six-sided die.

1 = Billy   2 = Suzie   3 = Rocky
4 = Sid   5 = Wally   6 = Stinger

2. Trial. In terms of the problem, we wish to find the average number of sticks of gum we would need to purchase in order to obtain a complete set of photos. Using our model, this translates into rolling the die until all six faces are obtained. This will constitute one trial.

3. Length of a trial. Record the number of rolls of the die (number of sticks of gum) required in step 2.

4. Repeat steps 2 and 3. The larger the number of trials obtained, the better (more reliable) is your estimate of the solution to the problem. For many problems, 100 trials provide a reasonably reliable estimate of the solution.

5. Find the mean (average) length of a trial. Divide the total of all the lengths of the

TABLE 2

Trial (Shopping Trip)	Outcome of Rolls of Die						Length of Trial (Number of Sticks of Gum)
	1 = Billy	2 = Suzie	3 = Rocky	4 = Sid	5 = Wally	6 = Stinger	
1	/	/ /	/ / / /	/ /	/ /	/ / /	14
2	/ /	⊤⊢⊬	/ / / /	/ / / /	/	/ /	18
3	⊤⊢⊬ /	/ /	/	/	/ /	/ / / /	16

trial (total number of sticks of gum) by the total number of trials. We carried out sixty trials and obtained an average number of rolls in a trial of 14.36, which is not far from the theoretical expected value of 14.7.

THE BIRTHMONTH PROBLEM

What is the probability that in a group of five people chosen at random at least two were born in the same month of the year (but not necessarily the same year)?

(An interesting variation is the zodiac sign problem: "What is the probability that in a group of five people at least two were born under the same sign of the zodiac?")

In terms of the Monte Carlo method, we have the following steps.

1. Model. Use a twelve-sided (dodeca-hedral) die, one side for each month of the year. Relatively inexpensive sets of plastic polyhedral dice, which work very well for Monte Carlo methods, are commercially available from toy stores. ("Dungeons and Dragons," for example, has a dodecahedron and other polyhedral dice.)

If these dice are not available, a spinner marked off in twelve congruent sectors would serve the purpose. We could also use twelve marbles that are different colors (one for each month), but otherwise identical. The marbles would be placed in a bag and mixed thoroughly. One is drawn, the color noted, and the marble returned to the bag.

2. Trial. A trial consists of rolling the twelve-sided die five times, once for each of the five persons in the group.

3. Successful trial. A success occurs when the same side of die (same month of year) is obtained at least twice in five rolls.

4. Number of trials. Repeat steps 2 and 3 about one hundred times.

5. Probability of success. Let's roll a twelve-sided die fifty times and complete our table for the resulting ten trials (five rolls per trial). We will follow common usage with random data by using an *O* to represent ten, *E* to represent eleven, and *T* to represent twelve (this keeps the format of the digits much neater). The outcomes of the fifty rolls are as follows:

92117   5*T*7*E*8   279*T*8   72*O*63   68292
96667   96*T*58   628*E*8   193*T*6   1*E*7*OT*

The outcomes of the first five rolls, 92117, translate into the months of September, February, January, January, and July, respectively. That is, our model of asking five persons their month of birth gave us two of those persons born in the same month (January). These outcomes are recorded in table 3. The circled slashes indicate that there were four trials in which at least two people had the same month.

Another 90 trials (sets of five rolls of the die) were conducted and of the 100 trials, sixty-four successes were obtained. So the probability that in a group of five persons at least two were born in the same month is estimated at 0.64, which compares favorably with the theoretical value of 0.618.

Let's take a closer look at the problem. How many people in the group would there need to be before we could be *certain* that at least two were born in the same month? To

Polyhedral objects serve well as models when using the Monte Carlo method.

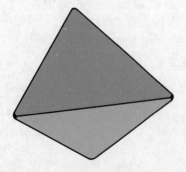
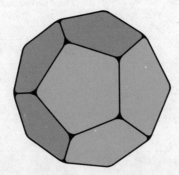
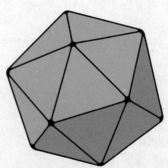

TABLE 3

Groups of 5 Persons	1 = Jan	2 = Feb	3 = Mar	4 = Apr	5 = May	6 = Jun	7 = Jul	8 = Aug	9 = Sep	O = Oct	E = Nov	T = Dec	Successful Trials
1	⦸/	/					/		/				yes
2					/		/	/			/	/	no
3		/					/	/	/			/	no
4		/	/			/	/			/			no
5		⦸/						/				/	yes
6						⦸/	/	/					yes
7					/			/				/	no
8		/				/		⦸/			/		yes
9	/		/			/			/			/	no
10	/						/			/	/	/	no

realize that 13 is the number required to guarantee a match is helpful in understanding the birthday problem, which may be stated as follows:

What is the probability that in a group, say, of 25 persons, at least 2 were born on the same day of the year (not necessarily the same year, however)?

With the background of the birthmonth problem, students more readily accept the fact that in a group of 366 persons (ignoring leap year) it is certain that at least 2 persons share a birthday (there are only 365 days to go around). The surprising fact about this problem, however, is that for a relatively small number of persons, about 60, it is virtually certain (99.4 percent) that at least 2 persons share a birthday. In as small a group as 23 persons, the chances are 50-50 that at least 2 persons were born on the same day of the year.

The birthday problem can be handled in much the same way as the birthmonth problem, but this time we use as a model a "365-sided die." Although such a die does not exist in a real world, a simple computer program can provide the necessary random data (table 4). The variable T is the number of random numbers between 1 and 365, inclusive, which is desired.

BASEBALL—MONTE CARLO STYLE
by Larry L. Houser

Baseball announcers and sportswriters often say that a team is in a "hot streak" or that a player is experiencing a "batting slump." They imply that unusually good or poor performance is responsible for the streak or slump, with little or no suggestion that the streaks or slumps may be explainable by chance.

With the aid of what is known as a Monte Carlo procedure, baseball events can be simulated with little difficulty. A random-number table or a computer random-digit generator lends itself well to this task. Other sources of random digits include spinners with ten equal divisions and the last digits in a series of telephone numbers.

WINNING THE PENNANT

Information from previous baseball seasons indicates that good teams often win 60 percent or more of their games. For this example we assume that a hypothetical baseball team is expected to win 60 percent of its games (known as a 0.600 won/lost record). Using the six digits 0, 1, 2, 3, 4, and 5 to represent wins and the four digits 6, 7, 8, and 9 to represent losses, we can simulate a 160-game season as shown in table 5. A W denotes a win and an L denotes a loss. The team's won/lost record determined by the

TABLE 4

```
10    INPUT T
20    FOR I = 1 TO T
30    PRINT INT (365 * RND(1)) + 1;
40    NEXT T
50    END
```

TABLE 5
A Team Expected to Win 60 Per Cent of Its Games Could by Chance Win 92 Times in a 160-Game Season

W	W	L	W	L	L	W	W	W	W	W	W
3	3	7	5	8	7	1	5	1	5	2	3
W	W	L	L	L	W	L	W	W	L	L	L
1	3	7	9	6	2	7	3	2	6	6	9
W	L	L	L	L	W	L	W	L	W	W	L
0	9	7	7	8	2	6	5	7	2	4	7
W	L	W	L	W	L	L	W	L	L	L	W
5	9	5	6	0	9	8	0	9	9	6	1
L	L	W	L	W	W	W	W	L	L	W	L
9	8	0	8	3	4	1	1	8	8	5	9
W	L	W	W	W	L	L	L	W	W	W	L
0	8	3	2	4	6	7	8	3	3	5	8
W	W	W	W	W	W	W	W	W	L	L	W
4	4	1	3	1	2	2	3	9	8	3	1
W	L	W	W	L	W	L	W	W	W	W	L
5	7	5	0	8	5	8	0	5	3	3	9
W	W	L	W	W	W	W	W	W	L	W	W
0	5	9	2	5	4	4	2	2	9	0	1
W	W	W	W	W	L	L	W	L	L	L	W
3	5	2	3	0	9	8	4	9	6	6	4
W	W	L	W	W	W	W	W	W	W	W	W
5	1	7	0	5	2	5	5	2	3	1	2
L	W	W	W	L	L	W	W	W	L	L	L
9	5	0	2	7	9	1	1	4	9	7	9
L	L	L	W	L	L	W	L	L	L	L	L
8	7	9	5	9	8	4	8	8	8	6	8
L	W	L	L								
6	4	7	7								

TABLE 6
A Player Expected to Get a Hit 30 Per Cent of the Time Could by Chance Hit 162/600 = 0.27

5496	5870	6838	4937	0825	5128	4209	4596
7884	3459	8837	3101	5897	6510	9697	3275
6573	0601	6019	6810	4940	8490	1991	7541
5563	9825	0169	2957	7277	7595	2118	8799
9848	3812	6418	7850	4397	0407	8518	9887
0631	9951	2713	4321	0755	9035	2984	0870
6603	1896	5856	7514	1932	3515	4705	3854
9208	0872	7966	6520	8300	6174	7668	5867
3158	7793	9244	9416	0129	3219	5145	0535
1673	8043	4464	1914	5222	8162	7968	1337
9055	2793	3306	7642	1608	1681	8615	0979
3086	7477	6865	0579	8257	7822	3741	8244
0743	9889	7828	9604	5184	3498	0338	8712
7988	5788	4681	6256	9491	0659	8523	9201
8405	8364	6295	5144	0064	6886	5305	2616
3195	1427	8020	3696	8184	8836	6047	2239
7056	6641	9155	0231	4231	5472	4532	4376
8976	7404	7933	4691	4680	1025	9261	8383
5858	7146	2995	7238	8905	2605		

random digits in table 5 is 92 wins, 68 losses.

The 0.600 winning-percentage team would be expected to compile a record of 96 wins and 64 losses. However, in this particular simulation of the 160-game season, the team won 92 games and lost 68. The team in this example had a 9-game winning streak, two 8-game winning streaks, a 7-game winning streak, and a 6-game winning streak along with two 6-game losing streaks. Note that this variation from the expected win/loss record and the winning and losing streaks can be accounted for by chance.

In another simulation for a second "0.600 team," the team won 99 games and lost 61 games. By chance alone, this team won seven more games than the first team. In addition, this team had a 12-game winning streak, a 7-game winning streak, and two 6-game winning streaks along with a 6-game losing streak.

If the simulation is repeated, distribu-tions of won/lost records, winning streaks, and losing streaks can be obtained.

AN OFF YEAR

For this example we will assume that a batter playing a 150-game schedule gets exactly four opportunities to bat per game and is expected to get a hit 30 percent of the time (known as a 0.300 batting average). Let the three random digits 0, 1, or 2 represent a hit and a 3, 4, 5, 6, 7, 8, or 9 represent an out. The random digits in table 6 are grouped with four digits in a group to represent one game for the hitter. The four digits highlighted in blue represent a game in which the player gets a hit.

This particular player had two 10-game hitting streaks, a 9-game hitting streak, and several smaller ones in addition to a 4-game slump. In this instance the player batted only 0.270 (162 hits per 600 times at bat) for the season, which might be considered to be an off year. However, this particular Monte Carlo simulation shows that a 0.270 batting average can be obtained by a 0.300 hitter as a chance fluctuation.

Monte Carlo methods using random numbers can be designed to simulate almost all the events in baseball that generate the statistics found on the Sunday sports page □

UPI

A giant sinkhole destroyed homes and property in Winter Park, Florida, when soil collapsed into a cavern in the porous limestone stratum beneath.

EARTH SCIENCES

EARTH SCIENCES
REVIEW OF THE YEAR

Philippe Ledru/Sygma

The devastating earthquake that struck a southern province of Iran in mid-1981 killed more than 3,000 people, and was considered the country's most serious quake since 1978.

Earth Structure. Studies of the earth's structure during 1981 concentrated on testing and elaborating the theory of plate tectonics. This theory holds that the earth's surface is divided into major plates that move about and collide, carrying the landmasses and ocean floor with them. Studies of how the landmasses are very slowly drifting and of how the sea floor is spreading in certain areas have led to new and more detailed theories of how faults, or cracks, in the earth's surface, volcanic arcs, mountain systems, and continental crust have formed during the past 3,800,000,000 years. In one instance, geologists, studying views of the earth taken from space, have discovered a giant crack running diagonally across the face of America. Reaching some 2,700 kilometers (1,700 miles) from Washington state across south-central Missouri to the southern tip of the Appalachian Mountains, this rift is almost three times the length of the well-known San Andreas fault in California. Although much still remains to be learned about the rift, scientists believe that it may have formed when the European and North American landmasses collided more than 200,000,000 years ago—a collision that formed the Appalachian mountains. The crack is assumed to pose no danger, but could help explain why earthquakes persist in the Missouri Bootheel, where powerful earthquakes occurred in the early 1900's. ■ The relation of plate tectonics to fault movement in the San Andreas region of California and to volcanic activity in the Mount St. Helens region of Washington was also studied.

Earthquakes and Seismology. Seven major earthquakes were recorded during 1981. A major earthquake is one rated as having a magnitude of 7 or higher on the open-ended Richter scale, which is a widely used indicator of an earthquake's severity. The largest quake of 1981, magnitude 7.7, occurred September 1 in the Samoa-Islands region. The most damaging, however, was one of magnitude 6.8, which rocked southern Iran on June 11, 1981. It caused more than 3,000 deaths, countless injuries, and extensive damage in Kerman province.

Earthquake prediction research continued—but with more caution. A U.S. Bureau of Mines seismologist failed when he predicted that a very large quake would occur off the coast of Peru in 1981. The prediction, which was widely publicized, was never supported by the National Earthquake Prediction Council and was formally withdrawn on July 20. New guidelines are now being developed for handling earthquake predictions. And, in research areas, more attention is being focused on rock properties, observed natural phenomena, and risk and hazard estimates.

In 1982, the research submersible *Alvin* was used on an expedition to study marine communities surrounding hydrothermal vents off Baja California, Mexico.

NOAA

Volcanoes and Volcanology. Geologists continued to monitor seismic and volcanic activity at Mount St. Helens, which erupted violently in 1980. The volcano was relatively quiet during 1981, but in September small eruptions added considerable amounts of volcanic material to the dome. Now roughly 600 meters long, 560 meters wide, and 135 meters high (approximately 1,950 feet long, 1,600 feet wide, and 450 feet high), the relatively cool surface of the dome has temperatures that reach 815° Celsius (1,500° Fahrenheit). ■ Meanwhile U.S. Geological Survey scientists discovered the first evidence of submarine volcanic activity 430 kilometers (270 miles) off the coast of Oregon. The volcanic vent is associated with the Juan-de-Fuca ridge, which marks the junction of the Juan-de-Fuca and Pacific plates.

Underseas Minerals. Scientists dredged a number of minerals from hot springs associated with the volcanic fissures of the Juan-de-Fuca ridge. ■ Similar deposits of underseas ores, worth at least $2,000,000,000, were discovered by U.S. Department of Commerce scientists about 560 kilometers (350 miles) west of Ecuador. Samples included copper, iron, zinc, silver, cadmium, molybdenum, lead, vanadium, and cobalt. The ores formed along a fault at the Galapagos rift where mineral-laden hot water seeps up through the ocean floor. When the hot water meets the near-zero water of the oceans the minerals crystallize.

Sinkholes. A giant sinkhole developed in Winter Park, Florida, in May 1981. A sinkhole is a depression that results from the weakening and collapse of underlying bedrock caused by acid water. As much as 300 meters (1,000 feet) wide and more than 50 meters (170 feet) deep, the sinkhole developed when underground limestone caverns (usually filled and strengthened with water) collapsed after being drained by severe drought. Several buildings, an automobile, and part of a municipal swimming pool disappeared into the gaping depression. Groundwater geologists are studying sinkhole phenomena to see how such geologic hazards can be alleviated in the future.

Paleontology. Paleontologists were active on many fronts during 1981. Some continued research on dinosaur extinction, pursuing the possibility that many Late Cretaceous organisms might have become extinct when an extraterrestrial object—an asteroid—slammed into the earth some 65,000,000 years ago. Evidence for this theory is based on the amount of iridium—a mineral rare on earth but relatively common in extraterrestrial objects—found in clay deposits dating from the Cretaceous-Tertiary time. And geologists exploring for oil believe that they may have found the crater made by this prehistoric impact—a crater, about 190 kilometers (120 miles) across, located on the Yucatan coast of Mexico. Some scientists believe that this impact drastically changed the earth's temperature. (See "The Dinosaur and the Asteroid" on page 136.)

Meanwhile new fossils—and a new head for an old one—were discovered. A skull of an early Teleost-type fish of the genus *Saurodon* was found in Upper Cretaceous rocks west of Fresno, California. ■ A new bird fossil—which Argentine paleontologists believe to be the world's largest known flying bird—was found in Late Miocene rocks in Argentina. Known as a teratorn, the bird had a wingspan of 7.6 meters (25 feet) and weighed 75 kilograms (165 pounds). ■ The "missing link" between reptiles and mammals may have been found. Paleontologists working in Arizona's Painted Desert found the jaws and three teeth of a small shrew-like animal that lived some 180,000,000 years ago, and, as such, is one of the oldest mammalian fossils yet found in North America. ■ Is a dinosaur still living? A California couple report that they have seen and photographed a dinosaur-like creature in the African Republic of the Congo. Such creatures have been described in native tales for centuries. ■ And, finally, an old dinosaur got a new head. The 19-meter (65-foot)-long, 150,000,000-year old skeleton in Yale Peabody Museum has long been fitted with the wrong skull. Recent studies indicate that the Peabody *Brontosaurus* was mistakenly topped with a shorter flat-nosed skull of *Camarasaurus,* a contemporary dinosaur.

William H. Matthews III

© 1980 National Geographic Society

This drawing of a bald eagle and the world's largest known flying bird, the prehistoric giant teratorn, compares the dramatic difference in size between the creatures.

At long last, a new, sleek skull like the one below was fitted on the *Brontosaurus* at the Yale Peabody Museum to replace the snub-nosed skull of another dinosaur it had had by mistake.

Wide World

Fred Maroon

The ancient, man-made Great Sphinx may have survived so long because its creators fashioned it from a natural land formation that had already been streamlined by the wind.

DESERT BUILDERS

by Farouk El-Baz

THE pyramids of Giza were already ancient, their origins shrouded in mystery, when the Greek historian Herodotus visited them about 450 B.C. Today, these colossal structures are around 4,500 years old, and yet we still ponder: were they only tombs, or did they also function as markers, observatories, or public works projects? And how is it that they are still standing centuries after other man-made wonders of the ancient world have disappeared? The answer to that may be even older than the pyramids.

Imhotep started it all. He served as minister, adviser, physician, and astronomer at the court of Djoser, Pharaoh of Egypt, about 2630 B.C. Imhotep was a healer and master sculptor, but, more important, he was the architect of the Step Pyramid at Saqqara.

Until the reign of Djoser, royal dwellings and tombs were built primarily of sun-dried brick. Imhotep selected a site in the desert overlooking Memphis and began planning something more ambitious. He built a *mastaba,* or tomb, of stone, about 8 meters (26 feet) high and 63 meters (207 feet) on each side. Upon it, with several modifications, he built five additions, each smaller than its predecessor. The result is a six-stepped structure, about 62 meters (204 feet) high, that resembles on the whole a pyramid.

Not long ago in Egypt, I pointed at a hill that looked similar to Imhotep's Step Pyramid. My companions from Ain Shams University in Cairo turned to the hill, which became visible only after climbing a 30-meter (100-foot) sand dune. Eyes squinting from the glare of the desert sun, but cameras clicking, we discussed the form of the hill. There was no good reason for its existence amid a sea of dunes. Most of the terrain has been eroded to a plain by running water and desert winds.

As we continued our geological exploration near Siwa, we encountered other conical hills. They appear to have developed from mesalike elevations.

An entry in my field notebook says: "numerous conical and pyramidal hills; I wonder if the ancient Egyptians had studied such natural desert structures before deciding on the form of their towering monuments!"

Why not? The ancient Egyptians left their mark throughout the Western Desert.

ANCIENT GEOLOGISTS

"All the way out here to get a stone. It's incredible!" said Mahmoud El-Prince, governor of the New Valley province, who had joined one of our desert investigations in the bone-dry wasteland of the southern Western Desert.

"How in the name of heaven did they find out about that tiny rock exposure in the middle of nothing?" added the team's archaeologist.

"By being very good geologists, that's how," answered Bahay Issawi of the Geological Survey of Egypt.

This conversation took place at what is called the Chephren Quarries, more than 320 kilometers (200 miles) southwest of Aswan, in one of the driest, most hostile and featureless tracts of desert anywhere. From an exposure of rock that is only a meter or so high, the ancient Egyptians mined a rock and carved it in the likeness of Chephren, the builder of the second largest pyramid at Giza. This mysteriously dark statue was found virtually intact in the Valley Temple of Chephren's pyramid complex at Giza.

NATURAL SHAPES NO ACCIDENT

The ancient Egyptians not only knew where things were in the desert but, I believe, realized that the shapes they found were no accident. They must have wondered why— why, for example, is it that only tapered hills persist in the desert? Imhotep may have asked himself that question, as I did a few years ago. The great sage could have figured it out in no time at all. I had to work at it.

This landform, called a yardang, in the Farafra Oasis is wind-sculpted and aerodynamically-stable. Its sphinxlike shape will last for centuries.

Dr. Farouk El-Baz

Dr. Farouk El-Baz

In the Egyptian desert west of the Kharga Oasis, natural pyramidal forms eroded from solid rock (above) look like a mirror image of the famous, man-made pyramids of Giza (at left). Such resemblances led scientists to believe that the Egyptians copied nature in shaping their monuments.

Dr. Farouk El-Baz

On one of a dozen journeys into the Egyptian desert, 96 kilometers (60 miles) west of Kharga Oasis, I saw three hills looming in the distance in a mirror image of the pyramids of Giza. The sight heightened my curiosity. This was the windy season, when the wind carried enormous quantities of debris, redistributing it as it eroded obstacles in its way.

With a strong gust of wind, a large amount of fine dust was lifted from among the pebbles and sand grains on the desert surface. The wind hurled the dust toward one of the conical hills. With the first colli-

sion, the dusty wind rose swiftly upward as it whirled about the hill.

Eureka! The conical shape evades destruction by leading the wind upslope and funneling its erosive power to the peak where its energy dissipates in the air. Inhabitants of windy terrain must have learned this a long time ago. Images of conical or cone-topped structures that I have seen all over the world flashed in front of me: American Indian tepees; Bedouin tents in the Sahara; dwellings and storage bins in the Rajasthan desert of northwest India; Mongolian and Kazak yurts in central Asia.

Unlike conical hills, the pyramids have sides. Why don't they erode to the least resistant, smooth form? Roundness may not be necessary. We encountered natural faceted hills deep in the Western Desert, and there are others at Lake Nasser. The pyramids of Giza exist in near perfect harmony with their environment. They predate the rest of the Seven Wonders of the World by approximately 2,000 years, and yet they are the only ones still standing. Had the ancients built

Dr. Farouk El-Baz

A dramatic likeness exists between this natural step pyramid made of layers of eroded sandstone near Gilf Kebir Plateau (above), and the first man-made pyramid (at right), whose builders imitated the steplike pattern of the natural structure more than 4,500 years ago.

Dr. Farouk El-Baz

their monuments in the shape of a cube, a pentagon, or even a stadium, they would have been erased by the ravages of wind erosion long ago.

It makes sense, of course, to believe that the man-made structures were fashioned after natural forms, just as it makes sense that at least some of the pyramids were built over existing hills rather than up from flat ground. In his book *The Pyramids,* Ahmed Fakhry states that a rocky knoll of unknown size underlies the Great Pyramid, and that a large natural stone outcropping cores the tomb of Queen Khent-kawes.

ORIGIN OF THE SPHINX

Could the Sphinx reveal further knowledge? Its origins may even be more intriguing than we believe. Some scholars contend that the bulk from which the Sphinx was formed had been left by the quarrying for the Great Pyramid. But I favor another explanation.

Let us imagine a "staff meeting" of the master architect of Chephren's pyramid. The sun has already started to warm up the brisk morning air. Apprentice architects, quarry engineers, and a transportation expert unroll papyrus, on which site drawings are meticulously drawn, and place it on the table for a discussion. Chephren's pyramid was to be built next to its predecessor, the Great Pyramid, on the western bank of the Nile. Blocks of hewn stone would arrive by barge and then move over special roads or ramps to the building site.

The meeting progresses under the shaded, breezy shelter on the Nile bank near the pyramid hill. The transportation expert

Dr. Farouk El-Baz

The conical shapes of these natural limestone formations evade destruction by leading the wind upslope and funneling its corrosive, abrading force up toward the peaks.

appears preoccupied, for he repeatedly draws with his finger a rectangle with equidistant lines ribbing it from top to bottom. He is drawing in his mind the hieroglyph *inr* denoting stone or rock.

"How about the elongate *inr* on the east side?" he finally asks the master architect.

"What of it?"

"It's in the way. We really should think about removing it."

"Well," replies the aging master, "I have long enjoyed its streamlined contours. Such a carving of beauty should not be considered a *sedjeb,* an obstacle that must be removed!"

"Yes, I agree," says a young architect. "We can even enlarge it, dress it up and make a monument out of it—a monument to Pharaoh, of course."

"Good, I like this idea. Let us learn from nature as the great Imhotep did. I am sure our friend the mover can find roads about the *inr.* I will speak to Pharaoh about this."

What was the streamlined shape that the master architect spoke of? For clues to the original form of that elongate rock, we go back to the close of the 19th century, and journey into the desolate wastelands of central Asia. The tour guide is a rugged Swedish explorer named Sven Hedin. For nearly 25 years, starting in about 1890, he roamed the virtually unknown lands of the Asian interior.

In the rocky desert near Lop Nur at the east end of the Taklimakan Desert (in present-day China), he ran into a landform that was unknown to him: endless numbers of ridges arranged in parallel rows with gullies in between. His guides called the ridges yardangs, from the Turkic word *yar* meaning steep bank.

"With amazing regularity and without the slightest interruption," Hedin wrote in 1905, "this dry clay soil is furrowed throughout by pretty deep gullies, which separate the yardangs one from another. The only variety they present arises out of the consistency of the surface, that is to say, out of the varying resistance which it has offered to the corrosive, abrading force of the wind.... Each ridge was broken off pretty abruptly on the north-east, but had a gentle slope towards the south-west."

YARDANG TO START

Yardangs became a topic of investigation by three of my colleagues and fellow desert travelers—Carol S. Breed, Maurice J. Grolier and John F. McCauley of the U.S. Geological Survey in Flagstaff, Arizona. Their measurements and observations of

© Bruno J. Zehnder/Peter Arnold

Following nature's examples, people have designed circular shelters all over the world. Indian teepees, Mongolian yurts, and Bedouin tents have been successful for ages.

yardangs in deserts around the world indicate that the critical characteristic in the shape of a yardang, streamlined by the wind, is that its length greatly exceeds its width, by a ratio of about three to one or more.

Many such yardangs exist in the Western Desert of Egypt. In fact, one of the largest fields may be that north and east of the Kharga Oasis, where the wind-carved hills extend for hundreds of kilometers (miles). The hills look like inverted boat hulls with prows pointing into the wind. "Mind you," said McCauley, "these yardangs are not carved of soft silts or sandstone, but incised in hard, crystalline limestome."

What do yardangs have to do with the Great Sphinx of Giza? Breed, Grolier, and McCauley agree that the Sphinx was fashioned from a hillock, or small hill, of limestone that had already been streamlined by the wind.

You may think that the distinctive shape of the Sphinx must be quite different from a wind-eroded knoll of rock. Not true. As early as 1909 the British geologist H.J.L. Beadnell described in the Kharga depression "thousands of isolated hummocks [low mounds or ridges], disposed with their longer axes parallel and in the direction of the prevailing north winds." These same structures were described in 1924 as sphinxlike by the German geomorphologist Johannes Walther. Furthermore, in 1939 the British explorer Ralph Bagnold characterized similar forms between Kharga and the Gilf Kebir in southwestern Egypt as "mud-lions."

Thus, the reclining lion body of the Sphinx could have originally been shaped by the wind.

I proved the point to my own satisfaction when I was able to convince a skeptical graduate student. On a visit to the Farafra Oasis, I called him over to see the best example I had yet found. He stood there for a few minutes transfixed by the sight. He had heard us speak of yardangs and sphinxes, but he thought the analogy was farfetched. Even when I showed him yardangs in Faiyum and Kharga oases, he shrugged his shoulders, "I don't see the Sphinx in these; they have all been beheaded!"

The one he stood by in Farafra Oasis was not. It was complete with a neatly carved head in the shape of a dog's.

"My God!" he exclaimed. "The first thing I am going to do when we get back to Cairo is to revisit the Sphinx and pay respects to my ancestor engineers."

He walked toward the silent statue of limestone rock that dramatized the wind as a sculptor. For after the wind had created the inverted boat hull, it acted upon its prow, pruning it as it swirled in vortices.

DRESSED UP

The architects of Chephren could have studied such forms thousands of years ago, and decided to dress up in his image the yardang on the east side of their Pharaoh's pyramid. It looks this way to me.

We owe much of our understanding of ancient Egypt to Jean François Champollion, who in 1821 completed the decipherment of the Rosetta stone, the key to Egyptian hieroglyphic writings and thus founded the science of Egyptology. Jacques Champollion, an archaeologist and a descendant of Jean François, wrote: "The total length of the monolithic sphinx is one hundred seventeen feet (36 meters); the contour of the head at the forehead is eighty-one feet (25 meters); the height from the stomach to the top of the

Standing prominently above the dunes in Egypt's Western Desert, the wind-carved shape of this limestone form is in harmony with its environment.
Dr. Farouk El-Baz

head is fifty-one feet (15.5 meters)." He also says: "its height of forty feet (12 meters) above the ground is the witness and measure of the quantity of stone removed from the surface to leave this elevation on the plain."

Such a monumental task would not have been necessary if they had started with a yardang.

The evidence indicates that when they embarked on perfecting the form to make it more convincingly lifelike, they dug more rock from its sides. The farther west they went, the deeper they had to dig in the pyramid hill. The resulting moat was later filled by blown sand after years of neglect when civilization in Egypt declined. Most of the "addition" to the natural form remained buried until unearthed in 1926.

One writer has even suggested that in addition to decorating the head and shaping the paws, the ancients engineered the Sphinx to make it usable as a marker for studying the size and shape of the earth. It has also been suggested that the Sphinx once had an obelisk between its paws whose shadow could be used to compute the earth's circumference.

AND NOW TROUBLE

Today, the Sphinx is showing signs of old age; part of its surface is slowly wasting away. One reason may be the unusual rise of the water table.

"We can trace this to the Aswan High Dam," says Bahay Issawi. "The enormous Lake Nasser and the year-round irrigation of crop fields has caused a dangerous rise of water levels throughout the country."

As water seeps through the porous limestone rock of the Sphinx, it brings with it salts in solution. These salts expand as they crystallize at the surface, flaking off bits of the ancient Sphinx.

This is perhaps ironic. If the Sphinx is a symbol of the ancients' understanding of the environment, a monument in harmony with nature, then it is now being adversely affected by a modern symbol of our control of nature. In our rush to "develop" the earth, we may neglect to learn valuable lessons from what the ancients left for us, sometimes carved in eternal rock □

This violent twister destroyed nearly everything in its path when it struck Sayler Park, a suburb of Cincinnati, Ohio, in April 1974.

TAKING AIM AT TORNADOES

by Walter Sullivan

NINE hundred of them occur each year in the United States—sometimes as many as 20 in a single day. Many come without warning and pass so quickly that they cannot be studied. They leave behind dust strewn roads and bewildered people who wonder what, if anything, passed by, or they leave a trail of death and destruction. Such is a tornado—and despite its relatively common occurrence, it is the most poorly understood of all storms. Until now—maybe.

NEW ARSENAL

Using a variety of new devices and observation techniques, scientists are trying to learn what starts tornadoes, why their winds are far stronger than those in other storms, how to predict their occurrence, and perhaps, how to weaken them.

The tools include aircraft armored against hailstones, rockets mounted on an aircraft to probe tornado funnels, a shock-resistant instrument package to be implanted ahead of an oncoming tornado, as well as airborne and ground-based instruments to track storms, their winds and lightning.

Only about three per cent of tornadoes cause loss of life or severe damage. But those are so violent that no recording instrument has survived their full intensity.

About 70 per cent of tornadoes are not predicted, and their lifetimes, as a rule, are so short that it is difficult for researchers to catch one in full rage. Nor does anyone venture lightly into the area of such a storm. Many fatalities have occurred because persons tried to flee the funnel cloud by car.

Schemes for tornado modification range from cloud seeding that alters vortex-producing conditions to the use of explosions to destroy a newly formed vortex, which would raise legal and logistical problems.

Several years ago it was proposed that an instrumented tank be driven into a tornado's path. The scheme proved impractical if only because it was found that even tanks can be tossed by a tornado.

Dr. Stirling Colgate of Los Alamos Scientific Laboratory in New Mexico has fitted his own plane with small cardboard rockets akin to those used for fireworks and by amateur rocket clubs. He has spent time chasing tornadoes, hoping to fire the rockets through one. The rockets carry miniaturized instruments to report pressure, temperature, electrical activity, and other phenomena within the funnel. Target practice on waterspouts off the Florida keys has proved the scheme feasible and William Carley of Aerosystems Incorporated in Layafette, Colorado, has told Dr. Colgate that he has safely flown within 100 meters (yards) of funnels.

Dr. Alfred Bedard of the U.S. National Oceanic and Atmospheric Administration's Wave Propagation Laboratory in Boulder, Colorado, has built a rugged cylinder of instruments to be carried by tornado-chasers on the ground. It is to be anchored in the path of an approaching funnel cloud by stakes driven into the ground and the chasers will then flee. It can record pressure, temperature, electrical phenomena, and winds up to at least 320 kilometers (200 miles) per hour. The wind recorder was developed in collaboration with Dr. T. Theodore Fujita of the University of Chicago.

EXTREME WINDS

There is dramatic evidence that winds in the vortex of a tornado reach extreme velocity. Straws accelerated by them can pierce trees, and a windblown fragment of wood has penetrated a steel brake drum. Such incidents have led some meterologists to propose that funnel winds approach 960 kilometers (600 miles) an hour.

Direct radar measurements on tornadoes indicate, however, that the maximum velocities probably do not exceed 480 kilometers (300 miles) an hour. More precise measurement of wind patterns in the funnel should be possible with airborne lidar, a laser-based counterpart of radar, which has been tested on waterspouts.

Courtesy of Ted Fujita

Dr. Theodore Fujita, who devised the well-known F Scale for rating tornado severity, has studied patterns of twister damage for more than 20 years.

ROLE OF LIGHTNING

Dr. Bernard Vonnegut, of the State University of New York in Albany, and Dr. Colgate say that converging winds are not enough to sustain the tightly whirling vortex. They propose that heat generated inside the funnel by electrical activity provides added energy, although others are skeptical.

Because lightning plays a distinctive role in tornado-spawning storms, the U.S. National Severe Storms Laboratory in Norman, Oklahoma, is mapping electrical activity within storm clouds. Lightning in passing storms is monitored by radar, television, instrumented vehicles that race along Oklahoma's flat roads, and by electromagnetic tracking systems.

One of the latter is used by Dr. William L. Taylor of the National Oceanic and Atmospheric Administration's Wave Propagation Laboratory in Boulder, Colorado. With stations there and at another site about 50 kilometers (30 miles) away, the system determines in three dimensions the structure of each flash, including that part hidden above the clouds.

Another method, used by Dr. W. David Rust of the Severe Storm lab, records radiation produced by the electrical and magnetic effects of a lightning stroke. This can indicate the electric polarity and intensity of a stroke or where one struck the ground.

It has been found that cloud-to-ground lightning occurs near the front of an advancing storm, as does heavy rain. Tornadoes form near the rear, where rain and ground strokes are rare.

The tracking may help resolve one of the most stubborn problems in meteorology. What generates the electric charge that results in lightning? Decades of observation have shown that the top of a thunderhead develops positive charge, whereas the bottom becomes electrically negative, but why this occurs remains elusive.

Recordings here have indicated almost continuous lightning strokes between the upper and lower parts of a storm, as well as horizontally between storms. These, and cloud-to-ground strokes, should neutralize the accumulations of electric charge.

Yet the charge difference within the storm is continuously restored. One proposed explanation is that heavier cloud droplets and water drops became negatively charged, whereas smaller drops become electrically positive and are then lifted to the top by violent updrafts.

An armored T-28 airplane from the South Dakota School of Mines and Technology is being used to probe storms here at middle elevations, and two planes of the National Aeronautics and Space Administration are participating. One, a U-2, carries lightning sensors developed by Dr. Vonnegut to observe storms from above.

It is hoped that relating where lightning occurs in a storm to air motions and areas of heavy precipitation will help explain the generation process.

WARNING SIGNAL

A long-term goal of Dr. Taylor is to find some electrically induced "signal" that identifies tornado-producing storms, but so far the clues have not been reliable. Other warning signs are more useful. These include a hook pattern that tends to appear usually on the right rear side of the storm, in radar echoes from its clouds. Another tornado precursor is development of a vortex in Doppler radar images.

Doppler radar is able to display motion of the reflecting material, such as cloud droplets, because the wavelength of the returning signal is shortened if the material is moving toward the antenna or lengthened by a receding motion.

A miniature twister-generating machine, that Dr. Fujita built in his laboratory, roughly simulates a tornado's possible configurations.

Courtesy of Ted Fujita

The vortex recorded in this manner is not a tornado funnel but a rotating system, or mesocyclone, 3 to 8 kilometers (2 to 5 miles) wide. Mesocyclone formation is believed to precede that of one or more tornado funnels by about 20 minutes. The total rotational energy within a mesocyclone is ten times that of a single severe tornado but is far more dispersed, resulting in weaker winds.

That as many as seven vortices may coexist under a single funnel cloud has been indicated by the swirling patterns of straw stubble left on fields crossed by a storm. These vortices remain within a few hundred meters (yards) of the tornado's central axis and migrate around it.

AIR LAYERS OVERTURN

While, broadly speaking, conditions conducive to tornado formation are known, it is not clear why some storms produce them and seemingly identical ones do not. While they occur in every state, they are more common on the Great Plains. Warm, humid air flows in from the Gulf of Mexico, remaining below 800 meters (approximately 2,500 feet) elevation. Above it, cool, dry air blows in from the mountains to the west. The flat terrain enables winds to blow freely.

Such a layering of the atmosphere is potentially unstable, but may persist until there is an "explosive overturn," setting the stage for tornado formation. Great parcels of hot air thrust upward, forming thunderheads that march across the landscape, usually toward the northeast. Cold air ahead and behind them plunges downward, spreading over the land and producing the chilly gust that arrives ahead of the storm.

Some scientists believe that tornado-breeding vortices form in the descending cold air on the rear side of the storm. Others say it is inside the rising column of hot air or at the interface between the two air masses □

 SELECTED READINGS

"Divided winds." *SciQuest,* May–June 1981.

"Tornado" by F. P. Ostby Jr., and L. F. Wilson. *Weatherwise,* February 1981.

"Tornado factory" by Franklyn Peterson and Judi R. Kesselman. *Popular Science,* July 1978.

"Understanding tornadoes." *USA Today,* December 1979.

The spiral, looping marks seen in this aerial view of some Illinois cropland record the paths of funnels, or suction vortices, as they swirled across the ground.

Courtesy of Ted Fujita

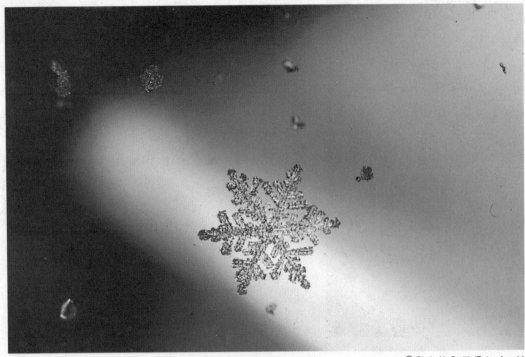

© Clyde H. Smith/Peter Arnold

This truly "classic" snow crystal, a near-perfect six-pointed hexagon, began its life by growing on a tiny particle of dust that had blown into a cloud.

LIFE OF A SNOW CRYSTAL

by Richard M. Preston

WHEN we think of a snowflake, perhaps we see in our imaginations the image of a feathery six-pointed star—the classic crystal of snow. Yet a snowflake, when examined under a magnifying glass, does not look like a star at all. It disappointingly resembles a puff of lint.

What we call a "snowflake" is in fact an airborne junk heap of many tiny individual crystals of snow, each of which formed separately in the sky and then, somewhere in its passage toward earth, crashed into a bundle of fellow crystals. When a snowflake is dissected into its separate and distinct snow crystals, comparatively few of those crystals even look like the classic six-pointed hexagons we see in our minds when we think of snow.

In fact, snow crystals come in a freak show of bizarre shapes: hexagonal tubes; hexagonal prisms; small bullets; pyramids; needles; six-cornered platters; knurled walnuts; wheels with axles attached; three-, four-, six-, and twelve-pointed stars; minuscule scrolls like Egyptian papyri; and hexagonal cups that look like cut-crystal shot glasses. The standard chart used by meteorologists to classify snow crystals contains eighty different categories, one of which (inevitably) had to be labeled "Miscellaneous." Examples of other categories are: "*P Seven a*—radiating assemblage of plates"; and "*CP Three c*—stellar crystal with scrolls at ends." Nature, the maniacal inventor, is never satisfied with a single design where a hundred will do equally well.

NOAA

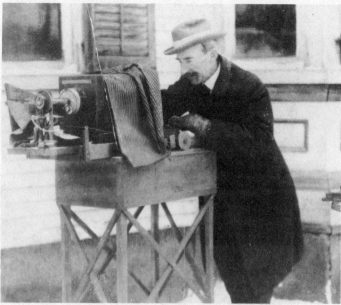

Courtesy of Duncan C. Blanchard

The photomicrographs at left reveal the infinite variety, beauty, and complexity that snow crystals can exhibit. Wilson ("Snowflake") Bentley, a pioneer in the development of photomicrography, displays the homemade camera he used to film more than 4,500 crystals in the photograph above.

But how is it that a simple substance like ice, when it drops in veils from the sky, can arrive in such a mysterious profusion of forms? The deep forces that shape a crystal of snow are not fully understood, any more than are many of the hidden urges that give rise to nature's most exquisite forms, from a spiral galaxy in the sky to the iridescent eye of a honeybee. But today, scientists know enough about the broad outlines of a snow crystal's growth to be able to chart its biography from birth to dissolution.

BIRTH IN DUST

Ulysses, Nebraska. A small farming town near the headwaters of the Big Blue River. The Big Blue is just a creek bottom here in this gently slopping fertile country in southeastern Nebraska, not far from Lincoln. The time was early December.

The sun was coming up over the Big Blue, rising through clear air over a bare corn field scattered with cut stalks. A farmer was walking in the field, once in a while scuffing at a chunk of earth with his boot. He glanced up and shivered. He put his hands in his jacket. Yesterday the wind had been out of the south, but sometime during the night it shifted, and now swept out of the northwest—hard and cold, he thought, a winter wind. He had heard on the radio this morning that a low-pressure storm system was brewing over Lake Superior. As he turned his back to the wind, he imagined a sea of polar air behind him rolling out of Canada, pressing over Nebraska, and curving up around to join warmer air from the south in a low-pressure hollow—a storm center—over the Great Lakes. The East, he had heard, was going to get its first big snow of the year.

The farmer absent-mindedly kicked a clod of dry earth. He looked up and saw a puff of dust from the chunk of dirt curling down his field. As the wisp thinned, it rose over hissing bone-colored cottonwoods waving in the riverine shoals of the Big Blue and was lost against the sky. That was the beginning of the life of a particular crystal of snow.

NEEDS A SEED

A snow crystal begins in dust and ends in dust, because without seeds of dust on which to grow, snow crystals cannot exist. A snow crystal cannot grow by itself inside a cloud unless it has a particle of something to grow on. It needs a seed, a nucleus. That was dramatically proven in 1946, when Vincent J. Schaefer, one of the grand veterans of modern meteorology, thought he would test the idea. Flying in a small plane over Schenectady, New York, Schaefer dropped less than 1.5 kilograms (3 pounds) of powdered dry ice into the center of a 6-kilometer (approximately 4-mile)-long cloud. The whole cloud immediately turned into a snowstorm.

How could such a small amount of powdered dry ice lead to a blizzard? A ripe cloud, ready to drop snow, is made up of free water-vapor molecules mixed with microscopic flying droplets of water. Even if the cloud is freezing cold—as cold as −40° Celsius (−40° Fahrenheit) the flying droplet cannot form into ice crystals. That is because water molecules gathered into a cloud droplet are unstable, constantly slipping and sliding past each other. They can't keep still long enough to form a crystal. But the crystalline structure of certain small particles can help start a snowfall.

When cold water molecules suddenly encounter the solid organized surface of a crystal, they act like green soldiers at boot camp bumping unexpectedly into a colonel—they fall into line. Soon other water molecules arrive, followed by more, and suddenly a snow crystal has flowered. Schaefer's dry ice worked beautifully because it was both crystalline and extremely cold. Once a few ice crystals grow, they tend to break apart and shed splinters as they tumble through the air. Each splinter of ice in turn can serve as a nucleus for another snow crystal, until the whole cloud is seething with snow.

Somewhere in the Nebraska farmer's puff of dust, a particular microscopic seed of clay was heading for the winds aloft, tumbling end-over-end as it was blown through the air.

In the atmosphere, there are plenty of dust particles to serve as ice nuclei, as scientists call these celestial seeds. Earth's atmosphere is a sea of dust. Dust rises aloft when winds race across the ground; when volca-noes belch; when the oceans toss off microscopic salt flakes; when factories simmer; when micrometeorites shower down from space; and when farmers scuff the dirt in their fields. Yet only certain kinds of dust will make snow.

The land around Ulysses, Nebraska, as in many of the river valleys of the Midwest, lies mantled in a famously rich, fertile, yellow-brown topsoil called loess. Loess contains a high proportion of the right kinds of clay particles needed to make snow. And strangely enough, loess, the icemaker in our story, was itself made by ice during the final act of a great geological drama some 10,000 years ago, when the last of the Pleistocene ice sheets melted away in the sun.

The snow that falls in New England may form from nuclei that come from across the country.

© Lynn McLaren/PR

Gene Aherns/FPG

As billions of snow crystals combined to create this typical, winter snowscape, their shapes changed radically as they blew from one temperature zone to another.

GRANDFATHER GLACIERS

At the beginning of the last ice age, during the time the North American glaciers advanced over much of the continent, these glaciers ground up millions of millions of tons of rock into powdery dust—"rock flour," geologists call it. Mixing it with gravel, they pushed this debris to their edges and left it in great mounds and moraines. Then, as the ice sheets melted, their meltwater streams rinsed this rock flour out of the piles of debris. Streams joined into great braided rivers streaming across the continent, carrying the rock flour in their milky currents.

As the glaciers vanished, their meltwater rivers dried up too, leaving curving mud flats cracking and bleaching in the sun. Then winds came, picked up the rock flour, and sifted it in rich blankets of loess over much of the Midwest. That is the origin of the clay particles that, swept into the air a second time, make snow. It seems strange to think that today, long after their extinction, the Pleistocene glaciers are still the grandsires of so much ice from the sky.

TRAVELS FAR

At first, the Nebraska farmer's seed of clay headed southeast, blown higher and higher by the Canadian wind, until it passed over the Missouri River at some 1,500 meters (5,000 feet), traveling at a steady 32 kilometers (20 miles) per hour. It crossed the Mississippi at nightfall near the town of Hannibal, Missouri. Then the clay particle began to veer to the northward, picking up speed and altitude, as the low-pressure storm developing over the Great Lakes began to draw cold air into itself. By morning, the rising sun found the clay particle some 3,000 meters (10,000 feet) above Indiana, coasting over the cloud deck. In late afternoon it mixed in with a haze of industrial smoke particles from the steel mills of Pittsburgh. As the second night of its journey fell, it was passing over western Pennsylvania beneath a rising moon.

PASSES INTO A CLOUD OF ICE

Meanwhile, some 480 kilometers (300 miles) to the northeast, a snowplow driver in Granville, New York, stepped onto his back porch to have a look at the weather and noticed a halo around the moon. Then he knew that snow was indeed coming and that he would be driving his truck by morning. Above him, a cirrostratus cloud made up of tiny hexagonal prisms of ice—a herald cloud bringing news of snow—was passing between the moon and New York, refracting a circle of moonlight into the man's eyes. At the center of each crystal prism was a nucleus of dust on which the crystal had grown. The nuclei were an assortment of clays, spores, blast furnace particles, diatoms from the sea, bits of decayed leaves, and even ash from Mount St. Helens—all traveling in a cloud of ice.

The Nebraska farmer's clay particle now was catching up with the storm front, which by this time had moved from the Great Lakes to upstate New York. Soon, the Nebraska farmer's particle would grow a crystal around itself, too.

Around 6 A.M., the speck of clay entered a newly formed, cold, water-filled cloud over upstate New York. It grew a shimmering hexagonal plate of ice around it, like a six-cornered disc.

ACTS LIKE A MAGNET

When an ice crystal grows in the air, it acts like a magnet. It pulls free water-vapor molecules directly out of the air onto its surface, where they lock into place in the bizarre and beautiful structures that make up a crystal of snow. As the farmer's crystal swept toward New England, its long aerial voyage was coming to a close.

It began to flutter and spin like a leaf as the winds aloft buffeted it up and down inside the storm. Several times it collided with other ice crystals, each time shedding splinters that went on to grow into other full-sized crystals. After half an hour of this, it had grown to a millimeter (0.04 inch)-wide flat hexagon. Now it blew higher into a part of the storm that was colder by a single degree, and each of its corners sprouted a branched feather.

The different shapes that snow takes are caused by the slightest variations of air temperature and, to a small extent, by the amount of water vapor present in the cloud.

If a snow crystal is blown from one temperature zone to another, which can happen several times during its period of growth, it radically changes its shape each time.

Nobody really understands how and why such small temperature changes can make a crystal look so entirely different. Physicists think that these transitions, such as from a hexagonal plate to a feathered star, have something to do with the way flying water molecules land on the surface of the crystal and lock into place, but nobody has yet developed an exact mathematical theory that explains how it works.

FALLS IN A SNOWFLAKE

As the Nebraska farmer's crystal grew larger, it grew heavier until it began to fall. Dropping to a lower altitude, it entered a warmer part of the storm, where whole droplets of water splashed onto the crystal and froze to its surface. The crystal's mutilated feathers disappeared under a pebbly lizard skin. Too heavy now for the winds to sustain its flight, it spiraled downward like Icarus with melted wings, until it caught in a puff of even faster-falling snow crystals, and at 7:45 A.M., joined to a snowflake, floated into the town of Granville, New York.

At that moment, a boy was on his way to school. He walked slowly through the first storm of the year, wishing it would snow enough for school to be called off. He stuck out his tongue; the snowflake holding the Nebraska farmer's crystal landed there. It melted instantly. Some of its water was carried back into the sky on the boy's breath; the rest of it he swallowed. The small portion of the state of Nebraska lodged on one of the boy's left molars, where it stayed until after dinner, when the boy's mother nagged him into brushing his teeth. The boy in Granville, of course, did not know that he had just eaten a snow crystal of the type *P Two g* □

 SELECTED READINGS

"No two alike" *Science Digest,* January/February 1981.

"Production of a diamond dust shower" by V. J. Schaefer. *Weatherwise,* August 1980.

"Preparation of snow crystal replicas" by V. J. Schaefer. *Weatherwise,* June 1980.

Brooks B. Britt

THE DINOSAUR AND THE ASTEROID

by Katherine Haramundanis

WHAT wiped out the dinosaurs some 63,-000,000 years ago? They had been among the most successful of animals, living in large numbers over both the Northern and Southern Hemispheres for over 130,000,000 years. (By contrast, human beings have been around for no more than 4,000,000 years.) And then, suddenly it seems, they disappeared. Why?

Scientists have long been seeking an explanation for the extinction of dinosaurs. Researchers call the disappearance of these often enormous creatures, and other animals that lived at the same time, "the Cretaceous-Tertiary mass extinction," referring to the period in earth's history when the change occurred.

Geologists divide the history of the earth into long sections of time called periods. Each period is characterized by certain climatic and geologic features and occurrences, and in more recent periods by the presence of certain plant and/or animal groups. During each of the more recent peri-ods certain groups of plants and animals came to dominate the landscape, often for periods of several million years, and then became less common, leaving other groups to dominate in the next period.

MASS EXTINCTIONS

Several times in the history of life on earth large percentages of the world's plants and animals have been wiped out in mass extinctions. Scientists believe that the fossil record shows at least six major extinctions. The first one known was some 500,000,000 years ago when more than one-half of the animal families disappeared. The most recent was just 6,000 to 10,000 years ago when mammoths, mastodons, and giant sloths disappeared.

The mass extinction that generates the most interest is, however, the one that occurred during the changeover from the Cretaceous to the Tertiary period some 63,000,-000 years ago. Around that time a large percentage of ocean life—giant shellfish and many sponges and bivalves—as well as many land plants and animals, including dinosaurs and flying reptiles, disappeared from the face of the earth.

No single explanation for these mass extinctions has yet been accepted by scientists. Some believe that all the mass extinctions were gradual, perhaps the result of slow changes in climate and ocean conditions. These scientists suggest that the apparent abruptness comes from gaps in the fossil record. Other scientists, however, hold that catastrophes—catastrophes from the sky— have caused the mass extinctions. These two general views have been formulated into many theories.

DYING TOGETHER

One suggestion, made in the 19th century, was that a kind of "species fatigue" occurs, when, after several million years of successful procreation, for some unknown reason, a species suddenly loses the ability to reproduce. The species then rapidly dies out. This theory does not, however, explain why several unrelated species would die out at the same time.

Another suggestion offered—this one just to explain the Cretaceous-Tertiary extinctions—is that some of the flying reptiles evolved into birds, rather than dying out altogether. This may explain the disappearance of flying reptiles like the pterodactyls, but it does not explain the simultaneous extinction of the dinosaurs, marine reptiles like the plesiosaurs, small-shelled sea animals, and tiny plankton.

CLIMATE CHANGES

Several theories center on possible changes in the earth's climate. According to these theories a change occurred in the earth's climate about 63,000,000 years ago, and the animals and plants living at that time could not adapt rapidly enough to the change and therefore died out.

One of these theories proposes that there was a change in the energy output of the sun. This theory depends on an understanding of how the sun's energy output changes and how climate can be altered as a result. Scientists, however, do not yet know exactly what

causes even small climate changes such as those that led to the ice ages. They are even less sure of how a large climate change could occur. Neither centuries-long observations of the sun nor recent understandings of how the energy output of a star like the sun could change, have provided any evidence that changes in the sun's energy output were responsible for the mass extinctions. The sun's energy output simply does not appear to change enough to create important changes in earth's climate.

Another theory suggests that changes in the earth's orbit may have caused changes in climate. The seasons of the year are caused by the amount of sunlight hitting the earth's surface. A change in the earth's orbit around the sun or a change in the angle the earth's spinning axis makes with the orbit would change the amount of energy received at different parts of the earth's surface. Such changes would then change the climate. The changes would not, however, appear to cause a pattern of mass extinctions like the one that occurred at the end of the Cretaceous.

There is also no known cause for such changes in the earth's orbit or spin axis. A massive object hitting the earth or entering the near-earth region of the solar system

A coin marks the site of an iridium-rich layer of clay in the Apennine Mountains in Italy. The layer may be debris from an asteroid.

Alessandro Montanari

could change the earth's orbit or spin axis, but there is no evidence of such events.

An increase in the level of volcanic activity has also been suggested as a possible cause of climatic changes at the end of the Cretaceous. The increased volcanism could possibly have been caused by the breakup of the huge Pangaea landmass into the present continents. Volcanic eruptions increase the level of carbon dioxide in the atmosphere. Carbon dioxide acts like the glass roof of a greenhouse. It allows the sun's rays to pass through to strike the surface of the earth but does not permit the reradiation of the light. Warm air thus becomes trapped close to the earth's surface and the climate becomes much warmer. According to these theories the dinosaurs did not adapt well to the hotter temperatures, eventually failed in their reproductive capacity, and died out.

ARCTIC SPILLOVER

Stefan Gartner of Texas A & M University suggests yet another possibility. He proposes that the Arctic Ocean, isolated and containing freshwater during the Cretaceous, broke looose at the end of that period and flooded the world's salt-water oceans. This flooding made the oceans much less salty and lowered ocean temperatures. The resulting destruction of much marine life would have affected the food chain and would have been felt throughout the world. This theory does not, however, explain the melting of the Arctic ice in the first place nor selective extinctions.

MAGNETIC CHANGES OR A SUPERNOVA?

Another theory looks at changes in the earth's magnetic field. Without its enveloping magnetic field, the surface of the earth would be quite unprotected from deadly radiation from the sun and outer space. Plants and animals bombarded by these deadly radiations would not survive. Some evidence exists that a major change in the earth's magnetic field occurred at the end of the Cretaceous period, but what caused it is not known. Furthermore, we do not know how bombardment of deadly radiation could selectively wipe out only certain plants and animals.

Another suggestion is that a supernova exploded nearby. When it exploded it vaporized the earth's protective ozone layer and left the earth exposed to lethal radiation from space. This theory could be substantiated by finding traces of such an explosion on earth (probably in the form of the isotope plutonium 244), but none have so far been found. Additionally, there appear to be few, if any, nearby stars that would qualify as supernovae. And finally, we are again left with the question of why only certain plants and animals would succumb to the radiation.

BUT, AN ASTEROID . . . MAYBE

Now a new—and very possible—explanation of the Cretaceous-Tertiary mass extinctions has been offered. It invokes a rare catastrophe to explain the extinctions. Walter Alvarez of the University of California at Berkeley, with his father, Luis Alvarez, the Nobel laureate in physics, and colleagues Frank Asaro and Helen Michel of the Lawrence Berkeley Laboratory, have developed this new theory. They suggest that an asteroid struck the earth, or exploded in the atmosphere, some 63,000,000 years ago and caused a long chain of events that led to the mass extinctions. (Harold Urei, in 1973, had suggested that a comet might have caused the Cretaceous-Tertiary Extinction.)

When the object struck the earth the debris and fine dust from the explosion was thrown up into the air and spread throughout the world. A similar pollution of the atmosphere was well documented when, in 1883, the volcanic island of Krakatoa between Java and Sumatra exploded. But while the Krakatoa explosion merely caused years of remarkable sunsets because of the increased amount of dust in the atmosphere, the Alvarez group suggests that the extraterrestrial object striking the earth polluted the atmosphere so heavily that it became dark for months. With no sunlight, photosynthesis gradually stopped and large numbers of plants and plankton died. When the plants and plankton died, animals that depend on them also died, and the mass extinctions became a reality.

Alvarez and his colleagues originally speculated that the dust thrown up into the

NASA

Manicouagan Lake in Quebec, Canada, fills a circular depression that may be the site of a great meteoritic impact.

atmosphere by the asteroid impact would remain there for as long as three years. Calculations by Brian Toon of NASA's Ames Research Center indicate that three months is more likely, and Alvarez has recently accepted that estimate. A three-month period of darkness could have caused the specific extinctions that have been found.

While Alvarez and his group favor the stopping of photosynthesis as the result of the asteroid impact, others, such as Kenneth J. Hsu of the Geological Institute of Zurich, suggest that the infall of the probable comet or asteroid heated the atmosphere, vaporized large amounts of cyanide, and released great quantities of carbon dioxide. The presence of these contaminants and the warming of the atmosphere caused the extinctions, he claims.

CHARACTERISTIC DUST LAYER

The new theory developed by accident. Alvarez and his colleagues were working in Italy, looking at sedimentation rates in limestone laid down during the Cretaceous-Tertiary transition. Quite by accident, they found a layer of dust in transition clay that had an unusually high amount of the element iridium. In fact, iridium was 30 times more abundant in the transition dust layer than in the adjacent limestone. The element iridium is rare in earth rocks but more abundant in extraterrestrial objects and rains gently and constantly from the sky in meteoritic debris.

Later Alvarez's group and others found this same iridium-rich layer at widely separated spots all over the world. It has turned up in Denmark (160 times richer in iridium than expected), Spain, New Zealand, New Mexico, the South Atlantic, and the North Pacific. On land the scientists analyze sedimentary rocks to find the layer. In the ocean they use deep-sea cores obtained from specially-equipped ships, such as the *Glomar Challenger*.

Besides containing unusual amounts of iridum, the dust layer also contains several other elements in unusual concentrations— elements such as osmium, palladium, nickel, and gold. These concentrations have made the dust layer recognizable wherever it is found.

Researchers like Billy Glass of the University of Delaware have pointed out that meteorites and microtektites often have element concentrations similar to those found in the dust layer. Alvarez and his group believe that the distinctive dust layer represents debris from the asteroid or comet that struck earth.

IMPACT CRATER

A comet or asteroid 5 to 15 kilometers (approximately 3 to 10 miles) in diameter could lay down the observed dust layer and contain the observed layers of iridium, osmium, and other elements. Such an asteroid would, if it fell on land, create an enormous crater, perhaps 175 kilometers (110 miles) in diameter.

Calculations by John D. O'Keefe and Thomas Ahrens of the California Institute of Technology indicate that the land impact of an asteroid could produce darkness and the observed chemical traces. Exactly how the dust and debris would be distributed worldwide is not yet understood.

However, since the ocean covers two thirds of the earth's surface, it is much more likely that an asteroid would fall into the ocean. Searching for an impact crater on the ocean floor is extremely difficult.

In the search for the asteroid-impact crater, scientists have suggested a site on the Yucatan coast of Mexico, another on the shore of Hudson Bay, and possibly the eruption of Iceland itself. However, scientists have not yet established ages of those sites, or proved that they were caused by extraterrestrial impact.

If the impact were in the sea, it is argued, a vast amount of water vapor would be thrown up into the upper atmosphere. This would, like carbon dioxide, create a greenhouse effect, warming the climate of the earth. An impact at sea could also have created a huge tidal wave that started the breakup of Pangaea. The breakup of Pangaea and resulting flooding of low-lying areas and changes in the ocean-land environment and climate—whether related to asteroid impact or not—are thought by some to have been major factors in the decline of the dinosaurs.

EVIDENCE FROM THE OCEAN

Using deep sea cores, Hans Thierstein of the Scripps Institution of Oceanography has provided clear evidence for a major environmental extinction of open-ocean species at the end of the Cretaceous. The extinction was both sudden and unique. He reports that almost one-half of all floating marine organisms, swimming organisms, and bottom-living organisms died out. At the same time 10 to 20 per cent of freshwater and land creatures were wiped out. Dale Russel of the National Museum of Natural Science in Ottawa has observed similar trends in his work on marine organisms.

REASONABLE SCENARIO

Perhaps the simplest explanation for the massive extinctions at the end of the Cretaceous is indeed darkness—the kind of darkness that could be caused by the pulverized particles of an asteroid impact cutting off the passage of solar energy for several months. With solar energy cut off, the microfauna of the seas would consume their food reserves in a week to three months. Land plants and certain animals would then have to contend with a changed climate and a disrupted food chain. With the collapse of the food chain and the dying out of many tiny sea plants and animals many land animals would suffer extinction. This scenario seems to follow fairly well the observed fossil record—a massive extinction of oceanic microorganisms and a slower, less severe extinction of certain animals and plants on land.

BUT DISSENTERS

As reasonable as this scenario seems, there are many dissenters among the scientific community. Some, such as Norman D. Newell of the American Museum of Natural History and Thomas J. M. Schopf of the University of Chicago, believe that withdrawal of the sea from vast continental areas during the end of the Cretaceous was fatal to many shallow-water species. Land areas where giant reptiles flourished in moist habitats became arid and drastic climate changes occurred. Others, including William A. Clemens of the University of California at Berkeley and Leo J. Hickey of the Smithsonian Institution, have described evidence that plant extinctions did not coincide with the extinction of land animals, including dinosaurs. According to the Alvarez hypothesis, animals died out because the plants they depended on for food died out. Clemens has also found deposits in western North America in which the iridium layer is about 1 meter (3 feet) above the remains of animals that evolved after the dinosaurs became extinct. If the iridium layer represents an event responsible for the extinction of dinosaurs and other organisms, it would be below that deposit.

Scientists cannot agree on what caused the dinosaur and other extinctions at the end of the Cretaceous or even on whether it was a catastrophic happening or just slow gradual change. They do, however, agree on certain things: mass extinctions did occur and a strange layer of dust does occur at the Cretaceous-Tertiary boundary □

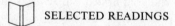 SELECTED READINGS

"The Mass extinctions of the late Mesozoic" by Dale A. Russell. *Scientific American,* January 1982.

"What killed off the dinosaurs?" [asteroid theory of W. and L. Alvarez] by Robin Bates. *International Wildlife,* May/April 1981.

"Belt of an asteroid" [Cretaceous extinction theory of Luis and Walter Alvarez] by Stephen J. Gould. *Natural History,* June 1980.

© Dan McCoy/Rainbow

Solar One, located in the Mohave Desert, is the largest solar-energy project in the world. Its 1,818 mirrors reflect heat, which is used in a process to generate electricity.

ENERGY

ENERGY
REVIEW OF THE YEAR

Tom Zimberoff/Sygma

Department of Energy (DOE) Secretary James Edwards has put his full support behind the Reagan administration's decision to dismantle his agency.

An energy-conscious individual uses a solar cooker made from masonite and aluminum foil to roast a hot dog. The innovative cooker can heat up to about 260° C (500° F).

The Suntwist Co.

U.S. Energy policy. U.S.-energy policy changed course dramatically and immediately under Ronald Reagan. Only one week after taking office, the President ordered complete decontrol of crude-oil prices. While not unexpected, the move expedited the withdrawal of the federal government's role in managing oil prices by nine months. Federal policies should strive to avoid "distorting" market forces "through indiscriminate subsidies," Reagan explained. That theme would be reflected over and over as the new administration reformulated energy policy throughout 1981 via budget proposals, executive orders, and guidelines issued to Congress.

In practice, the President's philosophy—to let market forces dominate—showed up best in attempts to cut the federal role in developing new energy technologies. A July 17, 1981 message to Congress offered strong clues as to how his administration would put this philosophy into practice. Specifically, the President said he intended to cut direct federal support for solar technologies, alcohol fuels, biomass projects, and urban-waste systems—slashing some $2,200,000,000 over a five year span. Steadily rising oil prices, precipitated by the January 28, 1981, oil-price decontrol measure, could be counted upon to encourage private investors to complete the development of the most viable of these technologies, he maintained. The same reasoning was used to justify ending support for five major synthetic-fuels demonstration projects including the Solvent Refined Coal I and II plants. By year end, the Department of Energy (DOE) budget had been slashed, relative to the previous year, 71 per cent for energy-conservation programs, 60 per cent for both solar and geothermal projects, and 58 per cent for fossil-fuels development.

Even the DOE itself saw cuts; by October, 2,000 persons, or 10 per cent of the agency's work force, had been let go. It was just the beginning of what Reagan promised would end the four-year-old Cabinet-level agency. "We do not need an Energy Department to solve our basic energy problem," Reagan explained in a September television address. "As long as we let the forces of the marketplace work without undue interference, the ingenuity of consumers, businesses, producers, and inventors will do that for us." This announcement neither surprised nor upset DOE Secretary James Edwards. When the former South Carolina governor assumed his post on January 22, 1981, he vowed he would do his best to try to work himself out of a job. However, by year's end details had not yet surfaced as to how the administration planned to dismantle DOE, or which programs within the agency might be spared for transfer to another agency.

Of all major energy programs in Reagan's fiscally-pared budget, only nuclear power was spared a real axing. In fact, federal support for nuclear programs rose 36 per cent in 1981, to $1,600,000,000. The nuclear industry, however, was never in more dismal straits. Not a single new commercial power plant has been ordered in more than three years. And in five years, more than 80 planned plants have been deferred or cancelled outright, including two major ones in 1981—Northern Indiana Public Service Co.'s Bailly-1 in August and Boston Edison's Pilgrim-2 plant one month later. Despite the fact that Boston Edison had already sunk $291,000,000 into its plant, the utility's directors reckoned that

142

initial cost projections for the plant—of $400,000,000—would ultimately prove to have been underestimated by at least $3,600,000,000. ■ Operating nuclear plants also experienced troubles. For instance, investigations showed that 16 pressurized-water reactors had steam generators with seriously cracked and leaking pipes. Utilities worried how they would ultimately cope with sheathing or replacing those pipes when the situation became critical—for some plants, such problems could be expected within a year.

In light of all these problems, Reagan issued a series of policy initiatives on October 8, 1981, explaining how his administration intended to "revitalize" the ailing industry. One directive instructed federal agencies to streamline regulation and the licensing of commercial power plants with the hope of reducing by as much as eight years the 10-to-14 years it now requires to get a new plant into operation. Reagan also asked DOE to work with the nuclear industry and with state governments in resolving obstacles to development of acceptable high-level radioactive-waste disposal schemes. However, the two most controversial provisions of Reagan's nuclear revitalization were announcements that the Clinch-River Breeder Reactor would be completed and that a ban on the commercial reprocessing of used nuclear-reactor fuel would end. Reagan's predecessor, Jimmy Carter, had attempted to kill the Clinch-River project throughout his presidency, claiming that the technology it was supposed to demonstrate was already obsolete. Carter had also initiated four years earlier a ban on the commercial reprocessing of reactor fuel. His aim was to limit availability of plutonium. Produced by the fission process that powers commercial reactors, plutonium would not only make an ideal fuel for breeder reactors, but also an ideal fissile material from which to fashion unsophisticated nuclear weapons—the type terrorists might be expected to attempt.

Perhaps more significant, it was in an attempt to shore up the nuclear industry that the President recanted for the first time on his ideological aversion to subsidies. On October 9, 1981, the Reagan administration announced it would commit "in excess of $100 million" toward removing the core of the Three Mile Island-2 reactor and disposing of radioactively contaminated material. The reactor had been shut down since damaged in a seriously crippling 1979 accident. In pledging aid, Office of Management and Budget Director David Stockman explained that Reagan had agreed to the subsidy in hopes of saving the plant's nearly bankrupt owner, General Public Utilities.

Oil and Gas Supply. The decontrol of oil prices had been expected to send gasoline prices skyrocketing. That never happened—largely owing to an oil-supply glut and a continuing fall in U.S. demand for oil products fostered by energy conservation. Though U.S. oil production maintained essentially its 1981 level of 8,600,000 barrels per day, exploration for new oil and gas supplies experienced a record level of activity. Global petroleum inventories also reached near-record levels with a surplus of roughly 2,000,000 barrels per day above consumption.

Passage of seven categories of financial waivers of law by the Congress on December 10 removed what appeared to be the last major obstacle blocking a commitment for private financing of the Alaska Gas Pipeline. When completed, perhaps as early as 1987, the $50,600,000,000 project is expected to provide a vast new avenue of natural gas supply to the lower 48 states.

Janet Raloff

Wide World

A parabolic mirror collects the sun's rays to power this unusual laser device. The device transmits television pictures over a laser-light beam deep into space.

A demineralizer system finally began decontamination of radioactive water left in the Three Mile Island reactor containment building more than two years after the accident.

TMI Photo

Solar energy, now in the mainstream of energy planning, may account for 20 per cent of U.S. energy consumption by the year 2000. Above: solar panels of an active system.

SOLAR-HEATED HOUSES

by William A. Shurcliff

THE more one reads about solar-heating systems for houses, the more one wonders what it all adds up to. Prospective homeowners are bewildered. So are architects and builders. All agree, "Solar heating is great!" However, there is no agreement as to which kinds of solar-heating systems provide the best thermal performance, or biggest fuel saving, or lowest construction cost, or greatest livability.

MANY SYSTEMS

I took some time recently to try to pinpoint the reasons for the widespread bewilderment. Instead of a few reasons, I found a whole basketful of them. The situation is both discouraging and encouraging: discouraging because of the long hard struggle that will be required before we can decide which systems really are best, which most cost-effective, which most livable; encouraging because so many options are available, so many avenues invite exploration.

One soon discovers that there are literally dozens of different kinds of solar-heating systems for houses. Furthermore, many of them have roughly the same cost—within about 25 per cent. Even systems that seem especially expensive cannot be ruled out: their advocates claim that once mass production gets underway costs will drop drastically. Also, the more expensive systems may be more reliable, more durable, and easier to operate. Dozens of competing designs are running neck and neck.

ACTIVE SYSTEMS

In active solar-heating systems a fan, pump, or other mechanism is used to direct a heat-transfer agent, such as air, water, or silicone, to the rooms of the house.

In active systems using air, air heated in rooftop collector panels is circulated by fans directly to the rooms or to a bin of stones in the basement. The stones store the heat for use at night or on cloudy days. Such systems have ardent backers. Air is free, they say. If it leaks out, no harm is done, and it causes no corrosion problems. One problem, however: air is not the most efficient heat-transfer medium.

In active systems using water, water heated in rooftop collectors is circulated directly to room radiators or to an insulated tank in the basement. Water is a far better heat-transfer medium than air and is a thousand times more dense and compact. If it leaks, you can see at once where the leak is—and plug it up. But freezing of pipes and corrosion can occur.

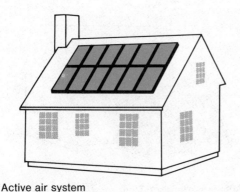

Active air system

There are ways—making collectors of rubber, which is not injured if freeze-up occurs, glazing panels with glass, or rigid plastic, or plastic film, for example—of dealing with some or all of these problems. Systems using silicone or phase-change Freon may also be used. With these systems freeze-up and corrosion problems are avoided, but cost may increase significantly.

Then there are active solar-heating systems that use concave mirrors that focus solar radiation onto a straight, slender tube. The resulting much higher temperature not only makes room heating especially simple, but also permits driving highly efficient cooling systems in summer.

PASSIVE SYSTEMS

Passive solar-heating systems require no fan or pump to move the heat. There are several types.

Thermosiphon passive system

The thermosiphon passive system is based on the fact that heated air or water tends to rise. In this system the solar-collecting panels are situated below the rooms to be heated. The solar-heated air or water then rises spontaneously into a storage system situated some distance—say, 1 to 3 meters (about 3 to 10 feet) above. No fan or pump is needed. Also, no controls are needed; when the sun sets, circulation stops immediately.

In a direct-gain passive system, the solar radiation enters the south rooms directly, warming massive floors and walls—which in turn give off heat throughout the night. But the south-window area may be so large that

Direct-gain passive system

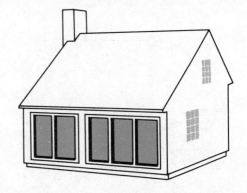

© Tom McHugh/PR

Solar-activated window louvers in this kitchen open and close automatically. The house belongs to Steve Baer of Corrales, New Mexico.

passive wall of concrete, or water-filled drums, or water-filled translucent-plastic containers. Warm-up in the morning is slow, however, and the massive wall takes up much space and blocks the view to the south. Large thermal shades may be needed at night.

The sunspace passive system is a variety of the indirect-gain passive system. Solar radiation is collected in a large glazed room (sun space, solar room, solarium, greenhouse) attached to the south side of the house. When the sun makes this room very

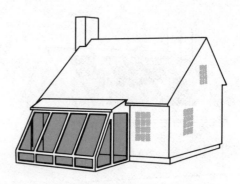

Sunspace passive system

problems arise: glare, overheating on warm sunny days, and excessive heat loss on cold nights (unless costly thermal shades are provided).

In an indirect-gain passive system, the solar radiation that passes through the large south-window area immediately strikes a

Indirect-gain passive system

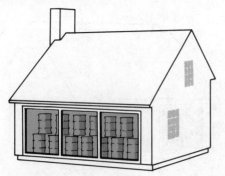

hot, the hot air is circulated into the living rooms. The sunspace is useful also for growing flowers and vegetables or as a daytime lounge area. But preventing it from becoming icy cold at night can be difficult.

In hybrid passive systems, the system is part passive, part active. Low-power fans may be used to assist energy collection, storage, or distribution.

THE UNDERGROUND HOUSE

Now we must fasten seat belts and discuss three new, glamorous, and highly controversial kinds of solar-heated houses: the underground house, the double-envelope house, and the superinsulated house.

An underground, or "earth-sheltered," house has large south-facing windows. As such it qualifies as a special kind of direct-gain passive-solar house. The east, west, and north sides may be truly underground or

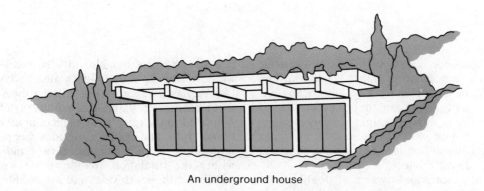

An underground house

may merely be flanked by large ledges or slopes of earth. The roof may be covered by 30 to 60 centimeters (1 to 2 feet) of earth topped with grass, shrubs, and the like. The building has thick concrete walls, floor, and roof that store an enormous amount of heat and keep the indoor temperature steady.

Why build a house underground? Different advocates furnish different reasons. Environmentalists stress the need to preserve green areas—that is, leaving the countryside natural in appearance and leaving the roof free for growing plants and for absorbing rainwater. Others stress keeping warm in winter: by living underground you avoid winter's icy grip. (But the effectiveness of superinsulation largely undercuts that argument.)

Others build underground to keep cool in summer; deep-down earth tends to stay at about 7 to 13° Celsius (45 to 55° Fahrenheit), even in summer. Still others go underground for protection against tornadoes—a frequent harassment in Kansas, for example. Others stress the quiet that underground living ensures. Others cite the low maintenance: an underground concrete building never needs new shingles or new siding.

Critics point out that most underground houses, with only one story and no basement, take up an unusually large area of ground; and with windows facing south only, the view is limited. To make the building strong enough to withstand the earth loads and waterproof enough not to take in water in rainy spells requires careful and often expensive construction. Many sites simply are not well suited to underground houses.

All agree that the houses keep warm in winter and that solar radiation plays a big role.

DOUBLE-ENVELOPE HOUSE

A so-called double-envelope house has two envelopes, or shells, with a continuous air space of at least 15 centimeters (6 inches) between them. It has a large greenhouse integral to the south side. The air can circulate in a complete circuit, or convective loop, around and under the interior envelope. A growing number of double-envelope house owners almost unanimously declare themselves well pleased and report that little auxiliary heat is needed. On the other side of the fence is the growing number of engineering reports on performance studies. These reports cast doubt on the adequacy of the natural airflow in the loop, indicate that significant amounts of auxiliary heat are needed, reveal considerable variations in temperature, and furnish estimates (ranging from $5,000 to $10,000 or more) of the added cost of the greenhouse. Many engineers question

Double-envelope house

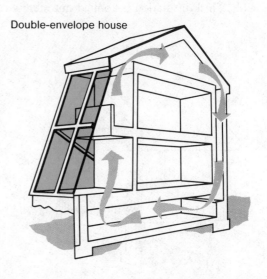

the cost-effectiveness of the within-wall air spaces, especially as much faster airflow could be provided by a small, cheap fan-and-duct system. Also, they question the desirability of closely coupling a large greenhouse (which can become so cold on winter nights and so hot on sunny days in summer) to the living rooms.

Engineers and owners of double-envelope houses agree that on cold winter nights enough heat is automatically supplied to the greenhouse so that plants growing there are not killed. Thus the system does have definite pluses—not the least of which are the pleasant, sunny greenhouse and the generally excellent insulation of roof and east, north, and west walls.

Another area of agreement is that there is a great need for more studies, more measurements of temperatures and airflow, more hard data on the overall thermal performance. Also, there is need for a much clearer understanding of the physical processes of transfer and storage of heat. With such an understanding, designers may be able to fine-tune the system so that it will perform much better. Or are there limitations inherent in the basic design?

SUPERINSULATED HOUSE

The so-called superinsulated house has such superb insulation and is so airtight that wintertime heating "almost takes care of itself." Thick insulation is applied not merely

Superinsulated house

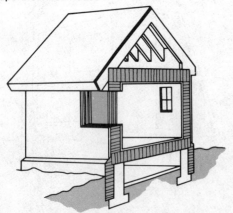

to walls and roof but also to sills, headers, window frames, foundation walls, and the like. A plastic vapor barrier [a large sheet of 0.015-centimeter (0.006-inch) polyethylene] is applied to the inner (warm) faces of all external walls and ceilings. Besides stopping infiltration it prevents moisture build-up within the insulation. Windows are small (except on the south side) and are double or triple glazed.

Even in New England, such a house keeps warm with little or no recourse to auxiliary heat. Much of the heat needed is supplied by human bodies, light bulbs, the cooking stove, and so on. Another large fraction of the heat needed is supplied by the solar radiation that enters via the moderate-sized south windows. There is no added mass such as a concrete wall or water-filled drums to heat. The normal mass of the house itself (10 to 15 tons of wood, gypsum board, and so on) suffices.

The amount of auxiliary heat needed is either none or very small. In any event, there is no need for furnace, oil tank, chimney, or radiators. One or two small portable electric heaters can supply the additional heat needed; or heat can be "stolen" from the domestic hotwater heater—its heater is idle 90 per cent of the time and there can be no objection to making it work a little harder.

Some of the earliest superinsulated houses, built according to schemes pioneered by a group at the University of Illinois, were simple and plain in appearance. Also, some were sufficiently airtight as to present problems of build-up of moisture or pollutants. These problems can be solved, however, by installing small air-to-air heat-exchangers that bring in fresh air, drive out the old air, and save most of the heat in the outgoing air.

AND SO—WHAT'S BEST?

Designers and prospective homeowners want to compare the various alternatives and select the best. Alas, the comparisons are very difficult.

One problem to be considered is the annual cost of auxiliary heat. This is a tricky subject. The cost depends not only on the location of the house (the average temperature, sunshine, and wind of the region) but also on

In the living room of Baer's home, stacks of water-filled drums in the south wall absorb the sun's heat and radiate it into the room.

the room temperature desired by occupants, the extent of cooking, and personal habits, such as opening windows and doors, and other factors.

The cost of the house itself must also be considered, and, in fact, this is far more important than the annual cost of auxiliary heat. But to find a "true cost" of the house may be impossible; building costs vary from locality to locality, and even in the same locality two different builders might set prices that differ by 20 per cent.

Many solar-house designers like to compute, for each new type of solar house, its "solar-heating fraction" or "solar-saving fraction." They regard it as helpful to compare the solar house with a "corresponding nonsolar house." They come up with accurate-sounding figures ("74 per cent solar-saving fraction for Smith's design, 52 per cent for Jones's design; thus Smith's is 22 per cent better"), but such numbers may have little real meaning and can interfere with comparisons. The computations, besides depending on many arbitrary and not-quite-correct assumptions, refer to some hopelessly irrele-

vant (and perhaps unlivable) house. The term "corresponding nonsolar house" cannot be defined satisfactorily, and who has the slightest interest in some sort of 100 per cent nonsolar house?

The process of comparing designs and choosing the most cost-effective may also be thrown off by government policy. Capricious tax-benefit rules and capricious building codes may force adoption of System A and rejection of B, even though, by every architectural criterion, B is better.

Esthetics must also be considered in thinking about which solar heating system to use. Some people insist on living in houses that appear elegant, modern, glamorous. But these are subjective matters—matters of opinion. They cannot be quantified. There is no systematic way of "figuring them in" when comparing different designs.

One might propose to visit many solar houses and simply ask the occupants how they like them—learn their overall judgments. Surely they must know. Who can know better? But, alas, their responses—more exactly, their favorable responses—are

A technician checks the performance of a newly installed solar panel for a hot-water system.

© Donald Dietz/Stock Boston

of little value. And as psychologists know, nearly everyone who makes a big, new, exciting purchase crows enthusiastically about it for a long, long time. ("My new car? The best! How smart I was to choose it!") Almost every solar-house owner I have talked to assures me that his house is not only successful but is outstandingly successful. Only in an unguarded moment will he reveal the mechanical troubles encountered or the excessive cost.

SOME RASH PREDICTIONS

I predict that the wide range of designs will become even wider for several years—until a great deal more performance data becomes available and designers have had time to think long and hard about comfort, cost, and esthetics. Eventually, many designers will fall from favor and the range will become narrower.

I predict that passive and hybrid designs will gain the ascendancy over active designs. Why? Because of superior economy, simplicity, durability.

I predict that houses with integral greenhouses will continue in popularity, but that designers will replace the large, awkward convective loop through which the air circulates with fan-and-duct systems. Several such houses already exist and perform excellently.

I predict that the superinsulated house will take the center of the stage as the design providing the greatest comfort for the smallest overall cost (construction costs plus annual cost of auxiliary heat). I expect that it will become the norm, or standard of comparison. Many may prefer other designs, and a prospective owner may, for example, ask his architect for a very different design—to satisfy certain needs and esthetic wishes. But he will add questions such as: "Will the performance match that of a superinsulated house?" "How much more will it cost than a superinsulated house of similar size?"

These are shaky predictions. The field is changing so fast. And with such rapid changes in the rate of inflation, interest rates, and the cost of auxiliary heat, anything can happen. Keep your woodlot in good condition □

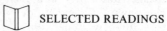 SELECTED READINGS

"Affordable passive solar home." *Mother Earth News,* June 1981.

"Eight solar add-ons that will help heat your home" by R. L. Dempewolff. *Popular Mechanics,* September 1981.

"High tech houses." *Popular Science,* May 1981.

"Research house for developing passive solar standards." *Architecture Record,* May 1981.

"Sunpower: earth's fair weather friend" by W. G. Reinhardt. *SciQuest,* March 1981.

"Super-insulated house" by Daniel Ruby. *Popular Science,* May 1981.

Super-Insulated Houses and Double-Envelope Houses by William A. Shurcliff. Brick House Publishing, 1981.

"Thermally layered retreat" by A. Lees. *Popular Science,* May 1981.

PEATLANDS

by Michael J. Philipp

THE vast peatlands of the United States are among the least appreciated of all wild areas. Though not as spectacular as lofty mountains or lush forests, they are nonetheless aesthetically and biologically varied. A peatland is a contained ecosystem, with its own patterns of water flow and plant and animal interrelationships.

But peat also has a high potential for energy production. As a result, energy companies and the federal government are examining the peatlands of Minnesota and other states with an eye toward mining and gasifying this fossil fuel.

WHAT IS IT?

What is peat? One can think of it as an early stage in the formation of lignite or coal. It is an accumulation of the undecomposed or partially decomposed remains of grasses, trees, mosses and other marsh and swamp plants in a wet and—in Minnesota—a cold environment. Anaerobic, or oxygen-deficient, conditions prevent fungi and bacteria from decaying the organic material as they ordinarily would. Peat accumulates at a rate of about 7 or 8 centimeters (3 inches) a century, although part of the material's definition is that it be at least a 20-centimeter (8-inch) layer. In most places in the Upper Red Lake peatland of Minnesota, the layer is 2.5 to 4.5 meters (8 to 15 feet) thick.

Although the formation and structure of peatlands are still poorly understood, slope may be an important factor. In the Upper Red Lake peatland, for example, there is a gradient of from 0.2 to 1 meter per kilometer (1 to 5 feet per mile). That may not seem much of a slope, but water will run down it. The current explanation of the Red Lake peatland's origin is that, after the warm climatic period of mid-postglacial times, organic material dammed up the water flow and peat built up on the slightly sloping surface. The Red Lake peatland is gradually ex-

© Brian Seed/Click/Chicago

In Ireland, youngsters load peat onto a donkey cart. Peat can be cut from the ground using a simple L-shaped spade, called a slane.

panding westward and, if left undisturbed, probably will continue into the Red River valley during the next several thousand years.

Like all other fossil fuels, peat is distributed unevenly throughout the world. A little more than half of the earth's 650,000,000 hectares (1,600,000,000 acres) of peat lie in the Soviet Union. The United States has about one-sixteenth of the total, much of it concentrated in Alaska. In the contiguous 48 states, Minnesota has about one-fourth of the peat, including the largest single peatland— the Upper Red Lake, or glacial Lake Agassiz land, which crosses the border from northern Minnesota to southern Manitoba.

© Richard Howard

A peat bog in Andover, Massachusetts, with characteristic low-growing vegetation. To get peat, the bog must be drained.

ENERGY SOURCE

Peat has an energy content about half that of coal. Like coal, it can be burned directly or turned into gas and used as fuel. The total energy content of all the peat in the United States is equivalent to about 20 times the amount of energy consumed by the United States each year.

Minnesota, with its large peatlands, could use its own fossil fuel to supply its energy for 200 to 300 years, depending on the exact rate of mining and consumption. A major natural gas company, Minnegasco, is already making plans to mine and gasify peat on a large scale at the still-wild Upper Red Lake peatland.

LAND OF MANY USES

The Upper Red Lake peatlands—and most major peatlands—have several uses.

Some uses that require extraction of the peat include: manufacture of coke, resins, waxes, and absorptive materials; production of potting soil and soil conditioners; and production of energy by burning or gasifying. Some uses of the land that do not require extraction include: farming, forestry production of biomass, provision of habitat for wildlife, and provision of subject matter for scientific investigation. Whatever use is in mind, however, officials and the public should be cautious when contemplating schemes for massive development—for many reasons.

DELICATE—AND UNKNOWN

The first reason is that peatland hydrology and ecology are in their infancy. (Hydrology is the study of the properties, distribution, and effects of water on the earth's surface, in the soil, and on underlying rock.) Scientists have barely begun to understand the complicated interactions among the water flows and vegetation patterns found in peatlands. Dr. Eville Gorham, a wetlands specialist at the University of Minnesota, has called peatland "the most delicate adjustment of vegetation to hydrology and water flow known to man."

The Upper Red Lake area provides a good example. Satellite photographs (the most effective method of studying bogs' patterns) show a large band of water called a "water track" that moves east, then north. East of the track is a fen, or bog, consisting mostly of sedges (closely related to, and resembling, grasses) and dwarf birch shrubs. For as-yet-unknown reasons, the shrubs are sensitive to the water flows in some way that often prompts them to grow in lines perpendicular to the flow. Some sources of water for the fen's tracks are also unknown. Mining an area whose dynamics are so unexplored seems risky.

The second reason to be cautious is that the effects of large-scale mining on regional hydrology are completely unpredictable but could be serious. Mining may exacerbate problems caused by spring run-off and may create acidic pools. If mined peatlands erode, nearby spawning beds in rivers' tributaries could be damaged by peat buildup. Mining in one area could also affect areas far from

© Peter Angelo Simon

These cooling towers are not part of a nuclear power plant. They are part of the Rhode milled peat-burning power station in Ireland.

Hobart G. Truesdale, president of a 100,000,000-acre peat-producing company in North Carolina, shows some of the peat briquettes he makes.

© Brian Seed/Click/Chicago

the mine site and could alter the whole region's hydrology. This potential suggests that development should take place first on small, isolated bogs to gauge the effects.

Another reason for concern is that past efforts to alter peatlands have often been ill-fated. Early in the 20th century developers undertook a vast project to dig a system of ditches that would drain the water and create lands suitable for agriculture in the Upper Red Lake region. But the grid of ditches succeeded only in altering the vegetation by making some areas drier than others; the land did not drain. Such mistakes are visible for years. Scars of large-track vehicles might well last for centuries, and marks made by small-track vehicles in 1966 are still visible.

In addition, peatlands are valuable habitat for many species of wildlife. They often provide living spots for some birds and stopping-places for others that are migrating, as well as habitat for large mammals—in the case of the Upper Red Lake area, for timberwolves and whitetailed deer. Plants including some rare species, are also found in peatlands.

Finally, peatlands are among the United States' last great wild areas. But the character of the lands, which depends on the delicate balance of water and plants, can be preserved only by setting aside a large portion of them.

ENERGY   153

POCOSINS OF THE SOUTHEAST

by Bill Thomas

POCOSIN—a strange-sounding word, used mostly in academia. Most people living near one would just call it a swamp. An Algonquin Indian word, "pocosin" literally means "swamp on a hill." But pocosins are distinctly different from most swamps. They are evergreen peat bogs, occurring only from southern Virginia down to Georgia along America's southeastern tidewaters. Usually higher than surrounding terrain, they tilt by 25 to 60 centimeters per kilometer (approximately 18 to 36 inches per mile), draining into the sea.

As landscapes go, the pocosin is not attractive. None has ever been nominated to become a national park. But climatically and

Dennis Rosney, who lives at the edge of the Boora Bog in County Offaly, in Ireland, uses his slane to cut a large supply of peat.

George Harrison

biologically pocosins are important because they store heat and protect salinity balances; and since the energy-hungry 1970's, they have become threatened.

Although some pocosins are timber producers, pocosins have, in general, been considered commercially worthless. Their spongy, acidic peat soil, wet most of the year, makes it difficult to build roads or transport equipment into them to clear their awesome undergrowth. In 1764 George Washington and a group of Virginia planters tried to clear a large section of Virginia's Great Dismal Swamp, some of it pocosin, for farming. The canal they built for drainage is still there, but the farming attempt failed because the would-be developers lacked the technology that would make it possible to farm such areas. Today the technology exists.

ENERGY SOURCE

First Colony Farms, which owns 150,-000 hectares (372,000 acres) of a pocosin on a peninsula just west of North Carolina's Outer Banks, has begun a $1,500,000 peat-mining operation that will strip up to 4.5 meters (15 feet) of the surface layers of organic peat and permit successful farming on the mineral-laden soils beneath. The peat removed is being touted as a major source of energy.

Machines designed in Finland—where peat has been mined extensively for many years—cut the peat from the ground in large sausagelike rolls that are then laid in fields to be sun-dried. Drying takes up to several weeks this way, but other methods have proved prohibitively expensive. Once dried, the rolls can be loaded and shipped to nearby power plants for burning.

A study by the Research Triangle Institute puts the farm's recoverable peat reserve at more than 400,000,000 tons on some 80,-000 hectares (200,000 acres), enough to fuel four 400-megawatt power plants for 40 years. Other large sections throughout 41 North Carolina counties may succumb to peat mining by the end of the century.

CRITICAL TO ECOLOGY

Virtually no opposition has been mounted by environmental groups against

George Harrison

For Dennis and his wife, Theresa, a hearth fired by peat from the Boora Bog means independence. They also use peat for cooking.

the peat mining. The local scientific community is less sanguine. Duke University's School of Forestry and Environmental Studies and the North Carolina Department of Natural Resources and Conservation Development cosponsored a symposium on the need for a pocosin land-management program.

Pocosins, according to the symposium report, are critical to a healthy natural environment. Besides providing habitat for flora and fauna, such as the carnivorous pitcher plant and the pond pine, the black bear and the rare *Hyla andersoni* tree frog, pocosins serve as giant sponges for an area's rainwater, storing it for gradual release into streams flowing to estuaries and, ultimately, the ocean. Pocosins may play a critical role in preserving the fresh- to salt-water balance in estuaries, though few studies have been done on the subject.

Finally, pocosins may have a far greater effect on the climate of the southeastern United States than is currently realized. "There's absolutely no question that wetlands have considerable direct impact upon climate," said Pat Gannon, Sr., meteorologist with the Environmental Research Laboratories of the National Oceanic and Atmospheric Administration.

Gannon has closely studied the muck lands of the northern Everglades in Florida, which he suspects bear great similarities to the pocosins. The Everglade muck lands are being used to raise sugar cane and cattle. Gannon believes that the continuing loss of the muck [1.5 meters (5 feet) in 30 years because of drainage and agriculture] may change local climate drastically, with southern Florida perhaps ultimately becoming a desert □

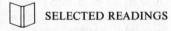 SELECTED READINGS

"Big bog: requiem for lonely wilderness?" [Minnesota Gas Company plan to harvest peat] by J. Luoma. *Audubon*, September 1981.

"Old world may teach the new an energy lesson." by Robert E. Sullivan. *Smithsonian*, October 1981.

"Peat to heat, light, and feed the world" by J. Mattill. *Technology Review*, October 1979.

"Young coal: big bogs of peat yield old energy source" by O. Davies. *Science Digest*, April 1979.

Courtesy of Chrysler Corporation

Chrysler engineers shoot colored smoke streams over a full-sized Plymouth to show air-flow patterns. These are studied to determine fuel efficiency.

WHAT A DRAG!

by Don Sharp

RECENTLY I acquired an old Saab 99 showing 148,000 kilometers (92,000 miles), ample reason for a noisy engine. Somehow, though, the engine noises were unusually distinct at highway speed, when the rattling of a noisy engine is usually muted. Eventually, I realized why: the engine wasn't noisier, rather, the wind was much quieter. Saab, with its experience building aircraft, has always sought good aerodynamics. A cigarette ejected through the window didn't come flying back into the car. It arced gracefully upward and over the roof, descending smoothly over the trunk lid. I reflected on this, comparing the Saab to 30-odd other cars I've owned and driven over 25 years. I thought of how some collected dirt on the rear windows while others did not. I remembered how some were pushed about by passing trucks while others were as steady as a blue-chip stock. I began to appreciate automotive aerodynamics more fully.

DRAG AND ROLLING RESISTANCE

Aerodynamics refers to the behavior of the air a car (or any moving body) moves through. The air, as it is pushed aside and swirls around, affects both the handling of the car and the amount of energy—*fuel*—required to move it.

As a car goes down the road, it sets up high- and low-pressure patterns of airflow. Generally, the aerodynamic forces that retard the forward motion of the car are called *drag*. These are the aerodynamic forces that consume energy.

Drag arises from a number of factors: the pressure of wind on the front of the car, the suction arising from the "hole" the car makes in the air as it rides along, all the interruptions in the car's smooth surface such as door handles and outside rearview mirrors, and finally, the friction of air moving over even a smooth surface. To deal with drag, engineers summarize all these elements in a single concept they express by a number called the drag coefficient, commonly expressed as C_d.

The drag coefficient does not, by itself, indicate how many miles per gallon a vehicle will get. For example, a full-size station wagon and an intercity bus may have the same C_d of around .55, but the station wagon might get 16 miles per gallon of gasoline, while the bus will get about 6 miles per gallon on diesel fuel (equivalent to about 3 miles per gallon on gasoline). Still, if all other factors were equal, the car with the lower C_d would get better mileage.

Once C_d and miles per gallon for a given car are established, engineers can project the fuel savings from given reductions of C_d. A rough rule of thumb is that reducing C_d by a given percentage reduces fuel consumption by half that percentage, with the qualification that the fuel saving will be greater at higher speeds, where aerodynamics has a much more noticeable effect.

In the past, engineers thought of aerodynamics as a way of improving high-speed performance and practically ignored aerodynamic drag at lower speeds. They paid more attention to rolling resistance—a catch-all phrase used to describe the loss of energy due to the friction of moving parts, such as tires against the road. Rolling resistance affects gas mileage at low speeds more than aerodynamics does. But now engineers aren't ignoring anything. They're trying to improve aerodynamics even at urban traffic speeds of 50 kilometers (30 miles) per hour or so. Indeed, engineers at BMW point out that since most driving is done in cities, low-speed aerodynamics may be more important to fuel consumption than high-speed aerodynamics. A point to bear in mind is that aerodynamic drag does not come only from the motion of the vehicle. The effect of wind must be included. For example, a car moving at 90 kilometers (55 miles) per hour against a 30-kilometer (approximately 20-mile)-per-hour headwind is subject to an "apparent wind" of 120 kilometers (75 miles) per hour.

PEOPLE AND ENGINES

If fuel economy were the only thing the aerodynamics engineers had to worry about,

their task would be simple. They could design for minimum drag and be done with it. Unfortunately, the car must carry people and luggage, and it must have an engine. The shape of the car must allow for room and ventilation (without excessive wind noise), even at some cost to aerodynamics.

Since the early 1900's aerodynamics has been subordinate to the needs of the passengers and the engine. Early experimental designs, some of which had a drag coefficient as low as .25, hardly served the human and mechanical needs of all. Even as promising an effort as the Chrysler Airflow models made between 1934 and 1937 weren't popular, apparently because they deviated too much from the boxy styling of that time. One of the early experimental cars had a long, swooping tail that was almost as long as the rest of the car. The long tail was there to create a smooth flow of air over the rear of the car.

To avoid the low-pressure suction area at the rear, the "hole" the front of the car made in the air would presumably be filled with the long tail, and the taper of the tail would give the air time to flow smoothly back to fill the hole. The idea was abandoned, partly because the tail added weight

At General Motors, a test engineer monitors the aerodynamic performance of a car, to determine its coefficient of drag.

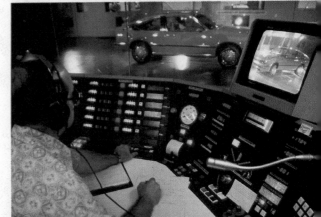

and cost, but also because the airflow behind a car contains vortices—spiral patterns of airflow—that are too complex for one particular solution. In 1935 the brilliant German engineer Wunibald S. Kamm discovered that cutting off the rear section abruptly was as aerodynamically effective as trying to streamline it, and the "Kamm effect" is now common on many cars.

SMOOTH AIR FLOW

For minimum drag, air must flow smoothly over all surfaces of a moving body. In such an ideal case, the air can be thought of as flowing over the body in a series of extremely thin layers, or laminae, that conform to the shape of the body and remain close to the surface. This kind of smooth flow is called laminar. If some irregularity, such as a door handle or outside rearview mirror, disturbs the airflow, or if the shape of the body

Two test engineers in a GM wind tunnel are dwarfed by a giant fan that generates 150-mile-an-hour hurricane-force winds.

Al Clayton

changes too abruptly, the laminar flow is disrupted. The air becomes turbulent, and turbulent air creates suction. The aerodynamics engineer seeks to minimize turbulence by creating the conditions for laminar flow. If the turbulence can't be avoided, the engineer tries to make it serve some useful purpose.

COMPROMISES NEEDED

The final shape of the car and its details represent a series of compromises among all those involved in the design. Consider the following dialogue among the mechanical engineer, the stylist, and the aerodynamics engineer.

Aero.: Let me round the front profile. That will reduce C_d from .46 to .41.

Mech.: You can't do that. Your round profile won't let enough air into my radiator.

Stylist: I don't like it.

Aero.: Well, O.K., leave the front. Suppose we slope the windshield a few more degrees.

Mech.: No good. That will create suction at the bottom of the windshield. I'd need a very large fan to get any fresh air into the car.

Stylist: I don't like it.

Aero.: I'd like to flatten the sides a bit to cut down the wind noise.

Mech.: No, that curved side is set up to make the body stiff and rigid.

Stylist: I don't like it.

Aero.: O.K., but at least let me change the shape of the roofline here at the rear.

Mech. and Stylist: What for?

Aero.: I want the flow of air to keep rain and dirt off the rear window.

Mech. and Stylist: To reduce C_d?

Aero.: Well, C_d may actually go up a few points, but I'll accept that to have a clean rear window.

EUROPEAN LEAD

Aerodynamics engineers have had more influence on European cars than on U.S. cars, partly because of Europe's higher speed limits and higher fuel costs. The first Swedish Saab of 1949 had a C_d of .35, and the 99 series made from 1969 to 1980 had a C_d of .37.

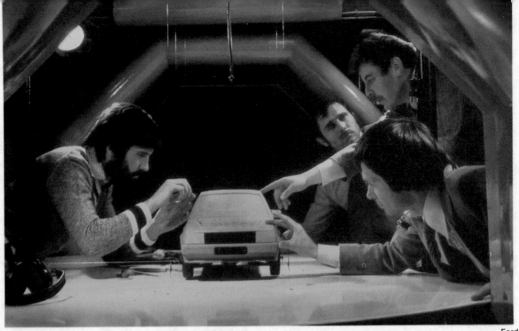

Ford

Ford engineers glue long strings over the model of an Escort to analyze airflow over the car's body. The scene is in Ford's wind tunnel in West Germany.

The tiny French Dyna Panhard of the 1950's had a C_d of .26. The European model of the current Renault 18i registers a C_d of .39. (The U.S. version registers .41, an increase arising from U.S.-government mandated headlights and bumpers.)

Researchers at Volkswagen have established .46 as the average C_d for all European sedans. No similarly documented figure is available for U.S. cars, but the common assumption is of a C_d range from .45 to .56. The Chrysler two-door K-body series has been reported as having a C_d of .47. General Motors gives its X-body family a C_d of .43, an excellent number, and Ford gave its 1980 Escort/Lynx an even better rating number of .40.

These numbers show that U.S. designers are as capable as their European counterparts when both work toward the same purposes. Historically, however, U.S. designers have pursued aerodynamics for purposes other than fuel economy. Chrysler, for example, examined the relationship between aerodynamics and high-speed stability in the 1950's. Chrysler's vertical or near-vertical tail fins of the late 1950's (in contrast to more horizontal fins on other makes) contributed significantly to directional stability at high cruising speeds.

To increase road holding at high speeds, the Dodge "muscle cars" of the late 1960's had a wind wing. This appendage, shaped like an upside-down airplane wing, was mounted above the trunk on two vertical posts. It pushed the car downward to improve traction on the rear wheels.

SMALL CHANGES, BIG EFFECTS

The work on the Volkswagen Rabbit and Scirocco models exemplifies the compromises the aerodynamics engineer faces. Volkswagen took the stylist's design as basic and, as they say, sought to optimize the details. Some very small changes made significant reductions in the drag coefficient of the whole car. For example, the original hood for the Rabbit and Scirocco had a right-angled edge. The corners at the fenders were also right angles. Since airflow could not conform to these abrupt changes of direction, a turbulent area, or "separation bubble," was created above the hood as laminar flow was disrupted. By simply rounding these edges and corners, the aerodynamics engineers improved the airflow over the hood and windshield and reduced C_d from .48 to .41. The raised seams that replace the conventional rain gutters at the sides of the roof of the Renault 18i, the turned-up lip on the trunk lid of a number of cars, and the smoothly contoured housing around the outside rearview mirrors of the current Volvos are all details that improve airflow.

Mercedes-Benz has a reputation for paying attention to aerodynamics. Even the sedans of the late 1950's had headlights and taillights smoothly faired into the body contours, and the body shape avoided abrupt angles. One distinctive detail of the Mercedes-Benz family is the ribbed taillight. The surface consists of a series of parallel ridges and valleys. Dust settles on the ridges, but the airflow keeps the valleys clean, so a substantial portion of the taillight area remains bright. To enhance this effect, the engineers designed a taillight unit that would duct air from the sides to help remove dust.

NO MIRACLES

One should bear in mind that aerodynamics engineers cannot work miracles. They presume a car will always be perfectly level on the road and its form as smooth as it was when it left the factory. Unfortunately, drivers are not as scrupulous as the engineers, so they load the trunk of the car with too much weight. The rear end squats, the car puts its nose into the air, and that laboriously achieved drag coefficient soars. Or a spring in the suspension system breaks, and the car goes down the road listing to one side. Luggage racks on the roof or trunk lid spoil airflow, and even wheel covers with "spinners" or simulated spokes, or a broken muffler hanging close to the ground can raise drag efficient by several percentage points. The beautiful "optimizing" of the Volkswagen engineers carries the seeds of its own weakness: if a small detail such as hood profile can lower drag coefficient, what happens when the driver crinkles the hood or crumples a fender?

The engineers have enough to do without trying to figure out the consequences of a bent fender. Perhaps as time goes on, automotive aerodynamics will become familiar to everyone, and people will be more conscientious about preserving the original lines of the cars, both by avoiding collisions and by timely repairs of minor scrapes. The engineers have done very well in their effort to save fuel. The rest, of course, is up to the driver □

SELECTED READINGS

"Flying on the ground" by R. Voegelin. *Motor Trend*, February 1981.

"Turbulence and tunnels" by D. Sherman. *Car and Driver*, August 1981.

"Aerodynamics to Save Gasoline" by Natalie Angier. *Discover*, October 1981.

Ford's Mercury LN7 (left) is the U.S. car with the lowest drag coefficient. Its European counterpart is the Porsche 924 (right), Weisach edition.

Dana Duke/DISCOVER © 1981—Time Inc.

Of the twelve major commercial duck farms in the United States, only three supply nearly 70 per cent of all native-grown plumage. The country imports most of its down.

DOWN

by Heller McAlpin

PEOPLE sport it on their backs and on their feet, sleep with their heads cushioned by it, their bodies smothered under it. When on camping trips, they envelop themselves in it. The substance is down.

Whether home-grown or mass-produced, channeled into coats or pillows or sleeping bags, as long as it is dry, it remains nature's best insulator—and an increasingly popular and costly one. The cost of down and its loss of insulating ability when wet are its chief disadvantages, but even after nearly 100 years of extensive efforts, we cannot produce a synthetic equal to it.

MORE AND MORE DEMAND

Despite competition in recent years from manmade fibers such as DuPont's Dacron Hollowfil II polyester, demand for down is at an all-time high, and still on the upswing. It is coveted by everyone from the U.S. government—which, in 1980, ordered 182,000 sleeping bags containing at least 50 per cent down—to the skier who wouldn't consider braving the slopes without a down-filled nylon parka and leg warmers, to chic urban women who have taken over restaurant cloakrooms with their bulging comforterlike coats.

Down was named a "basic strategic and critical material" in the late 1940's when shipments from the Far East were cut off, leaving no suitable substitutes for military use. Today, the supply is not increasing in pace with demand despite the reopening of trade with China in 1972. As a consequence, prices keep rising. When one learns that it takes on the average nine commercially raised geese to fill a single good-quality sleeping bag, one can't help wondering where all the plumage is coming from.

WHERE IS IT COMING FROM?

The answer, by and large, is from abroad. The United States imports about 80 per cent of its down. That's because down is a by-product of geese and ducks raised for food, and people in the United States simply do not eat enough waterfowl to sustain an industry large enough to keep the country well supplied with native plumage. According to Howard C. Winslow, executive director of the Feather and Down Association, approximately one-half of the more than 7,500,000 kilograms (approximately 16,600,000 pounds) of feathers and down imported by the United States in 1980 came from the People's Republic of China.

A supplier carries heavy sacks stuffed full of down to a processing factory, which will manufacture comforters and pillows with the plumage.

Hubert Schriebl

The Chinese eat ducks the way we eat broilers—as do the other leading exporters of waterfowl plumage, including France (famous for its pâté de foie gras, made from the enlarged livers of force-fed geese), Germany, Yugoslavia, and Taiwan. Although some of the feathers are still collected from small village farmers, as they were before the 1940's, the vast majority of down feathers come from geese and ducks commercially raised on large farms or, in China, on communes.

Similarly, nearly 70 per cent of U.S.-grown plumage comes from just three of the twelve major commercial duck farms in the United States. C&D Foods, Incorporated, of Franksville, Wisconsin, is the biggest single producer, turning out more than 5,000,000 ducks a year, which yield more than 550,000 kilograms (roughly 1,250,000 pounds) of feather and down.

BIRDS AND FEATHERS PART

The ducks are slaughtered at seven weeks of age, by which time they have reached the live weight of 2.5 to 3 kilograms (about 6 or 7 pounds). That's too early for them to generate the quantities of feather that full-grown wildfowl produce, but that is the age at which growth slows and it would no longer pay to feed them. The live birds are hung by their feet on shackles on an assembly line, and killed. They are then bled and "scalded" in a hot (but not really scalding) water bath to saturate their plumage. While wet, the ducks are plucked by hundreds of rubber fingers that "stroke" off their feathers, which drop into a trough.

At this point the birds and their plumage part company for good. The ducks continue on to another assembly line, where they are waxed to remove any remaining bristly pinfeathers and then dressed to make them oven-ready. The feathers are rinsed and dried and sold to processors and manufacturers of down-filled bedding and clothing. Meat accounts for 76 per cent of a duck's revenue, but feathers and down are a good secondary source of income, and getting better all the time as demand continues to exceed supply.

Geese are even less prevalent in the United States than ducks. Among the fore-

Standing in a blizzard of white goose feathers that have been washed and blown dry, a worker empties the sacks into a sorting machine that separates down from feathers.

most growers of these waterfowl are the Hutterites of South Dakota, a German-speaking Anabaptist pacifist sect started by Jacob Hutter in Slovakia in 1533. The Hutterites live on large communal farms and wear traditional European dress, although they use modern equipment to run their successful goose business.

The U.S. Federal Trade Commission (FTC) defines down as "the undercoating of waterfowl, consisting of clusters of light, fluffy filaments (barbs) growing from the quill point but without any quill shaft." Down's lack of quill shaft distinguishes it from even the tiniest and most flaccid feathers, though down arrives at processing plants packed together with feathers in large sacks or in compressed bales.

PROCESSING

Processing this plumage involves purifying, separating, and mixing. Preliminary cleaning is done in a machine that removes dust by means of mechanical agitation in combination with compressed air and suction. From the dusting machine, the feathers are transferred pneumatically to washing machines, where special detergents are used to remove all blood, grit, and impurities. The plumage is then centrifuged to squeeze out excess moisture—as in the spin-dry cycle on a home machine. The next step is drying, at a constant 100° *Celsius (212°* Fahrenheit), until all traces of dampness have completely disappeared.

Now that the plumage is clean, it's time to separate the feathers from the down. This is done by means of air currents that blow the plumage into separate compartments lined up, one behind the other, at increasing distances from the source of air. The feathers are deposited into these chambers according to their weight with the largest (and heaviest) settling closest to the blower. Because down is the lightest material, it will travel to the farthest compartment.

One processor of down is Northern Feather, Incorporated, a Danish concern whose U.S. division manufactures down and feather bedding in eight factories, which supply department stores nationwide. According to James England at Northern Feather, about 18 to 20 per cent of a duck's plumage (by weight) is down, and the rest is feathers. But as much as 25 per cent of the total plumage (by weight) will settle in that farthest down bin.

As a result, some feathers will still be mixed in with the down, but Mr. England explains that it would be commercially impractical to run the separating machine slowly enough to yield purer than 90 per cent down. In fact, 85 per cent down in that last compartment is more normal.

LABELING

That impurity is no cause for alarm, however, because virtually all down-filled products contain some feathers, as well as varying amounts of the following: plumules (underdeveloped feathers with barbs indistinguishable from those of down), down fiber (detached barbs from down and plumules), and remainder (waterfowl and nonwaterfowl feathers and fiber, as well as residue such as quill pith, quill fragments, and foreign matter).

The percentage (by weight) of down and plumules in down-filled products varies, and there are tight—if complex—labeling regulations to protect consumers. The labels can, however, give an incomplete and therefore misleading impression of a product's make-up. For example, a top-quality soft pillow labeled "down" can by law contain a combination of up to 20 per cent feathers, chicken and turkey plumage, damaged feathers, and debris, and not mention them on the label. Similary a medium-soft pillow labeled "50 per cent down, 50 per cent waterfowl feathers," need contain only 35 per cent down and plumules.

The tremendous demand for down-filled products in the United States has kept business booming for many bedding and clothing manufacturers.

Hubert Schriebl

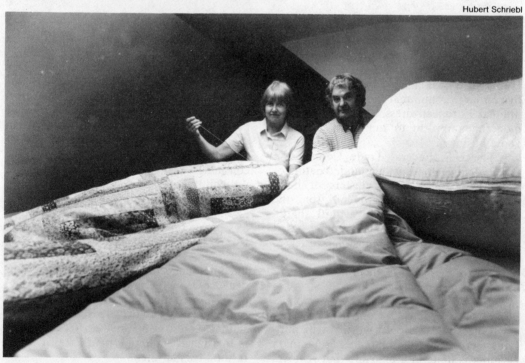

Hubert Schriebl

Down, whose insulating ability is better than that of any natural or synthetic fiber, is coveted by some people for practical purposes (above), and by others for fashionable ones (at right).

Hubert Schriebl

To complicate matters further, there is the added question of how rigidly manufacturers adhere to guidelines.

Some final advice about down labels: if you are tempted to play it safe by going for the product that boasts "100 per cent down," "all down," "pure down," or "prime down," don't. It probably isn't a superior product at all—just a false and illegal label. If, on the other hand, you have a preference for goose or duck, you can rest assured that an item labeled "goose down" or "duck down" consists of at least 90 per cent of the plumage of the named species. The manufacturer needn't specify species, however, and most products contain a mixture of duck and goose plumage, depending on availability.

INSULATING VALUE

Although there is no shortage of rules and regulations governing the labeling of feathers and down, quality control is another matter, and down does not vary widely in quality from one lot to the next. Determining the quality of a comforter's filling can be much more difficult than pinpointing its components, and as frustrating as trying to capture the contents of a burst pillow. But there is a test, which is neither standardized nor included on the label, that measures one aspect of down—its "loft" or "fill power."

Down's value lies primarily in its ability to insulate without weight. When dry, it does that better than cotton, wool, silk, feathers, or any manmade fiber. That insulating ability results from its structure. When magnified, down looks vaguely like a snowflake. Like a snowflake, its filaments have hooks that latch onto the barbs of other down fibers, forming clusters that trap dead air in between. (When wet, down becomes a sodden mass, clumping together with no air trapped at all). The more air trapped, the better the insulation.

The less down it takes to fill a given space, the greater the air-to-down ratio and the better the down. That characteristic is measured by dropping 28 grams (1 ounce) of the feather-down blend in question into a graduated plastic cylinder, followed by a light weight called a platten that slides down the cylinder until it comes to rest naturally opposite a marking. The industry standard is that 1 gram of down should fill 320 cubic centimeters (or 1 ounce fill 550 cubic inches), although the manufacturer is not required to comply with that. But if the feather-down mix fills only 235 cubic centimeters per gram (400 cubic inches per ounce), the manufacturer will have to use more down to fill an item properly, which will cost more (unless the down is cheaper) and result in a slightly heavier garment.

Generally, a good cold-weather sleeping bag requires 0.9 to 1.4 kilograms (2 to 3 pounds) of down; a jacket, 369 grams (13 ounces). You wouldn't want the down in either article to weigh much more, but for use under less frigid conditions, less down—and more feathers or even a synthetic blend—might be appropriate.

GOOSE VS. DUCK

The factors that affect down's quality (and fill power) are numerous and controversial—breed, feed, climate, age at which the birds are slaughtered, processing, and mix of the plumage, and species. The most hotly debated issue in the feather and down industry is the merits of goose versus duck down. Polish goose down is traditionally considered the best commercial grade of down, probably because it often has a fill power of 410 cubic centimeters per gram (700 cubic inches per ounce).

There are those who contend that goose down has longer filaments than duck down, and thus can trap more air. Duck defenders argue that goose down's special appeal lies soley in its color, which tends to be lighter than duck down—but color actually depends on breed, not species. Several points, however, are uncontested in the duck versus goose debate:

• Commercially raised geese yield more per bird than commercially raised ducks. It takes about five geese to produce a down-filled jacket, while it requires twelve ducks just to insulate a vest. One goose can produce about 84 grams (3 ounces) of down, while one duck yields as little as one-fifth of that.

• Goose down is currently about 13 per cent more expensive than duck down.

• The hands-down best down is eiderdown, which is from the eider duck, an endangered wildfowl that resides near the Arctic Circle (lending credence to the argument that native habitat affects the quality of down). Eiderdown is gathered by robbing the eider duck's nest. By law, feathers can be taken only from abandoned nests. These nests are hard to reach, often perched on cliffs or in caves.

According to the Feather and Down Association's figures, between 1,500 and 2,000 kilograms (3,300 and 4,400 pounds) of eiderdown are collected annually, mainly in Iceland, of which only half is exported. Its fill power is approximately double that of top-quality goose down, and it is considered by all to be the best noncommercial grade of down—noncommercial because the substance is so rare as to make its cost prohibitive—more than ten times that of top-quality goose down.

Beware, when buying a down-filled article, of the fabric encasing the plumage. Make certain it is truly downproof, for there are few things more annoying and messy than a leaky pillow or comforter. Special nylons and cotton cambrics with 220 to 260 threads per square inch are generally the best covers. Cotton can be made downproof by treating it with hot-wax, but that process is only temporary. A superior method of downproofing is the application of tremendous pressure on the fabric, which causes the cotton to seal itself with its own resin □

SELECTED READINGS

"Dovekies, dollies, and down: keeping warm in arctic waters" by J. Dillon. *Oceans*, July 1978.

"Getting down to business" by Val Ross. *Maclean's*, February 4, 1980.

"Producing your own down" by K. Bernsohn. *Organic Gardening and Farming*, March 1978.

ELECTRICITY FROM THE WIND

by John J. Pullen

AT midmorning of April 12, 1979, a pleasant day with the still-leafless treetops swaying in a moderate breeze, I joined an unusual group gathered at the home of Rosemary and Alan Hanks in Madison, Connecticut, on a hill overlooking the East River about a mile north of its outlet into Long Island Sound. Conspicuous on the scene, and most curious, was the presence of men in yellow hard hats from the Connecticut Light & Power Company (CL & P). They were there on private property to help install a windmill, which might have moved a casual observer to ask, "What hath the energy crisis wrought? Are the wind folk now in bed with the electric utilities?"

When I arrived the CL & P fellows were digging a hole in which to plant a 70-foot wood pole, which was lying nearby. The generator which was to be mounted on top of the pole was about 6 feet long and 2 feet across, with a three-bladed propeller 13 feet in diameter. Across its gleaming fiber glass nacelle was lettered the word ENERTECH, the name of the manufacturer.

The Enertech 1500 represents something new in windmill technology. It produces alternating current (ac) that is identical to the 115-volt, 60-cycle utility power supplied to your home. It is connected by a simple plug to any 20-ampere wall outlet, and wind-generated electricity then flows directly to lights and appliances in the house. If there is a shortage, the electric utility automatically makes up for it. If the wind produces more electricity than is being used, the surplus flows into the utility's distribution system. This arrangement eliminates the need for a set of storage batteries, which has traditionally been one of the costliest components of a wind-powered system.

The system also has an important fail-safe feature. It automatically stops generat-

Ben Wolff

This wind-generated electricity system is a vertical-axis, or eggbeater type, model that makes use of wind from any direction.

ing when there is a utility power failure, so that wind-generated power cannot be fed into a "down" utility line and shock people who may be repairing the line. As this feature indicates, the Enertech 1500 is not at present a stand-alone, or back-up, system. It is designed to slow down your consumption of utility power and reduce your electric bill.

By early afternoon the pole at the Madison site was in place and securely guyed. The generator was lifted to the top of the pole and attached. The connecting cable and accessory equipment were installed. At 2:40 P.M., whirling with a sound like the distant beating of wings, the propeller started making red, white, and blue circles in the sky. Almost involuntarily, everybody cheered. On a control box inside the house, a meter showed that the Enertech 1500 had begun to deliver.

Windmills with a horizontal-axis configuration are very common. Fins on the powerful blades keep the blades facing into the wind.

Enertech Wind Systems

A fast, simple operation. The cost? In this case, I was told, Northeast Utilities had contributed the pole and the installation out of its research budget, but the normal cost is reasonable. The wind turbine generator and its control system as of the end of 1979 was priced at about $3,475 F.O.B. Norwich, Vermont.

The additional cost—the pole or tower, installation, and wiring—may run from around $1,000 to $4,000 depending primarily on the height and the type of pole or tower. A wood utility pole, if it can be used, is less expensive than one would think.

NEW SYSTEM

It was obvious that much planning and technical expertise had gone into the Madison-site accomplishment, so I was not surprised to learn that Enertech's chief design engineer is Henry Clews, a nationally known pioneer in wind-energy systems. Back in 1974, struggling by himself in Maine, Henry Clews was a distributor for a couple of imported wind machines, and he quickly learned a lot about the windmill business as distinct from the windmill art. He then built several prototype windmill systems. He explains, "They were direct-current (dc) battery-charging types, and the problem was that none of them could ever be competitive with utility rates. So it didn't seem to me that they'd ever have widespread acceptance. It wasn't until I went to work for Enertech that I got started on the new idea.

The new approach came about as a result of a project we did at Enertech for Xerox Corporation, making a bicycle-powered generating system. They wanted a bunch of little units that children could pedal to generate electricity that could be fed directly into a power line to light up the White House Christmas tree—a sort of public relations project. We built twenty of these. In doing so, we learned a lot about using induction generators to feed power directly into an ac line."

This is a key point. The machines traditionally used in wind systems—the dc-producing generators and the ac-producing alternators—cannot accomplish this direct feed-in, because as wind speed changes they turn out an electric current with varying voltage and frequency, not synchronous with utility power. Therefore their output must be stored in batteries. Since batteries accept and supply only dc, the current from an alternator must be changed to dc by an appropriate device before storage. When electricity is drawn from the batteries it can go directly to lights and some appliances that will function on dc. But many appliances require ac, and for these there must be an inverter to change dc to ac. The inverter is expensive and uses up a good deal of power just in running itself. All rather complicated.

RELIABLE AND TROUBLEFREE

The induction generator that Henry designed into the Enertech 1500 produces ac that is always synchronous with that of the electric company. Therefore it can simply be plugged into a wall outlet, eliminating the need for batteries and inverters. The induction generator is actually (and should be called) a motor-generator. When electric power is fed into this machine it causes a rotor to turn and a mechanical driving force to be produced. It is then acting as a motor. But mechanical force, such as that of the wind, can be applied to turn the rotor and do the opposite—that is, cause electricity to be produced. It is then acting as a generator. Induction motors (generators) are standard, off-the-shelf items, so their cost is quite reasonable, and millions of them have been in use for decades, so their reliability has been proven, and the bugs have been pretty well worked out.

Another noteworthy feature of the Enertech 1500 that would seem to make for simplicity and troublefree operation is the power train. One problem in windmill design is to get all the power possible at low wind speed, but to prevent high-speed operation that could destroy the machine. Traditionally, many manufacturers have provided this overspeed control by means of a variable-pitch propeller. Instead of adding this mechanism, Enertech uses a fixed-pitch design based on a "rather subtle" (as Henry calls it) aeronautical principle that sends the blades into a progressive stall when wind speed gets too high.

At the same time, the propeller is efficient at low wind speed. It is not self-starting, but this potential difficulty is easily overcome. Utility power is used for the first few seconds to bring the machine up to synchronous speed as a motor; then the wind takes over, and the motor becomes a generator. Even after start-up a small amount of electricity from the utility continues to flow through the machine to energize the magnetic field necessary for generating electricity. If there is a utility "outage" and this flow stops, wind-generated electricity also stops perforce. This is the ultimate fail-safe feature that protects utility linemen.

BUT DOES IT PAY?

The amount of electricity a wind turbine generator produces varies with wind speed. On a general basis, wind systems are not for everyone. They are best suited for windy locations where the cost of commercial power is unusually high. They are better suited for rural or semirural locations than they are for urban or suburban areas where building and zoning regulations, as well as interference with the wind caused by nearby structures, may be encountered. Given a location that seems generally favorable, the most critical remaining factor is average wind speed at that site. As little as one mile per hour at ground level can make the difference between a system that will pay for itself and one that will not. And winds can vary consid-

Top drawing: the locations of these windmills show decreasing levels of efficiency from highest to lowest. Middle: trees can create turbulence which hampers performance. Bottom: wind flows up and over this house, bypassing the windmill.

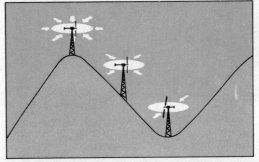

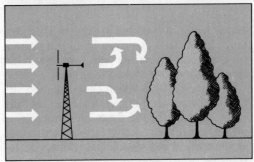

Technicians assemble an Enertech 1500 windmill, which has many ingenious features, at the company's plant in Norwich, Vermont.

erably between sites that are only a short distance apart. It is therefore highly important to determine carefully the average wind speed for each individual location.

Starting with a visual check, a good site is one where treetops sway or a flag flies fully extended most of the time. Deformed trees may also provide a clue. Strong continuous winds tend to reduce foliage on the side toward the wind. Sites may benefit from irregularities in the local terrain, such as narrow valleys that compress, or rounded hill crests that speed up, wind flow.

For preliminary estimates, it may be enough to measure and record wind speeds at eye level twice a day for two or three weeks, using a simple hand-held instrument that costs about $10. If the average of these measurements is less than 8 miles per hour and commercial power is available, Enertech advises you to go no further; the site is prob-

ably not satisfactory. Other manufacturers may suggest different minimum wind speeds. If the site appears to be promising, the next step is to install an anemometer, a recording device to measure and record wind speed over a period of several months or even a year. You need to take into account seasonal variations in determining if the site is worthwhile.

The next step is choosing tower height and type. One purpose of the tower or pole is to raise the wind machine above and away from turbulence, which may damage it, and from "wind shadow," caused by nearby trees or buildings. A site on a hill doesn't necessarily lessen the need for a high tower. Some authorities suggest that both turbulence and wind shadow can be avoided by erecting a tower that is at least 30 feet higher than any obstacle within 100 yards, or 40 feet high, whichever is greater. Others say the tower should be at least 60 feet high.

Another purpose of the tower relates to wind speed. Wind measurements at ground level can be misleading. Here winds are slowed by the drag of the earth's surface and by various obstacles. Wind speed generally increases with height, and even though this increase may be only 4 or 5 miles per hour, it is significant, because power varies with the cube of the wind speed.

The cost of attaining the desired height is an important consideration. The real trade-off is between a low-cost 40- or 50-foot utility pole and an 80- or 90-foot tower. Generally, however, since tower increments are not too costly, the least expensive way to get more power is to increase tower height.

LOOKING AT TRUE COSTS

Having arrived at the type, size, and gross cost of the wind system, the next step is to determine net cost after taking advantage of federal and state benefactions. There are generous federal and state incentives for installing windmills. These incentives generally take the form of tax credits.

The cost of utility power in your area and what, if anything, the utility company will pay you for wind-generated power that is fed into utility lines must also be considered □

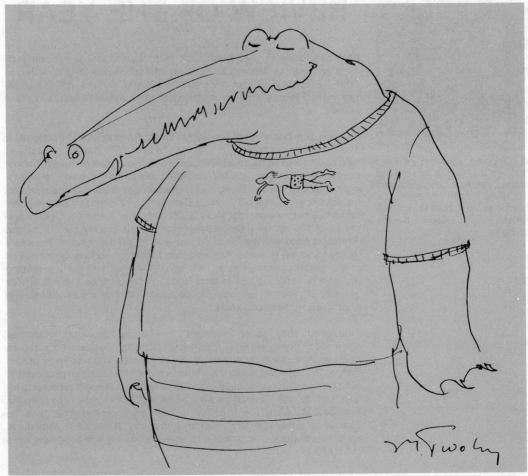

© 1982 M. Twohy. First appeared in AUDUBON.

THE ENVIRONMENT

THE ENVIRONMENT
REVIEW OF THE YEAR

Wide World

A logging truck rambles through a once-dense stand of timber that has been denuded of trees. Such clear-cutting practices can cause severe soil erosion and pollute nearby streams.

Politics and the Environment. Little more than a decade ago, environment and politics seemed to have as little affinity as oil and water. In 1981 by contrast, politics dominated the environmental realm, and environmental issues leapt to unprecedented prominence on the political scene.

The new administration of President Ronald Reagan was both originator and subject of much of the environmental news. Mr. Reagan himself has long been accused by conservationists of being at best ambivalent about environmental values, and his accession touched off a rapid and unending succession of controversies. The most contentious development was his selection of James G. Watt, a Denver lawyer identified with industry and anti-environmental litigation, as Secretary of the Interior, chief custodian of the nation's natural resources. Watt quickly took a course directly at odds with his line of conservationist predecessors. "President Reagan told me to swing the pendulum back from excessive protection and excessive preservations," he said. Watt then laid out a sweeping program of "opening up" federal lands, offshore tracts, and wilderness areas to oil, mining, and logging development. There was widespread opposition to these programs.

Throughout 1981, as the President's chief adviser on natural resources and environmental matters, Secretary Watt was considered the source of many other major policy shifts. Environmental controls were placed high on the list of administrative areas in which Mr. Reagan proposed to cut back on federal regulation and expenditures. Among numerous retrenchments, the Council on Environmental Quality, which advises the President and Congress on policy, had its budget cut by 64 per cent; the coastal-zone management program was cut by 36 per cent; allocations for solar-energy development and energy conservation programs were cut by 83 per cent.

Secretary Watt and environmental activists became embroiled in reciprocal caustic criticism and name-calling that culminated in the virtually unprecedented presentation to Congress in October, 1981, of a petition with over 1,000,000 signatures demanding the Secretary's removal. The White House ignored the protest, but environmental groups kept up their pressure, and they credited Mr. Watt's militance with causing record spurts in their membership and financial support. Watt's aggressive actions likewise evoked opposition from coastal states concerned about offshore drilling and in Congress. Several of the Secretary's major initiatives were blocked at least temporarily by court decisions and Congressional votes, and in several instances, he was impelled to reverse policy announcements.

Anne M. Gorsuch, Administrator of the Environmental Protection Agency, must cope with drastic cuts in budget and personnel, and a relaxation of regulatory environmental safeguards.

UPI

The EPA. Another focus of attention was the Environmental Protection Agency (EPA), which in 11 years had become one of the government's biggest regulatory arms. To head the agency, President Reagan named Anne M. Gorsuch, a Denver lawyer little known in the environmental field. Mrs. Gorsuch announced that while she had no intention of compromising environmental safeguards, she proposed to weed out excessive and overcomplicated rules and procedures, streamline the agency's operation, and transfer some responsibilities to the states.

Sharp personnel and budget cuts followed, along with a series of relaxations of federal requirements.

Action on Air, Water, Noise, and Recycling Regulations. Pressures from industry made the Clean Air Act a prime target for modification in deregulation plans, but defensive public and congressional reaction led the Administration to defer concrete proposals for revisions. One change favored by scientific groups, government officials, and conservationists was a drastic reduction in allowable emissions of sulfur dioxide from eastern industrial chimneys to lessen waterway and land pollution from acid rain. (Acid rain, rain heavily laden with sulfuric acid and other contaminants from power plants and heavy industry, is damaging to many life forms.) ■ Existing water pollution control legislation likewise escaped any major amendment. Congress formulated a compromise on Administration proposals for phased reduction of federal subsidies for sewage-treatment plants and reauthorized the multi-billion dollar sewage treatment grant program. ■ The Administration proposed virtually to end the federal program to curb noise, most ubiquitous of the pollutions, but Congress voted to continue it on a reduced basis. ■ Waste-recycling advocates, pressing an arduous state-by-state campaign for mandatory deposits on beverage containers, persuaded the Massachusetts legislature to override the governor's veto, making it the eighth state in the "bottle-law" fold.

Toxic Substances. Problems of toxic substances stirred political reverberations from coast to coast. Conservationists, with corroboration from the federal General Accounting Office, accused the EPA of moving much too slowly in the billion-dollar program enacted in 1980 to clean up toxic-waste dumps. ■ An outbreak of the Mediterranean fruit fly in California and the controversy over spraying with the pesticide Malathion also occurred. (See also "The Fly in Our Fruit," on page 80).

Public Opinion. One reason for the widespread controversies that developed over environmental matters was that while President Reagan repeatedly cited an electoral "mandate" to reduce federal regulation, citizens generally did not seem to want this extended to environmental controls. National opinion surveys (Louis Harris, N.Y. Times/CBS, NBC) repeatedly found strong majority support for environmental protection and improvement even if this involved larger expenditures and restricted economic growth. Pollster Louis Harris told a Congressional hearing, after a September 1981 survey, "While the public thinks that some regulations in other areas ought to be relaxed or even abolished, they will oppose vehemently any measure that might have the effect of reversing some of the environmental gains that have been made in the last ten years . . . They will not tolerate any reductions in environmental cleanup efforts . . . The American people's desire to battle pollution is one of the most overwhelming and clearest we have ever recorded in out 35 years of surveying public opinion."

Global Outlook. The year 1981 marked the passage of nearly a decade since most of the world's peoples, at a United-Nations conference at Stockholm in 1972, endorsed a massive program for dealing with global environmental problems. In pre-anniversary stocktaking, U.N. experts concurred that while there had been much progress, too much remained undone. The International Union for the Conservation of Nature then drew up a "World Conservation Strategy," emphasizing tightened linkage between developmental and environmental planning and augmented protection of vital but dwindling global resources such as soil, forests, fisheries, and diversified species.

Gladwin Hill

Charles Steiner/Sygma

In January 1982, radioactive steam escaped from the Robert E. Ginna nuclear power plant near Rochester, New York, when a steam-generator tube was damaged and ruptured.

Rutgers University's Smith Hall was closed in February 1982, after air samples revealed excessive levels of estradiol benzoate, a hormone believed to be carcinogenic.

Harvey Bilker/The New York Times

Charles Krebs/Aperture

Cavity-nesting birds, like this saw-whet owl, need old-growth trees to survive. But logging operations are ruining the last large stands of old trees in the Pacific Northwest.

TEN ENDANGERED HABITATS

by Mark Wexler

AMERICANS have been tinkering with the landscape ever since the first Europeans set foot on the continent. All too often, nature has come up the loser. Until fairly recently few people seemed concerned about how the land was used. After all, weren't all the nation's resources unlimited? To make way for development, forests were cleared and never replanted. Swamps were drained and mountains leveled. Entire rivers were diverted. In the process, some pieces of the natural domain vanished forever.

Since the beginning of the 20th century several battles have been fought over the use, abuse, and protection of America's vast outdoor treasures. But perhaps at no other time in the history of the United States have so many different ecosystems been so threatened with disruption—or have so many different confrontations over land use been in the offing. The reason: the United States is at last paying the price for too many years of uncontrolled growth. The resources of America are indeed finite. Finding the best and most responsible way to use them may be the toughest judgment Americans have ever had to make. "Obviously, some resources must be developed," observes Dr. Jay Hair, executive vice president of the National Wildlife Federation (NWF). "The real argument is over manner and degree." How that argument is settled could have a lasting impact on large portions of wild America, including the ten crucial habitat areas discussed on the following pages.

In some cases, the land is now threatened because of programs started years ago. In others, the situation is exaggerated by recent changes in federal policies. Early in 1981, Interior Department Secretary James Watt announced his intentions to open some previously closed natural areas to development. "He seems to have a different vision of what stewardship of public lands should be," says Hair. This opinion is shared by many in the environmental community.

ALL TYPES OF ECOSYSTEMS

The lands in trouble as a result of past and present policies include almost every type of natural ecosystem found in the Lower 48 states—from the fragile California desert and diminishing old-growth forests of the Pacific Northwest to the dynamic barrier islands that buffer the Atlantic and Gulf coasts. Each of them provides irreplaceable habitat for a wide variety of plant and animal life.

Yet each is under siege. Wyoming's Bridger-Teton National Forest, for instance, is a primeval wilderness of towering peaks and dense woodlands that shelter the largest elk herds in North America. Unfortunately, the same geological forces that shaped this pristine region also created vast reserves of oil and gas below ground. If those reserves are exploited unwisely, large pieces of elk habitat may simply disappear.

Meanwhile, in the prairie pothole region of the Upper Midwest, where millions of migratory ducks are hatched each year, some 140 square kilometers (55 square miles) of valuable wetlands are being drained an-

nually. Since 1960, researchers estimate, nearly ten per cent of the 202,000 square kilometers (78,125 square miles) of wetlands in the United States have been lost to dredging projects and commercial development. Wetlands are crucial to the survival of many animals. They also filter out pollution from underground water supplies.

DEVELOPMENT AND/OR PRESERVATION

In the early 1970's, the U.S. Congress set up a system of checks and balances to protect U.S. wetlands. The heart of that system is Section 404 of the Clean Water Act, which requires an environmental review of proposed activities in most marsh areas. Currently, however, several bills have been introduced in Congress that would remove some of the safeguards designed to preserve wetlands.

Congress is also feeling pressure these days from industrial lobbyists, who charge that the Clean Air Act hampers economic growth and stymies energy development. Some industries are trying to reduce dependence on foreign oil by switching to coal—

Prairie potholes serve as breeding grounds for millions of migratory waterfowl each year. Yet these valuable wetlands are being rapidly drained for agricultural purposes.

the largest single source of sulfur pollution in the United States—without taking significant steps to clean up their air emissions. Those emissions often return to earth as acid rain, which has already killed almost all life in half of the high-altitude lakes in New York's Adirondack Mountains. Scientists now point out that if acid rain continues to fall unabated, more than 50,000 other North American lakes will "die" in the next two decades.

"We must not be shortsighted," comments Hair. "Preserving resources today still allows for development at a future time, perhaps after we've solved some of our most serious pollution problems." According to

Increased oil and gas exploration in Wyoming, where this young calf lives, may endanger the habitat of the largest elk herds in the United States.
© Tom and Pat Leeson

many public opinion analysts, the American people agree. "There is plenty of data to show that most Americans do not think they must trade off environmental safeguards for energy, or for anything else," says California pollster Mervin Field.

At stake in the current land-use dilemma is the future of several of the most important habitat areas in the United States. Who will ultimately decide their fate? Abraham Lincoln may have provided an answer to that question more than a century ago, when he observed: "Public sentiment is everything. With it, nothing can fail. Without it, nothing can succeed."

LAST STAND FOR OLD GROWTH

To the early European colonists, America's dense forests were merely obstacles in the path of westward expansion. Relentlessly, the pioneers cleared the woodlands to make way for crops and settlements. By the late 1800's, nearly 80 per cent of all virgin woods east of the Mississippi River had been cut down. In their place, foresters eventually planted different, faster growing trees that could be harvested in a few decades. As a result, standing dead trees—called "snags"—have become quite rare throughout most of the United States—and so have many of the 85 or so species of cavity-nesting birds that depend on them.

Today, the nation's last large stands of old-growth forests are found only in the Cascade Mountain region of the Pacific Northwest. Though not virgin woods, these stands are made up of trees 150 years of age or older. They are crucial to the survival of a variety of animals. Researchers have found that the lush old-growth Douglas fir stands in the western Cascades support the most dense breeding bird populations of any forest system in the United States. Old growth also provides food and shelter for big game, and it is vital to the overall forest ecology.

Unfortunately, because of their size and bulk, old-growth trees are also valuable for timber production. On many federal lands, they are now being cut at a rapid rate, and some officials are seeking to increase that rate. Already in Oregon's Willamette National Forest, for example, about 85 per cent of present harvesting is taking place in old-growth stands.

The U.S. government is now conducting an inventory to decide which of its forest areas should be designated as "wilderness," and thus be closed to logging. However, environmentalists anticipate a tough fight to gain such protection.

DRAINING THE DUCK HATCHERY

During the last Ice Age, mammoth glaciers blanketed the entire northern Great Plains. As they retreated, the glaciers left millions of scattered depressions in their wake. Today, these depressions—called prairie potholes—are spread over thousands of square kilometers of central Canada, and about 12,000 square kilometers (4,688 square miles) of the Dakotas and Minnesota. In some areas, it is not unusual to find 40 potholes per square kilometer (100 or more per square mile). When the potholes fill with rain or snow, ideal wetland conditions develop.

Though this water-speckled landscape provides habitat for all kinds of prairie wildlife, millions of migratory ducks could not survive without it. Each year, almost 50 per cent of all North American ducklings are born in the pothole region. Nevertheless, large areas of these vital wetlands are being drained every year in the United States. Already, in fact, more than one-half of the potholes that once existed in the United States have vanished forever. The reason: the region contains some of the richest agricultural soil in the Midwest.

In Minnesota, where most of the potholes have already been drained by private landowners, the state legislature recently passed a law that encourages wetland protection through tax incentives. In the Dakotas, however, there is still no overall marsh protection plan.

Prairie wetlands are important for more than just waterfowl production. They help maintain ground-water levels in the high plains and prevent flooding in years of heavy rainfall. They also act as buffers against water pollution. "There's obviously much more at stake than migratory birds," says biologist Alan Wentz, NWF assistant director of Resources Defense who worked in the pothole region for six years. "But the birds alone are a valuable enough resource to warrant greater protection of prairie wetlands."

THE WILDCATTERS ARE WAITING

Within its 14,000-square-kilometer (5,469-square-mile) domain, Wyoming's Bridger-Teton National Forest has some of the most breathtaking scenery in the United States. It is an integral part of a massive 73,000-square-kilometer (28,125-square-mile) ecosystem that includes two national parks and numerous wilderness areas. But the Bridger-Teton is also located above a narrow band of the earth's crust known as the Overthrust Belt, which contains potentially

A surging current is not the only obstacle salmon in the Columbia River must face. Dams have depleted both the fish and their spawning habitat.
Art Wolfe

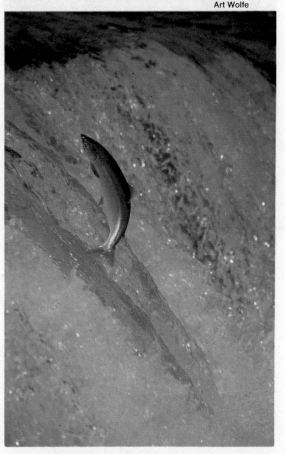

© Chuck Place

Off-road vehicles and other recreational activities are disrupting wildlife in the California desert and denuding it of prickly pear cacti and other plants.

vast reserves of oil and gas. The exploitation of those reserves could leave an indelible imprint on the region.

Stretching along a narrow path from Alaska all the way to Mexico, the Overthrust Belt was formed eons ago when two of the earth's tectonic plates crunched and overlapped one another. (The earth's crust is believed to lie on huge plates that move about very slowly.) For decades, geologists have known that this belt contained large pools of oil and gas. But it wasn't until the mid-1970's, when energy prices skyrocketed, that the cost of pumping out those reserves became competitive with foreign imports. During the Carter Administration, two-thirds of the Bridger-Teton forest was leased to oil and gas interests, who sought to drill exploratory wells. That activity is now being stepped up.

"Right now, the greatest loss of wildlife habitat is taking place on BLM [Bureau of Land Management] and private lands adjacent to the forest," sayd Dave Lockman, a Wyoming game department biologist. Nevertheless, in 1980, exploratory drilling activities disrupted large sections of Bridger-Teton woodlands, and researchers foresee problems as those activities increase. "We're particularly concerned about the effects of new roads and of potentially dangerous gases on such creatures as the grizzly bear, bald eagle, and elk," adds Lockman. Each year, some 28,000 elk migrate through the region, and federal officials have been slow in granting "wilderness" protection to some sensitive sections of the forest.

SWEPT AWAY BY A DEVELOPING TIDE

The 300 barrier islands that dot the U.S. coast from Maine to Texas represent one of nature's great paradoxes: their stability is based entirely on their ability to change. They are, in effect, large, shifting sandbars that are constantly being modified and moved by rising sea levels, storms, and ocean currents. Ranging in size from 8,094-square-meter (2-acre) Ship Pond Island off Rhode Island to the 280-square-kilometer (109-square-mile) Padre Island in Texas, they act as buffers between the sea and the adjacent marshes on their leeward sides. Those marshes are lush havens for hundreds of species of coastal birds, fish, reptiles, and furbearers.

Because they are constantly changing, most barrier islands are not suitable for development. Lands now considered safe for building may simply disappear in a few years. Despite that fact, the islands have been developed at a dangerous rate, and the U.S. government has played a role in that development. Though some federal agencies have purchased land on the islands for refugees and national seashores, other departments have encouraged people to move into the same areas by building roads and subsidizing flood insurance. What's more, in recent years, the U.S. government has spent $500,000,000 in a futile effort to stabilize shorelines. Jetties, seawalls, and other manmade barricades, however, interrupt the natural flow of sand, causing some islands to disintegrate even faster.

Jon Farrar

Mule deer and other animals once thrived in tallgrass prairies that grew from Canada to Texas. Today, these grasslands have been reduced to isolated pockets by development.

Presently, a measure is before Congress that would end federal subsidies to construction in these fragile systems. If passed, future builders will be developing these unstable islands at their own risk. But only time will tell if construction in the barrier islands will slow down as a result.

A DAM DISASTER IN THE MAKING

Perhaps no other waterway in the United States has such a profound influence on its surrounding environment as the Columbia River in the Pacific Northwest. Its enormous drainage basin extends over seven western states, providing habitat for everything from deer to songbirds. Its surging waters, ten times as powerful as the Colorado River, irrigate 28,000 square kilometers (10,938 square miles).

At one time, the Columbia was one of the world's greatest anadromous fish producing systems. Anadromous fish, such as steelhead and coho and chinook salmon, are born in fresh water, spend much of their adult lives at sea, and return to fresh water to spawn. Prior to this century, the fish ventured as far as 1,900 kilometers (1,200 miles) up the Columbia to deposit their eggs, and 1,400 kilometers (900 miles) up the Snake River and other Columbia tributaries.

Since the 1930's, however, more than two dozen dams have been built on the Columbia and the other waterways that flow into it. Many of those dams were constructed without any facilities for fish to pass over them. As a result, more than half of the creatures' spawning habitat has been eliminated.

Today, the fish have been reduced to only a fraction of their former abundance. Restoring their numbers, says the U.S. Fish and Wildlife Service, should be the number one fisheries priority in the United States. Currently, only one small stretch of the mainstem Columbia is open to spawning, and that area is now being considered for yet another dam. To make matters worse, much of the remaining fish habitat in tributary rivers has been ravaged by sediment flowing in from road construction and clearcutting. Those fish that do survive the dams often find their spawning areas heavily choked with silt.

DRAWING HEAT FROM ALL SIDES

Sprawling over one-fourth of the state, the California desert is an arid patchwork of federal, state, and private lands. It is one of the largest unified expanses of desert land in

THE ENVIRONMENT **179**

the United States, but according to a U.S. government study, the area has been "a victim of abuse and neglect" for more than a century. "It gives the appearance of being very rugged," says Wilbur Mayhew, a University of California-Riverside biologist, "but the desert is among our most delicate ecosystems."

In recent years, the region has become a particularly hot item. Currently, one-half of California's nonpetroleum mineral production takes place in the desert. What's more, because of its proximity to the Los Angeles-San Diego megalopolis, the desert is rapidly becoming the nation's most widely used outdoor area.

Since 1970, recreation in the area has increased by 350 per cent. During the same period, the U.S. Geological Survey estimates, off-road vehicles have denuded at least 4,000 square kilometers (1,566 square miles) of desert land. Not long ago, recalls Mayhew, there were 30-meter (100-foot)-high sand dunes on the outskirts of the community of Palm Desert. "I thought those dunes would be there for 1,000 years," he

says, "but they were bulldozed down to make room for a trailer park."

The effects of all this activity on the region's resources have been, in some cases, devastating. The U.S. government now lists eight species of California desert wildlife as endangered, but according to the BLM, "there are 31 other species in various states of jeopardy." Nearly 100 desert plants are also considered endangered.

In the spring of 1980 the Department of the Interior approved an intensive management plan for the 47,000 square kilometers (18,000 square miles) under its jurisdiction. "At least it's a start," says Mayhew. "We just can't have everyone out here doing as they please—not anymore."

AN ENDLESS SEA NO MORE

It was once an incredible sea of grass, growing along a wide midwestern corridor from Canada all the way to Texas. It sheltered wildlife by the tens of millions. But in less than a century more than 1,000,000 square kilometers (400,000 square miles) of eastern tallgrass prairie in the United States

Sulfur-dioxide emissions from coal-burning power plants are the primary cause of acid rain. This deadly pollution has killed all life in many lakes—especially in the Adirondacks.

Clyde H. Smith

were reduced to only one per cent of their original size. And those isolated pockets that remain today are still being converted to agriculture and destroyed by other development. They represent one of the last major ecosystems that has yet to be federally protected in this country. "Grasslands just have not inspired strong national or regional support," notes T. Destry Jarvis of the National Parks and Conservation Association.

Legislative efforts to preserve sections of prairie as a national park began in the 1930's and continued up until 1980. Since 1961, six separate bills seeking grassland protection have been introduced in Congress. All have been stopped by agricultural interests. Most recently, landowners in Kansas and Oklahoma, where three major tallgrass reserves were proposed, successfully fought a measure.

As a result, conservationists are now going to the "grass roots" to work with local governments. Their immediate goal: establish tax incentives and other benefits for landowners who preserve prairie land. "We still hope to protect a significant portion of the tallgrass ecosystem," says Joel Smith, president of the Oklahoma Wildlife Federation. "The steps we are now taking represent a new attempt at achieving that goal."

WE'RE FOULING UP THE FOOD FACTORY

Tidal estuaries develop where fresh water from the land meets salt water from the sea. The two forces combine to produce a coastal area that is unbelievably rich in life. That is particularly true of the nation's largest estuary, the 11,000-square-kilometer (4,-400-square-mile) Chesapeake Bay. Each year, the Chesapeake Bay yields an average of 23 kilograms of seafood per hectare (approximately 125 pounds per acre) to sport and commercial fishermen. The bay supplies 90 per cent of the country's soft-shell crabs, and one-half of its oysters and blue crabs. More than 200 species of fish feed and spawn there, and the bay is a major wintering area for waterfowl.

In recent years, however, the Chesapeake's environment has been increasingly under attack by pollution. Every day, an estimated 1,500,000,000 liters (400,000,000 gal-

Thase Daniel

The great egret and about 300 other kinds of birds make their home in the lush Atchafa laya Basin—a target for agricultural projects.

lons) of municipal sewage are dumped into the bay. Toxic chemicals, such as the Kepone that still persists in the adjacent James River, also find their way into the estuary. In addition, because of heavy tanker traffic, some 800 oil spills occur in the bay each year.

According to a U.S. Army report, "oil spills have the greatest negative impact on estuarine waters. It's desirable that tanker traffic avoid these areas." Despite that assertion, a major oil refinery has been proposed in the lower bay at Portsmouth, Virginia. In the fall of 1980 the NWF and its Maryland affiliate, along with four other conservation groups, filed suit to block construction of the refinery. "Our suit does not mean we are opposed to all East Coast refinery sites *if* a need can be shown," says Tom Tomasello, counsel for NWF. "But we are against any plans that threaten nationally important resources where reasonable alternatives exist."

VICTIMS OF AN INVISIBLE KILLER

In 1965 scientists first discovered an alarming trend: in certain lakes in New York's Adirondack Mountains, thousands of fish were dying. The researchers now know the reason for those deaths: acid rain, an invisible and very insidious form of pollution. Today, fish are still perishing in the Adirondacks, and acid rain is spreading throughout the North American continent at an almost uncontrollable rate.

In early 1981 researchers in New York reported that one-half of the 2,800 high-altitude Adirondack lakes tested are now devoid of fish, and that ten per cent of them are completely "dead"—they contain neither fish nor plant life. Furthermore, 1,000 Adirondack lakes have yet to be tested. The problem stems primarily from sulfur dioxide emissions, released from coal-burning power plants as far away as Ohio.

Rising high into the sky and blown hundreds of kilometers east by prevailing winds, these chemicals mix with water vapor to form acids. Those acids return to earth in rain and snow, damaging everything from buildings to living organisms. "In the Southeast," notes NWF Executive Vice President Jay Hair, "the acids are destroying the waxy cuticle layer on plants, making them more susceptible to pests."

The problem, environmentalists say, could grow much worse if the federal Clean Air Act is weakened. Some industries are seeking relaxed U.S. standards that would allow them to burn domestic coal without incurring additional air pollution clean-up costs. Unfortunately, coal combustion is the largest source of sulfur emissions in the United States. "We can't just sweep the problem under the rug," notes Hair. "We must pay heed to the tragic lesson of the Adirondacks." Doing nothing about acid rain today could lead to major environmental nightmares in the future.

LOSING GROUND FAST

If the wheat fields of Kansas were blowing away, it would be delcared a national disaster," exclaims Sammy Nunez, a Louisiana state senator. "Yet in this state, we're losing 100 square kilometers (40 square miles) of land a year, and we're having trouble getting people to listen to us." Nunez is referring to the lush swamps and marshes of the Mississippi Delta, which are literally vanishing into the Gulf of Mexico. During the past 30 years,

at least 2,000 square kilometers (800 square miles) of Louisiana wetlands have disappeared from an area that provides more than one-third of the nation's annual fisheries harvest.

For centuries, there was a net land gain in the delta region, created by the periodic overflow of the Mississippi River. As silt was deposited, wetlands developed. But in building levees and drainage canals, human engineers interfered with the natural flow of fresh water. With nothing to hold back the open sea, the marshes began to deteriorate. "At one navigation channel near New Orleans," notes federal biologist David W. Fruge, "we can actually see big chunks of marsh falling into the water as ships go by."

Nearby, an equally precarious situation has developed around the Atchafalaya River and its floodplain, which is home to some 300 species of birds and nearly 100 species of fish. Until recently, the region's bottomland hardwood swamps were being cleared at a rate of 15 or 16 square kilometers (6 square miles) a year for agricultural projects. In 1979, however, a U.S. District Court ruled in favor of an NWF lawsuit, granting protection for bottomland hardwoods under provisions of the Clean Water Act. Now, those provisions are being challenged in Congress. "Without legal protection, the bottomlands and delta are gone," says Oliver A. Houck, an NWF official who is now studying the region at Tulane University. "Acre for acre, creature for creature, we're talking about losing one of the most productive ecosystems in North America □

SELECTED READINGS

"Dune busting: how much can our beaches take?" by H. R. Mahoney. *Sea Frontiers,* November/December 1980.

"How much of this land is our land?" by A. H. Westling. *Environment,* July/August 1981.

"Physical effects of vehicular disturbance on arid lands (Mohave Desert)" by R. M. Iversen. *Science,* May 22, 1981.

"Protection for barrier islands." *International Wildlife,* July/August 1981.

"Spare that snag" [dead trees for cavity-nesting birds] by K. Dann. *Country Journal,* May 1981.

"Value of forests, virgin and otherwise" by H. R. Delcourt. *Natural History,* June 1981.

THE BOWERBIRD

by Corliss Karasov

DO tales of explorers leading scientific expeditions in search of exotic species belong only to history books—to the days of Darwin and Audubon? Or are there some remote corners of the world left to be explored?

In 1981 a discovery was made which helped shake many notions of the world as a conquered territory. A scientist surprised many when he announced his discovery of a bird that was assumed to be extinct. He found the tropical species in a remote uninhabited rain-forest mountain range of New Guinea, in an area probably few other humans have ever visited.

The discovery of the yellow-fronted gardener bowerbird, *Amblyornis flavifrons,* is not only a personally rewarding find for the scientist—Jared Diamond of the University of California at Los Angeles—but is also a valuable contribution to our understanding of bowerbirds and the ecology of the tropics.

BIRDS THAT BUILD LOVE PARLORS

Bowerbirds are so-called because of the elaborate bower structure the males build to woo females. Ornithologists are excited by the discovery of the yellow-fronted gardener bowerbird for many reasons. Bowerbirds are among the most fascinating of birds—their bowers may well be the most impressive structures built by birds—and certain aspects of their behavior have long puzzled ornithologists. With each new species discovered and studied, ornithologists look for patterns to help explain the puzzles. What, for example, is the exact function of the bower and why do such little animals put so much work into elaborate architecture?

The different species of bowerbirds—there are 18 known species (family Ptilonorhynchidae)—vary in their bower design. Bowers of the Vogelkop gardener bowerbird were once mistaken for manmade huts by an explorer in the late 1800's. His mistake is quite understandable when you consider what he saw: huts, made out of sticks, that

Lee Jones/Courtesy of Jared Diamond

An artist's realistic rendition of the rediscovered yellow-fronted gardener bowerbird.

were 1.2-meters (4-feet) tall and 2.4-meters (8-feet) across. Like other bowerbirds, Vogelkop gardener bowerbirds decorate their "love parlors," as Diamond calls them, with brightly colored objects such as fruits, shells, flowers, and bones. No wonder the explorer mistook the structures for manmade huts; who would have thought that songbirds were the actual architects.

As only a few other animal do, bowerbirds use tools. They make use of twigs or leaf stems to paint their bowers with bright colors from crushed fruits. Once the bower is built the male displays his brilliantly colored crest and holds fruit in his bill to entice and enthrall a female.

Of the 18 known species, 15 are thought to build bowers—some more elaborate than others. According to Diamond, there seems to be an inverse relationship between the

This drawing depicts a pair of yellow-fronted gardener bowerbirds displaying courtship behavior near the male's unusual bower.

Lee Jones

bowers and the male's coloring—the more brilliantly colored the males the less elaborate the bower. Ornithologist E. T. Gilliard has suggested an explanation for the evolution of this pattern. While males of some species may lure females with brightly colored feathers, others may build bowers and hold twigs to attract the females. The bower-builders may not need the bright coloring and this may, in fact, serve as an advantage for them: they are less visible to their predators.

THE SEARCH—LITTLE TO GO ON

The long-lost species was found after a dozen other expeditions had failed to locate the bird. The live bird had never been seen by an ornithologist. The only evidence that the bird even existed was three specimens (skins) of male bowerbirds that a plume merchant brought to Europe from an undisclosed location and sold to a museum in 1895.

Plume gathering was a thriving business in the tropics throughout the 1800's. Plume merchants often kept their collecting locations secret from competitors. No date or locale accompanied the skins, which were later placed in the American Museum of Natural History in New York City.

Ornithologists knew from the specimens that the long-lost bowerbird males were relatively average in appearance for bowerbirds. The male yellow-fronted gardener bowerbird is a rusty brown 25-centimeter (10-inch) long bird with a bright golden-orange crest. The lower breast and belly are earthy orange. Until Diamond's discovery no one had any idea of the female's appearance, the structure of the bower—if indeed that species built bowers—or the behavior of the bird.

THE DISCOVERY

When he discovered the yellow-fronted gardener bowerbirds, Diamond was conducting a bird survey and helping the Indonesian government plan a national park.

Diamond discovered the species in the Gauttier (Foja) Mountains of western New Guinea, a totally uninhabited and inaccessible range of rain forest mountains. The lowlands below are sparsely populated, and the dense mossy forests are difficult to reach. Diamond and his team were airlifted by helicopter to an elevation of nearly 1,600 meters (5,200 feet).

Diamond saw and heard the birds the first morning after his arrival. The crest of the male was even more brilliant than those of the museum specimens, which were apparently fading. The females were relatively plain. They were identical to the male, except that they lacked the golden-orange crest. Diamond's greatest delight must, however, have been the discovery of their bowers—he observed eight in all.

THE BOWER AND COURTSHIP

The center of the bower of the yellow-fronted gardener bowerbird was a tree fern against which the male had stacked twigs crisscrossing one another to a height of 1.2 meters (4 feet). The bowerbird had also built a moss platform about 1 meter (3 feet) in diameter around the pole and created a rim. He had formed three piles of fruit on the platform: one yellow, one green, and one blue pile. How did Diamond rate the bower design? Average, for a bowerbird, just as their coloring is average.

The use of three different colors of fruit surprised some ornithologists. Each bowerbird species was thought to show a color preference, with some species choosing a berry color to match their crests and others selecting colors that contrasted sharply with their own colors.

Diamond made detailed records of courtship behavior. He was able to get within 3 meters (10 feet) of a male courtship display. When the female approached, the male picked up a fruit from the blue pile and held it in his beak, always pointing it at the female in such a way that she could see the blue fruit against his golden crest.

Vocalizations are another important part of the bowerbird's repetoire. According to Diamond the birds had a variety of sounds. They made a series of sounds like clicks, croaks, screeches, rasps. Some noises sounded like someone shoveling gravel, some like crumpling paper, and some like an axe striking a tree.

REPRESENTATIVE OF THE TROPICS

Diamond's extensive notes on the 20 to 30 individuals he observed will be very helpful to ornithologists. It will increase their understanding of how the long-lost species fits into the rest of the bowerbird family and enable them to learn more about bower building and other unusual behaviors. But beyond these points, the information may add further to an understanding of the complexity of the tropics.

As mentioned before, the yellow-fronted gardener bowerbird may have been difficult to locate because of the inaccessibility of its habitat. But there is another characteristic of tropical species which may have added to the difficulty. Like many tropical species, bowerbirds may have an extremely limited range. Diamond estimates that there may be a few thousand, or even fewer, members of this species in a 260 square kilometer (100 square mile)-area at elevations above 1,200 meters (4,000 feet). (He based this estimate on the density and amount of suitable habitat he observed.) And this may be the only place the species exists.

The tropics are renowned for their remarkably diverse plant and animal life. For example, more than 535 bird species have been seen in New Guinea. But the species all tend to have more limited distribution than temperate species. The Archbold's bowerbird, for example, has been found only in four isolated mountain ranges at opposite ends of New Guinea; the Aledbert bowerbird is found only in one mountain range.

This patchiness of distribution is of concern to many ecologists. If a plant or animal species is restricted to one location, the entire population could be decimated by a single catastrophe in that region—a catastrophe such as fire, disease, overhunting, or, as in the case of exotic birds, plume gathering. A more widely distributed species has more opportunities for survival. By understanding the habitat requirements of species such as the yellow-fronted gardener bowerbird biologists may be able to prevent the loss of species from vulnerable patches of the tropics □

 SELECTED READINGS

Birds of Paradise and Bower Birds by E. T. Gilliard. Natural History Press, 1969.
The Birds of Paradise and Bower Birds by W. T. Cooper and J. M. Forshaw. Collins, 1977.

Monserrate Schwartz/Shostal Associates

A fisherman enjoys a magnificent vista as he wades into the tranquil waters of Stanley Lake in Idaho. The spectacular lake is located in the Sawtooth National Recreation Area.

OUR TROUBLED LAKES
by Roger B. Swain

WATER has become a fashionable drink. At clubs, bars, the most gala receptions, it is *de rigueur* to stand about holding a glass containing nothing stronger than ice, water, and a slice of lime. But the water that is being sipped doesn't come from the faucet. It's being poured from bottles, more than 2,000,000,000 liters (nearly 500,000,000 gallons) in 1980 alone. Water, with no calories, no artificial sweeteners, no caffeine, is the essence of lightness, the drink of the elite, the elegant, the sophisticated, or so the advertisements whisper. Samuel Clemens, who observed that to increase something's popularity you have only to increase the price, would smile to learn that while city tap water costs less than 0.0002 cents a liter (about 0.001 a gallon), bottled water is selling at an amazing price of more than $1.10 a liter (approximately $5.00 per gallon).

ALL WATER IS NOT ALIKE

Whether you are rich or poor, whether you drink water out of choice or necessity, the attention that has been devoted to the bottled variety has reminded everyone that all waters are not alike. Bottled water is being judged with the same concentration and articulation used in wine tasting. Consumers Union convened a panel of taste experts to judge 36 kinds of bottled water. "Excellent water," the experts explained, "should be clear: free of sediment and color. Its aroma should be clean: free of obvious off-odors such as those of chemicals or manure. An excellent water's flavor should also be clean, though it may stimulate just slightly the tastebuds that sense sweetness, bitterness, or sourness. But most of all, an excellent water should be refreshing."

These experts were drinking water by the glassful, a common enough way to judge its quality, but not the only way. Throughout the summer people test water in another way. Instead of merely raising a glass of water to their lips, they first remove all or most of their clothes. Then, after slowly (or rapidly) immersing their entire body, they swim.

Sipping water while seated at a table is simply no match for swimming. There is no comparison between swirling a sample of water around the inside of a glass and swirling yourself around the inside of a sample of water. A swimmer cannot escape the odor of the water; at most, it is inches from one's nose. To judge its clarity and color, you have only to look down. To taste it, open your mouth and an unlimited draught will flow in.

Those people who never drink while they swim have spent too long in the ocean or in chlorinated pools. Fresh water is meant to be drunk, and anyone who has ever been thirsty, desperately thirsty, delights in the knowledge that even the most gargantuan drink will not drain a lake.

Ask swimmers which kind of water they prefer to swim in and most will say a lake, one that is deep and clear, with nothing floating on the surface and only rock or sand on the bottom.

CLEAR DEEP LAKES

Choosing a lake is more complicated than choosing a brand of bottled water. Lakes come in all sizes and shapes, of different depths and different ages. Some have streams flowing into them; others are spring-fed. The most common way of classifying them, however, is in terms of their productivity—the amount of organic matter that is produced per square meter per year. Swimmers, whether they realize it or not, are looking for an oligotrophic lake. Oligotrophic means poorly fed, and an oligotrophic lake has a low concentration of plant nutrients in its water. With few nutrients, there are few plants, and such lakes are most likely to be deep and clear and to have a sandy bottom.

Nutrient levels in the lake are hard to measure, but there is a simple device for measuring clarity, called a Secchi disk. Simple enough for any swimmer to use, the Sec-

chi disk is a white disk 20 centimeters (8 inches) in diameter that is lowered into the water on a string. The clearer the lake, the farther down the disk can be seen. In most oligotrophic lakes, the Secchi disk can be seen at a depth of 6 meters (20 feet) or more. In Crater Lake in Oregon, which is 587 meters (1,932 feet) deep, the disk has been seen at depths of 40 meters (131 feet).

There was a time when it was easy to find an oligotrophic lake. Most of the lakes in the northern United States were formed by glaciers. These glaciers scoured out basins in the native rock, or piled up dams of glacial debris, or left behind big buried blocks of ice that ultimately melted and created kettles (steep-sided hollows without surface drainage). Shortly after the last glacier receded, there were oligotrophic lakes all across the United States. They were deep, clear, clean-water lakes, all with bare bottoms. But that was 10,000 years ago.

A pair of rusty sewage pipes spew out gallons of polluted wastewater into a stream that feeds into a nearby lake.

© Maurice E. Landre/PR

This clean, clear lake is still in a rather early stage of human colonization. It will remain in good condition if used only by a summer community.

DILUTE LAYERED BROTH

To see what difference a hundred centuries can make, you must realize that even the clearest lake is not sterile. There are things growing in it. Suspended in the water is phytoplankton—minute plants, such as diatoms, desmids and filamentous green algae. These plants require sunlight for photosynthesis. The photoplankton are eaten by zooplankton—equally minute animals, with names like rotifer, copepod, and cladoceran. They, in turn, are being eaten by nekton, those larger, free-swimming animals that include aquatic insects and fish.

As pure as an oligotrophic lake may seem, it is actually a dilute broth, and, like a broth on which a layer of fat is floating, the water in a lake is stratified. Any swimmer who has dived toward the bottom of a lake has discovered that there is a much colder layer of water a short way down. This is the hypolimnion, a layer of cold—and hence heavy—water on which floats the lighter, warmer water of the epilimnion. Between the two layers there is a zone of rapid temperature change called the thermocline.

During the summer, there is very little mixing of the layers. In the fall, when the surface water cools, it sinks to the bottom, carrying its dissolved oxygen with it. At the same time the bottom water, carrying nutrients, is displaced to the surface. A similar turnover of the lake water occurs in cold areas of the country in the spring when the ice melts.

Turnovers of the lake, in which nutrients are carried to the well-illuminated surface waters, are often accompanied by a proliferation of phytoplankton. The minute plants, freshly supplied with nutrient-rich waters and receiving sufficient sunlight in surface layers, increase their rate of photosynthesis, growth, and reproduction. During the summer, many of the zooplankton migrate vertically, moving to the surface once a day to feed on the phytoplankton and then settling back to the depths. Largemouth bass and muskellunge also live in the food-rich upper layer. Lake trout, however, move deeper into the cold hypolimnion as the summer progresses.

SLOWLY BECOMES A SWAMP

Although there is a long list of things that live in oligotrophic lakes, the water is not crowded. In fact, there is virtually no chance that a mouthful will contain anything detectable. But while the creatures in an oligotrophic lake have little effect on swimming conditions during their life, their death is another matter.

© Adam Woolfitt/Woodfin Camp

Serving the recreational needs of a sizable population of year-round residents, this lake
has been significantly deteriorated by man-made sources of pollution.

As they die, their remains drift to the bottom. There they contribute to the bottom ooze, an organic muck where bloodworms and phantom midges survive on what little oxygen is left after decomposition. This muck builds up very slowly, about 1 millimeter (0.04 inch) a year, but after 10,000 years, the rain of tiny corpses may have resulted in 9 meters (30 feet) or more of sediment. In a lake that was originally very deep, this probably will have no effect on the water quality, from a swimmer's point of view. Provided there is a large volume of water deeper than plants can grow, the lake will remain in something of a steady state.

However, some lakes are shallow to begin with, and when sediment has further decreased the depth, much more of the lake bottom will be shallow enough for rooted plants to grow. What was once only a fringe of rushes and sedges around the edge of the lake becomes broad expanses of pickerelweed, arrowheads, and cattails. The rest of the lake's surface may be plastered over with waterlily pads. Such a large amount of aquatic vegetation consumes equally large amounts of oxygen as it decomposes. The lake is then said to have a high biological oxygen demand. This situation depletes the oxygen in the colder lower level and trout can no longer live in the lake. Instead, perch,

pike, bass, pan fish, and bullheads become the dominant fish. Eventually, as sedimentation continues century after century, the lake will fill in completely, becoming first a marsh or swamp and then a forest.

When lakes change from deep, relatively unproductive ones to shallow, highly productive ones, the process is called eutrophication. Lakes at an intermediate stage are called mesotrophic. Mesotrophic lakes often have well-developed fish populations and thus are very popular. The progression of lakes from oligotrophic to eutrophic doesn't always occur the same way, but when it does occur it is perfectly natural—natural and incredibly slow. Immeasurably slow from the point of view of an individual swimmer. Find a lake that is still oligotrophic and from the perspective of a human life span it will remain oligotrophic indefinitely—deep, clear, clean, inviting. Or at least that's the way it should remain.

BUT WHEN IT'S SPEEDED UP

Oligotrophic lakes, however, attract swimmers the way a bare arm attracts mosquitoes, and many of the best swimming lakes have gone through the following stages of human colonization.

The first summer, a tent is pitched on the shore of a wild and deserted lake. Next

THE ENVIRONMENT   189

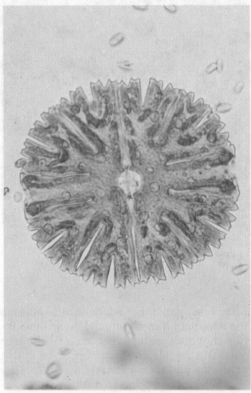

© James Bell/PR

Fresh-water phytoplankton, like this minute, one-celled plant called a desmid shown highly magnified, reproduce rapidly in nutrient-rich waters.

year, the tent acquires a platform, and since word has got out about how clear the lake is, how fine the swimming, the tent has acquired neighbors. Before long, the tent platforms have evolved into the floors of small cottages. Since there are too many people in the summer community to "go around behind a bush," outhouses are constructed. In short order, these are replaced by indoor toilets. The toilets, in turn, are connected to cesspools made by filling large steel drums with rocks.

As long as the community remains a summer one, the water in the lake remains as clear and as clean as it was when first discovered. But summer communities have a tendency to change into year-round ones. Roads are paved for winter use. Drains are dug and culverts are laid. The trees surrounding the lake are cut down and grass seed is sown. Businesses are established, so that residents won't have so far to commute. The cottages all around the lake are themselves improved: roofs are raised, furnaces put in, dishwashers and washing machines installed. But one thing stays the same, the steel drums filled with rocks, the drums by now very rusty and the rocks coated with grease.

The human body produces about 4.5 kilograms (10 pounds) of nitrogen and 0.6 kilogram (1.3 pounds) of phosphorus in the form of sewage every year. Homeowners who do their wash in detergents containing phosphates can double the phosphorus content of their waste water. Both nitrogen and phosphorus are essential plant nutrients. In fact, the growth of plants is usually limited by the availability of these nutrients, especially by the availability of phosphorus. Letting nitrogen and phosphorus drain into a lake is like spreading fertilizer on a garden. It causes the lake to bloom.

LAKE BLOOM

The bloom, a population explosion of algae, is not a pretty sight. Swimmers, the first to detect a change in the water quality, don't need a Secchi disk to tell that the water is cloudy. They can no longer see their own feet. What was once clear all summer long is now a pea-green murk by July. What's more, the water tastes funny and smells bad.

The nutrients flowing into the lake aren't just from the homes on the lake's perimeter. Lakes are low points in a landscape, and the nutrients come from wherever water flows toward the lake. This area of drainage, or watershed, as it is called, extends from the lake shore to the tops of the nearest mountains. Street drains carry lawn fertilizer and waste from thoughtfully curbed dogs. The smoke from coal and oil furnaces contains significant amounts of nitrates, and these may be washed down in rains. In the more rural parts of the watershed, the runoff carries manure from horses, cows, and other livestock. Here and there, a town sewer or a pump on a sewer line is leaking raw sewage.

The more of this that reaches the lake, the more the water deteriorates. Large mats of blue-green algae appear on the lake surface and are blown onto the beaches by on-shore winds, where they look like human excrement and smell worse. Lakefront residents may end up closing their windows, preferring the heat to the stench. As unpleasant as the algae is to people, it's worse for the fish. The more algae, the more oxygen needed to decompose it when it dies and the less oxygen available for fish to breathe. Ultimately, even the carp, the last species in the lake, are gulping air from the surface. Soon they too are asphyxiated and float belly up, as the entire upper layer of the lake becomes depleted of oxygen.

What has happened to this once oligotrophic lake is that it too has become eutrophic, and in a period of only years or decades, not centuries. Furthermore, the lake has reched its state of high productivity by a very different route from natural eutrophication. Natural eutrophication is the result of gradual filling of a lake with sediment. This artificial enrichment of a lake produces a similar outcome but is called cultural eutrophication to reflect the fact that it is associated with the activities of humans. Cultural eutrophication is not an isolated occurrence. The National Eutrophication Survey, conducted by the U.S. Environmental Protection Agency from 1971 to 1977, looked at 800 lakes receiving municipal waste water and found that 68 per cent were eutrophic.

HEALTH HAZARD

Just because the water in a lake is green, tastes bad, and smells funny doesn't stop some people from swimming in it. It's probably a good thing that people don't drink very much water when they swim or a lot more of them would get sick from swimming in culturally eutrophied lakes. For mixed in with the plant nutrients there are usually plenty of bacteria. As it is, many bathers contract "swimmer's ear" and "summer diarrhea," the former a staphylococcus infection of the outer ear, the latter a coliform bacteria infection in the gut.

The public-health hazard that a polluted lake represents is too often overlooked until something serious happens. Perhaps a number of people contract a more serious water-borne disease or someone goes under

for the third time and rescuers can't find the body in the green murk. Then the Public Health Department, which has been reluctant to shut down a recreation area, formally closes the lake to swimming, citing coliform counts greater than 2,000 per 100 milliliters, or Secchi disk readings of less than 1.2 meters (4 feet).

TEMPORARY HELPS

Long before the lake is a public-health hazard, however, it is an eyesore, not to mention a pain in the nose. The lake that was once the raison d'être for the community has become its bête noire. Lakefront residents storm into selectmen's meetings and demand that something be done. In response to such pressure a number of things have been tried.

Copper sulfate, spread in judicious amounts, kills algae without harming fish or aquatic invertebrates. From 1926 to 1936, between 27,000 and 45,000 kilograms (60,000 to 100,000 pounds) of copper sulfate were applied annually to Lake Monona in Madison, Wisconsin. The result was copper-rich layers of sediment on the bottom of the lake and an annual reappearance of the algae. Whether copper sulfate is used or one of the modern biodegradable algicides, there will be no lasting benefit unless the flow of nutrients into the lake is stopped.

A microscope enhances the fine features of this tiny, fresh-water crustacean called a copepod.
© James Bell/PR

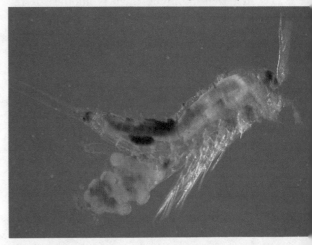

The same is true of efforts to restock a lake. Fishermen lamenting the passage of trout may demand that the town rid the lake of carp and other "trash" fish and restock. Rotenone, the familiar garden insecticide, is spread on the lake, and since fish are exquisitely sensitive to the chemical, which blocks their respiration, they all die. Trying to introduce trout into such a lake, however, is a waste of fingerlings, for unless the biological oxygen demand has been reduced and oxygen has been restored to the cold deeper layers, the trout will die, just as surely as if they themselves had been given rotenone.

BUT IT IS REVERSIBLE

Cultural eutrophication can, however, be reversed. This fact distinguishes it from natural eutrophication, which is essentially irreversible. Reversal requires that the entire watershed be treated, not just the lake itself. The improvement in the water quality of the lake will not be as instantaneous as poisoning all the algae, but in the long run, treating the sources of lake degradation rather than the byproduct is more cost-effective.

Finding where the excess nutrients are coming from can be as simple as noting where the storm drains empty. Septic-system seepage is harder to locate. Tracking the path of household waste is made easier by flushing a die down the toilet. Sometimes the dyes show up immediately. Even if they don't, they can be detected in analysis of lake water.

Identifying pollution sources is only the first step. Stopping them is another. It requires understanding, public concern, and money. Lots of money. If the lake offers public access, some of the money comes from the state and Federal governments. Ultimately, however, lake restoration depends on local landowners and officials, on lakefront associations, conservation groups and sportsmen's clubs. There are still plenty of culturally eutrophied lakes that need improvement. But gradually watersheds are being improved, the destructive flow of nutrients into lakes is being halted.

LAKE RESTORATION

Once the flow of nutrients to a lake has been halted, it makes sense to begin restoration of the lake itself. Lakes with large enough streams flowing in and out of them may have enough water exchange to make in-lake treatments unnecessary. In some lakes it takes only a few days to replace the water. In Lake Superior it takes a few centuries. In a closed, spring-fed lake with no outlet, the phosphorus content of the water may remain high and continue to promote the growth of algae for a very long time. Spreading aluminum sulfate in the lake will incapacitate the phosphorus by binding with it to produce an insoluble compound that settles to the bottom.

Stands of larger aquatic vegetation can be destroyed with herbicides. If chemical control is objectionable, mechanical harvesters can be used. These harvesters are usually self-propelled floating machines that mow or uproot submerged plants.

Another way to destroy vegetation along the shore is to lower the level of the lake with pumps and allow the weeds in shallow water to dry out or freeze depending on the season. Called "drawdown," the lowering of a lake's level also makes it easier to dredge sediment from the bottom. Dredging, however, is controversial. If the sediments are contaminated with toxic chemicals, they may be more dangerous on land than at the bottom of the lake. Simply stirring up the bottom sediment may resuspend herbicides, pesticides, and industrial wastes and reintroduce them into the food chain of the lake.

Then there is biological control, whereby species are introduced to the lake to control the growth of plants automatically. Eutrophic lakes have been experimentally stocked with a variety of organisms, from algae-eating water fleas to water-hyacinth-consuming manatees. Although the use of predators rather than poisons to keep the water clear is attractive, exactly how to do it remains to be worked out.

WHICH? HOW MUCH?

Knowing how to restore lakes is one thing, but deciding what to restore them to is quite another. Obviously, it is impossible to return every lake to its postglacial origins. The Federal Water Pollution Control Act Amendments of 1972 set some national

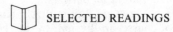
Tom Stack

Covering the water like a carpet, this thick, green mat of algae seriously depletes the amount of oxygen that is available to fish and other animals living in the lake.

goals, specifying 1983 as the year in which all water in the United States should be swimmable and 1985 as the year by which all discharge of water pollutants will be halted. Swimmable doesn't mean oligotrophic. It simply means safe, and even that goal seems unlikely to be realized on schedule. There is talk of "accepted levels for projected use," words that sound like an excuse to do nothing, to claim that since a lake is too disgusting to swim in, no one will want to go in it anyway.

Lake restoration is expensive. Installing new sewage treatment plants is very expensive. But any method is going to be expensive. It's a matter of deciding what to spend one's money on. The dollars being spent for bottled water would buy a lot of lake restoration.

Deciding which lakes will be restored and to what level they will be restored will require a community consensus involving not just the lakefront residents but all those who live in the watershed and all those beyond who ever have or ever might enjoy the lake's water. In the end, the decisions will involve almost everyone, for one-third of the U.S. population lives less than eight kilometers (five miles) from some publicly owned lake and 99.4 per cent live within an hour's drive.

GRANDFATHER CLAUSE

From all the debate over which lakes to restore, a simple suggestion emerges—a sort of "grandfather clause" for lake restoration. If the lake was oligotrophic when your grandfather swam in it two generations ago, then it should be made oligotrophic once more. The water should be deep and clear—clear enough to see the bottom all year round—and clean—clean enough to drink with impunity. No, not just impunity. One should be able to float in the middle of all that water and drink one's fill with the same enthusiasm bestowed upon the finest bottled import. The first person in the lake each summer should be able to call back, "Come on in, the water's fine," and mean it □

SELECTED READINGS

"Bring a lake back to life" [Lake Erie] by E. Keerdoja and J. Lowell. *Newsweek,* September 8, 1980.

"Nitrogen-fixing anabena" [surface bloom] by P. E. Kellar. *Science,* May 11, 1979.

"Quality vs quantity: is a U.S. water crisis imminent?" by T. Bodde. *BioScience,* August 1981.

"Slow poisoning of our water" [chemical pollution] by C. Keough. *Organic Gardening,* March 1980.

"Water"—Environmental Quality Index. *National Wildlife,* March 1981.

DOE/Battelle Memorial Institute

Currently, high-level commercial nuclear wastes, or spent fuel assemblies, are in temporary storage pools at reactor sites such as Illinois' Dresden Nuclear Power Station.

NUCLEAR WASTE DISPOSAL

by Linda Garmon and Ivars Peterson

THE magician taps the box with a mystical wand and assures that the volunteer's missing watch will be inside. But upon opening the first good-sized box, the volunteer discovers a second, smaller box. Likewise, opening box number two reveals only a third box, and so on until the missing article is retrieved. The nest of boxes leaves the impression that the trickster somehow overcame multiple barriers.

On stage, the multiple barrier effect is, of course, an illusion. In the scientific arena, however, a diverse group of researchers and policy makers are enlisting the aid of the real-world correlate of the nest of boxes to tackle one of the toughest problems of the nuclear age—the "disposal," or isolation from the biosphere, of high-level radioactive wastes. The biosphere is all the regions of earth that support living systems. Under the multiple barrier plan, such wastes—often called radwaste—would be immobilized in a solid form, then would be placed in a canister, which in turn would be encompassed by a series of additional barriers—the ultimate one being a mined, or underground, repository.

While the U.S. Congress mulls various pieces of legislation regarding these repositories and the U.S. Department of Energy (DOE) plans exploratory shafts at selected geologic sites, much activity remains focused on the smallest in the nest of boxes—the initial barrier, or the form used to immobilize the high-level waste. For instance, DOE in late 1981 capped years of intensely competitive research when it decided to consider solidifying certain liquid radioactive military wastes into either a glass or a ceramic. At the same time, a long-standing controversy over what to do with civilian (commercial) radwaste has been rekindled.

SOURCES OF RADWASTE

High-level radwaste has been accumulating in the United States for nearly 35 years. The waste results from commercial power generation and from the extraction of uranium and plutonium isotopes for military weapons manufacture. In both instances, the process begins with reactor fuel composed of uranium-oxide pellets sealed in metal tubes. During a fission-type nuclear reaction, the uranium atoms in this fuel assembly release heat as they split into the fission products—new and lighter atoms such as krypton, strontium, ruthenium, iodine, and cesium.

In addition to the fission products—which constitute only about 5 per cent of the used fuel—the waste contains residual uranium and heavier elements, such a plutonium, produced in the fuel when uranium atoms capture neutrons. Some of the waste is stable (nonradioactive), but other components—dubbed "radionuclides"—emit hazardous bursts of radiation. Certain of these radionuclides continue to decay for thousands of years. Plutonium 239, for example, has a 24,000-year half-life—this means that it takes 24,000 years for one-half of the atoms to decay. And therein lies the reason why nuclear waste is no ordinary trash. It radiates, and it radiates for a long time.

TIME RUNNING OUT

The brunt of the responsibility for isolating that radiation from the biosphere falls on DOE. Since 1980 or so, the department has come to favor the multibarrier mined-repository strategy over more exotic proposed radwaste disposal schemes. These schemes include burial in polar ice caps and storage on remote islands or in outer space, for example. Mostly by default, aging radwaste by temporary storage has become the first step in this strategy. Used commercial fuel assemblies now lie in water-filled pools adjacent to power plants, and the mostly liquid defense wastes sit in double-walled steel tanks at three government facilities and at one commercial site in West Valley, New York.

But time is running out on temporary storage. Not only have commercial pools of used fuel assemblies been plagued with overcrowding, but also "some defense high-level wastes have been stored for 35 years, approaching and sometimes exceeding the life expectancy of their storage tanks," according to a recent General Accounting Office (GAO) report. "More importantly, some tanks have cracked and leaked significant amounts of radioactive materials into the ground," the report goes on to state. As a result, DOE has stepped up its efforts in dealing with the 8,000 tons of used fuel assemblies and the more than 282,000,000 liters (75,000,000 gallons) of defense wastes it now has on its hands.

IMMOBILIZING THE WASTE

Approximately 30 per cent of the defense waste is from a land of sandy soil and pine trees. These wastes—generated by the E.I. du Pont de Nemours & Company-operated Savannah River Plant in Aiken, South Carolina—are first in line to be treated. They are DOE's radioactive guinea pigs, and precisely how to treat them has been the subject of much recent discussion.

There are a lot of different ways to treat a waste. You can make it into a glass. You can incorporate it into concrete. You can even make ceramic pellets out of it and then cast those pellets in metal. In each case, the objective is the same: to immobilize the waste with a barrier by making it a part of that barrier. In 1979, DOE recognized about 11 potential ways of achieving this effect. Recently, with the Savannah River Plant wastes in mind, the department decided to take a closer look at what it believes are the two most effective forms: borosilicate glass and a crystalline ceramic called SYNROC.

GLASS vs. SYNROC

Borosilicate glass is formed by melting together nuclear-waste components and glass-forming additives such as boron oxide and silicon oxide. SYNROC, made famous by A. E. Ringwood and colleagues of the Australian National University in Canberra, is a ceramic material whose three minerals accept waste components into their crystal lattices.

Most waste-form researchers already feel borosilicate glass is the shoo-in. Some go so

DOE/Battelle Memorial Institute

Deep drilling at various sites, including the Paradox Basin in Utah, will help provide vital information for repository site selection.

far as to say that SYNROC was listed by DOE merely for political reasons. "I think they [the DOE panel] believe SYNROC—the idea of a synthetic rock—has a big PR value," said one waste-form developer. "My own personal opinion," he continued, "is that glass is quite acceptable . . . I think the thing that we need to worry about now—that we have not put enough thought into—is the actual [waste-treatment] plant. We want to put in a process whereby the people who have to work there eight hours a day get the minimum exposure. If we engineer a complicated plant—and I think SYNROC would require one—we're going to endanger these people."

Glass also earns extra points for being tolerant of a wide variety of waste forms. "Defense wastes are not uniform," explains Stephen V. Topp of the Savannah River Laboratory. "A lot of different fuel has gone into those reactors over the years," he says, and an immobilizing form that is insensitive to the resulting variations in defense wastes is desired. This should be a factor when deciding between glass and SYNROC, says Topp. "Ceramics must be precisely tailored to the precise waste form, and that would vary from tank to tank [of wastes in temporary storage]," says Topp. "You'd like to make a waste form that would take a wide variety of junk," he says. "That's why glass shines."

Nonetheless, the show-down continues—at least officially—with the final DOE choice between borosilicate glass and SYNROC due by October 1983. DOE plans then call for the first high-level waste immobilization facility to be in operation at the Savannah River Plant by 1988. Treatment of the high-level waste at the Hanford defense site in Richland, Washington, and at the Idaho Fall, Idaho, defense site will be dealt with thereafter.

REPROCESSING COMMERCIAL FUEL?

But what's to become of the nuclear waste from the private sector? At least for now, neither glass nor SYNROC can solve this problem, because most commercial waste is not in a state that can be converted into these waste forms. Most commercial waste is in the form of spent-fuel rods—the used uranium fuel that has been removed from a nuclear reactor. But the fuel isn't really completely "spent," and technically, it is not even considered a waste: 95 per cent of it is re-cyclable uranium.

The high-level defense wastes, on the other hand, result from reprocessing military spent fuel. At reprocessing plants, the fuel is separated into streams of uranium, plutonium, and high-level waste. The uranium and plutonium are solidified and converted into either fresh reactor fuel or nuclear-weapon material. The high-level waste—which contains fission products and chemical solvents used to dissolve the spent fuel—remains in a liquid state, awaiting immobilization into a waste form.

Reprocessing commercial spent fuel in this fashion was banned by Presidents Gerald Ford and Jimmy Carter, who feared the plutonium produced could be stolen and used to make nuclear weapons. President Ronald Reagan lifted that ban October 8, 1981.

Still, "The private sector is saying, 'You've got to be kidding—the risks are too high,' " says Colin A. Heath, former director of DOE's Office of Waste Isolation. Because the future of nuclear power in the United States is uncertain, and because succeeding administrations could easily reverse current policy, investors fear pouring money into commercial reprocessing plants, Heath explains. Indeed, despite DOE's current search for methods to encourage commercial reprocessing, it now is viewed as the long-shot in civilian nuclear-waste disposal.

The treatment processes that are likely for commercial waste range from simply packaging the intact spent fuel assembly to chopping it, dissolving the resulting exposed fuel in acid, and converting the solution to a glass. DOE now is testing how stainless-steel encapsulated fuel assemblies fare in granite formations at the Nevada Test Site in southern Nevada and in a basalt out-cropping at Hanford.

The GAO sees several drawbacks to this method. It notes that spent fuel disposal only defers the nuclear proliferation threat to future generations who may exhume and reprocess the fuel. In addition, the disposal method would require several times the repository space of high-level waste forms.

Finally, GAO reports, "DOE's contractors and scientists believe that a waste package [all of the multiple barriers, save the repository] can be designed that will completely contain either spent fuel or high-level waste for 1,000 years." This thousand-year guarantee appears adequate for fuel that has been reprocessed. The high-level waste resulting after reprocessing consists mainly of fission products that can decay to a relatively nontoxic level of radioactivity in that time period. Spent fuel, however, takes more time to detoxify, because it still contains plutonium and uranium, which decay to a nonradioactive state only after hundreds of thousands of years. Consequently, reports GAO, spent fuel eventually would "knock down" the multiple barriers in its waste package. In that case, the only box left in the nest isolating it from the biosphere would be the geologic repository.

MINED VAULTS

DOE has endorsed geologic isolation in mined vaults deep inside the earth as the primary option for high-level waste disposal. Attention is focusing increasingly on three sites and three types of rock. Although the sites under consideration appear promising, they also have potential problems that raise questions about their ability to contain the waste indefinitely without leakage. And some scientists are concerned the evaluation process is becoming too rushed.

At the Nevada Test Site, a data instrumentation package is placed in a hole that was drilled in volcanic rock called tuff.
Courtesy of Sandia National Laboratories

DOE's timetable calls for the sinking of exploratory shafts at the three selected sites during 1983. Two years later, the drilling should be completed, and one of the sites will be chosen for the development of a test facility.

"We could expect to have a repository available by about the year 2000," says Carl Cooley of DOE's nuclear waste management office.

HANFORD BASALT

One of the three finalists is likely to be a site on the DOE's Hanford Reservation in the state of Washington. Astride a bend in the Columbia River, this sprawling piece of federal land is the location of a spent-fuel reprocessing plant that extracts plutonium for building nuclear weapons. Large quantities of high-level liquid radioactive waste rest in "temporary" storage tanks on the site.

Geologic studies indicate the Hanford site lies over a series of thin lava flow layers. These layers are composed of basalt, a dense, strong, dark-colored volcanic rock, interspersed with clay minerals. The most promising candidate is a layer about 1,000 meters (3,300 feet) below the surface. The interior of the layer has a relatively constant thickness of about 50 meters (165 feet), a texture rich with glass and some minerals that can take up moisture.

Basalt has a low permeability and moisture content and remains strong even at elevated temperatures. However, basalt structures are typically jointed and generally consist of irregular and inconsistent columns. These joints are potential channels for water flow and influence the strength of the rock. Water flow is an important consideration in evaluating any potential radwaste disposal site. Water flowing near the packaged rad-

Crash tests are conducted on heavy-duty trucks like this one to determine their safety for transporting spent nuclear fuel.

DOE/Battelle Memorial Institute

Vitrification, a waste solidification concept being studied, is a process of mixing nuclear waste with glass at very high temperatures.

DOE/Battelle Memorial Institute

waste could become heated or contaminated by any leakage from the radwaste capsule or could possibly present a threat to the overall suitability of the packaging materials themselves.

Paul A. Witherspoon, head of the earth sciences division at the Lawrence Berkeley Laboratory, has doubts about basalt. "A crucial issue is the vertical permeability within the basalt flow," he says. The lava flow lies between two permeable, water-bearing layers, so possible leakage paths need to be identified. "It's become a major issue that people are now beginning to recognize," he adds. Witherspoon is also uncertain a shaft to the basalt layer can be completed within the time allowed.

John Robertson of the United States Geological Survey (USGS) agrees that not enough is known about the groundwater sys-

tem at Hanford to make good, well-founded judgments.

A variety of technical studies are in progress, including investigations of groundwater flow and earthquake activity.

TUFF ROCK

Another likely candidate, but a relatively new entry in the race, is the Nevada Test Site, federal land in southern Nevada used for weapons testing. Investigations have concentrated on a volcanic rock called tuff, found at Yucca Mountain. Tuff is a light-colored rock composed of small volcanic rock fragments and ash compacted into a material that has a rough, gritty feel.

Welded tuff is a high-density rock that contains many water-filled fractures. A second form, zeolitic or non-welded tuff, has a low density, high water content and retains some important radionuclide ions. Some researchers believe a waste repository mined in a welded tuff formation surrounded by non-welded tuff might make an attractive waste-disposal facility. The welded tuff would dissipate the heat, while the surrounding non-welded tuff would form a barrier capable of absorbing migrating radionuclides. Additional research is, however, required on water-flow conditions, general rock stability, and tuff's response to long periods of heating from waste products.

SALT SITES

The third candidate, a salt site, is the veteran. Salt has long been considered a prime candidate as a radioactive waste disposal medium. Salt is plastic and flows under pressure. This assures cracks and discontinuities will seal automatically over time, but this may make waste difficult to retrieve, if necessary. The existence of salt beds and domes indicates long-term stability, although both forms are not dry and often contain brine inclusions. However, salt is soluble in fresh water, which may enter as the result of drilling into the salt, and becomes more soluble if heated. This property allows brine inclusions to move through salt in the direction of a heat source, such as a radioactive waste package. The possibility of brine movement—and contamination—in the area of radwaste disposal is one concern about salt repositories.

Although salt has been studied longer than the other candidate rocks, and continues to be studied in a wide range of research projects, many uncertainties remain.

STILL MANY UNCERTAINTIES

A draft USGS report dated April 1980 said, "The major impediment to the resolution of technical questions leading to the establishment of a mined geologic repository for commercial radioactive waste is the lack of specific sites on which to conduct detailed *in situ* geologic research." Now the field is narrowing to a few specific sites. However, key questions concern the amount of information needed to characterize a site adequately, whether engineering can overcome the inherent faults of a given site, and what an appropriate timetable for the required research and construction effort may be.

The proposed radwaste packaging system uses multiple barriers: a canister to contain the waste, a mineral filling (backfill), and the host rock.

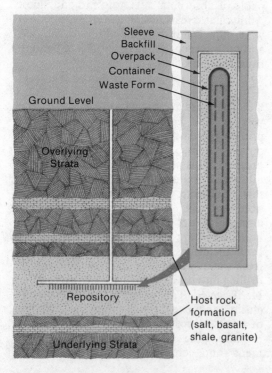

Sleeve
Backfill
Overpack
Container
Waste Form

Ground Level

Overlying Strata

Repository

Host rock formation (salt, basalt, shale, granite)

Underlying Strata

One of the most difficult problems is understanding a site sufficiently to make predictions about future performance, says Colin Heath, formerly with DOE and now in the consulting division of NUS Corp. Some critics, however, claim that the choices have narrowed to sites that were best known and most accessible or convenient, rather than most simple or suitable geologically.

In selecting a site, some agreement must exist on what sufficient characterization is, but this is tied in with funding and scheduling. USGS geologists have indicated they are not comfortable with DOE's new, accelerated schedule. Robertson says, "We agree that it's still possible to arrive at a good site on the schedule, but it's being extremely optimistic to think it'll go so smoothly. The way earth science works, we know there'll be some surprises."

Irwin Remson, applied earth sciences department chairman at Stanford University and a member of several federal committees dealing with nuclear wastes, tackles the engineering problem. He says, "My perception is that these repositories are going to be the most overengineered installations ever built in the history of humanity. There are going to be so many redundant safety factors that it is absolutely inconceivable that we shall ever have any problems with them."

Remson believes engineering and other considerations can overcome geologic deficiencies in a particular site. Witherspoon is more doubtful. "This business of engineering around problems as they occur may prove to be very naive," he says. Time and money are needed to do full-scale underground tests at depths and conditions expected to be encountered in an actual repository. Other researchers have pointed out that geologic repositories are to be constructed in environments that have many more unknowns associated with them than those of, for example, nuclear power reactors constructed on the earth's surface. They list several conditions that may be found underground that are undetectable from the surface: for salt, trapped brine, trapped gas (methane, carbon dioxide or nitrogen), cavities or faults; for hard rock, excessive water, explosive or toxic gas, excessive rock pressure, faulting or folding.

ALTERNATIVES

Work has not stopped completely on alternative high-level waste disposal strategies, although most of the funding is concentrated on the near-term goal of preparing the three potential sites. Continuing studies concentrated in 15 states are being supported to maintain granite as an option for a later repository. The DOE has also established a cooperative program with the Canadian government, which is testing at a granite site in Canada.

In addition, the USGS in the summer of 1981 began a study of an eight-state area in western United States to identify places that appear favorable for a repository site. The focus in earlier site surveys had been on specific rock types to find out where they were present and then to see if other factors were suitable. The new approach in this study is to look at rock type and hydrology at the same time, because any waste is going to be carried in the ground water if it gets loose from the repository.

TOO MUCH RUSH?

Critics of the current DOE program are concerned about the rush to characterize sites and begin developing a permanent repository. They point to plans in other countries that provide more time for testing and evaluation. One significant idea that is accepted in Sweden, England, and other countries is surface storage of high-level waste for up to 50 years so its temperature will decay to much lower levels. Most U.S. repository design studies have used as a design basis the assumption waste has been cooled about 10 years since removal from the reactor.

Several years ago, a USGS report suggested that one little-understood geologic problem was the interaction between the host rock and the waste due to the heat of the wastes. Robertson says, "That remains a question that we are concerned about. The geologic answer to that is don't put hot waste down." The DOE appears to be bending in the direction of allowing waste to cool longer before final deposal. This relaxes the requirements for a suitable geologic host and makes the choice of a suitable disposal medium easier.

DOE/Battelle Memorial Institute

This micro-earthquake monitoring station records geologic data important to determining the suitability of a repository site.

In the end, the NRC, through its licensing procedure and design specifications, will decide how safe is enough. The DOE, whatever timetable it follows, will need to meet those requirements □

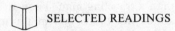 SELECTED READINGS

"Geological storage of radioactive wastes: field studies in Sweden" by P. A. Witherspoon. *Science,* February 27, 1981.

"Governors urge national radwaste policy" by S. Mack. *Science,* April 28, 1981.

"Japanese solution" [proposed disposal in Pacific Ocean] by W. J. Davis. *Oceans,* June 1981.

"Nuclear waste disposal: United States eyes burial at sea" by S. Walton. *BioScience,* November 1980.

"Nuclear waste management" by Rustum Roy. *Technology Review,* April 1981.

"Radwaste bound in crystals" by B. M. Schwarzschild. *Physics Today,* April 1980.

"Strategy for radioactive waste disposal in crystalline rock" by J. D. Bredhoeft and T. Maini. *Science,* July 17, 1981

"Space disposal of nuclear waste: keep the option open" by J. Mattill. *Technology Review,* July 1981.

U.S. Army Corps of Engineers

In September 1934, the wide Missouri River had dangerous currents, innumerable sand bars, and was host to a wide variety of wildlife.

RIVER IN A STRAIGHTJACKET

by James P. Jackson

I have lived for 25 years by the lower Missouri River, and recently I read a marvelous description of it, written in 1907 by one George Fitch:

"It is a perpetual dissatisfaction with its bed that is the greatest pecularity of the Missouri. It is harder to suit in the matter of beds than a traveling man. Time after time it has gotten out of its bed in the middle of the night, with no apparent provocation, and has hunted up a new bed, all littered with forests, cornfields, brick houses, railroad ties, and telegraph poles . . ."

But this is not the river I have known; that description has not been applicable for many years. The dissatisfaction with its bed still occurs, I'm sure, but the Missouri no longer has any freedom within its floodplain. It is today a straitjacketed channel that has been narrowed and drastically shortened. It is only half the river it was prior to the 20th century. For anyone who has stood on its stabilized banks and somehow got caught up in the drama of its history, there is a sadness in the loss of its freedom and greatness.

GLORIOUS HISTORY

It was upward against the river's treacherous currents, past its countless sandbars, and along its wilderness floodplain that one of the greatest of all American explorations was begun in May of 1804, from St. Louis. That was, of course, when Lewis and Clark led their two-year expedition through the Rockies to the Pacific and back. They were followed by mountain men, those rugged individuals who trapped beaver and traded with the Indians—John Colter, Jim Bridger, and many other real characters of legendary fame.

Later came the settlers who followed the river routes, the cattlemen and sodbusters who became adversaries on the plains. And finally, still remembered by old-timers of today who knew them personally, the skillful river pilots who dared the shifting river channels with their well-crafted steamboats. More than 100 such boats were lost to the wild Missouri between 1830 and 1860, when railroads finally began to take over their trade. The early history of the river was im-

SEPT. 1935

In just one year, the Missouri underwent drastic changes when the U.S. Army Corps of Engineers built pilings from the banks to deepen the channels.

mortalized in 1947 by Bernard De Voto's Pulitzer prize-winning book, *Across the Wide Missouri.* Today we know that river only as the nostalgic title of a book, or the words of a song.

OVERKILL

Some harnessing of the Missouri was necessary and inevitable. But, as so often is the case in today's world, we find ourselves in the position of having yielded to engineering and technological overkill.

Changes to the Missouri have been extensive and drastic. They have been particularly devastating to the wildlife and recreation resources that we have grown to value so highly. To dam a tributary stream is to pinch off an artery; to dam a major river is to sever a vital part of its life. The upper Missouri is now permanently dissected by six mainstream dams. Beginning in northeastern Montana and going downstream, these dams are: Fort Peck, Garrison, Oahe, Big Bend, Fort Randall, and Gavin's Point. The three lower impoundments (a body of water formed by confinement, such as that in a reservoir) each back up to the dam above.

The major purposes of these dams were to provide flood control and aid in navigation far downstream while at the same time furnishing irrigation water to the adjacent plains states. But in matters of holding or releasing water from the impoundments, these purposes have often been in conflict with each other and with yet another purpose: to generate hydroelectric power. There are only so many uses that water can be put to at any one time; no one purpose has been completely met in spite of monumental costs to the taxpayers. Recreation, meanwhile, has received attention mainly in the form of public campgrounds around the six impoundments. Wildlife values have been short-changed.

LITTLE STILL WILD

Today the only wild, truly natural stretch remaining along the upper Missouri is in north-central Montana, from the town of Fort Benton to where Fort Peck Lake backs up into the Charles M. Russell National Wildlife Refuge. This amounts to 250 kilometers (155 miles) of pristine river with high, rocky headlands, abundant wildlife, and the kind of solitude no longer available anywhere downstream.

Down below Gavin's Point Dam, between Yankton, South Dakota, and Sioux City, Iowa, there is another segment, 90 kilometers (55 miles) long, that is supposed to be

MAY 1946

U.S. Army Corps of Engineers

As a result of channelization, the natural, physical features of the Missouri have suffered tremendous shrinkage and have been greatly degraded.

preserved in its "natural state" by federal designation as a Recreation River. Here the problem is that the river—although unchannelized and relatively wild—has been adversely affected by the series of dams above it. What is happening along this segment is proving to be a growing headache for the Corps of Engineers. It is known technically as degradation.

BECOMING A DITCH

Degradation of a river such as the Missouri, which does not rest directly on bedrock, occurs when sand and gravel moving downstream are not replaced. This gradually causes a lowering of the channel. At such points the river is not merely changing beds, as Fitch described in 1907; the bed is collapsing in place. Previous to damming, the inherently silt-laden Missouri maintained an ever-shifting balance between building sandbars in places and finding a new bed for itself in others, but always at the same general elevation. Since closure of Gavin's Point Dam, however, the balance has been destroyed.

All dams serve as silt traps, so the water passing through Gavin's Point Dam is always clear. It has great velocity, which makes it able to pick up and carry large volumes of sediment downstream. Thus the channel below is constantly robbed and deepened;

the banks on either side are left higher and less stable; and whatever backwaters previously supported aquatic vegetation and harbored wildlife are being drained. To date the Missouri between Yankton and Sioux City has degraded nearly 3 meters (10 feet) in places. It is becoming a ditch, and the process of degradation is continuing downstream in Omaha, Nebraska.

Much of the Missouri above Gavin's Point is impounded by dams. A short segment just below—the stretch officially designated as a Recreation River—is being degraded. And downstream from Sioux City, Iowa, which is the head of navigation, the entire 1,175 kilometers (735 miles) to the mouth is completely channelized.

STRAIGHTJACKET MADE

The monumental task of channelizing the wide Missouri—that restless, bed-shifting challenge to all riverboats—was begun in 1910. That was the year that Congress first appropriated funds to the Corps of Engineers with specific authorization to guarantee a 1.8-meter (6-foot)-deep channel from the mouth of the river to Kansas City. Funding continued year after year, and the authorization was extended to Sioux City in 1927. With creosoted-wood pilings and a variety of riprap, a straightjacket was created and

By 1977, the once-magnificent river had been straightened, shortened, lowered, dissected by dams, and decimated of its wildlife values.

tightened. (Riprap is a loose assemblage of broken stones erected in water or soft ground as a foundation.) Wingdikes of piling were built outward and downward from the banks into the channel to narrow and deepen it; riprap was used where necessary to stabilize crumbling banks; side channels that skirted behind islands were cut off to prevent the river from changing beds; and sharp bends were gradually straightened over the years.

The purposes of all this work were to stabilize and deepen the channel for commercial barges, to protect the lands of floodplain residents, and to help them gain new land from added-on islands. The landowners, especially farmers, have received ample benefits, but river traffic remains a disappointment to the Corps.

In further taming the lower Missouri River, engineers have replaced wooden pilings with rock to provide even greater stability.

In 1945, with commercial river tonnage not yet exceeding 163,000 tons in any one year, the Corps asked for and secured congressional authorization for a deeper, 2.7-meter (9-foot) channel for the entire navigable distance of the Missouri. Supporters claimed that this would encourage more use by barge lines, up to an estimated average 12,000,000 tons per year. Funding was increased, rock began to be used in place of old wooden pilings and other riprap, and channelizing progressed. Today the entire project—at a total cost approximating $1,000,-000,000—is nearly completed. Nevertheless, barge traffic has yet to exceed 4,000,000 tons per year.

SHRINKING—IN AREA AND IN WILDLIFE

The natural, physical features of the Missouri River have meanwhile suffered amazing shrinkage. The states of Iowa and Missouri have each conducted studies to document this. For example, Iowa reports the following specific changes, as deciphered from maps drawn between 1890 and 1976:

Harnessed for flood control and other purposes, the river is a victim of technological overkill.

Missouri Department of Conservation

total length of the river bordering the state was shortened by 51.5 kilometers (32.25 miles), or 15 per cent; total water area was reduced by 85,784 square meters (21,197 acres), or 58 per cent; the area of unconnected, vegetated islands which originally covered 23,509 square meters (5,809 acres) was totally eliminated.

In Missouri, through which most of the lower river flows, a comparable study reported the following changes between 1879 and 1972: total length of the river was shortened by 73 kilometers (45.6 miles), or slightly more than 8 per cent; total water area was reduced by some 240,000 square meters (60,000 acres), or 50 per cent; the land area of unconnected islands was reduced by more than 98 per cent.

What do these figures mean in terms of fish and wildlife, fishing and hunting? The losses in these resources cannot be measured as accurately as those of physical features, but the latter represent habitat for living things, and losses should be roughly comparable. One revealing reference point is what channelization has done to reduce commercial fish harvest over the years. It is a matter of record in Missouri that during the year 1908, 237 commercial fishermen harvested more than 450,000 kilograms (1,000,000 pounds) of fish. In 1945, the year when the largest number of fishermen, 771, reported their catch, it was down to 228,213 kilograms (503,117 pounds). By 1970, with 404 Missouri fishermen reporting, the haul was further reduced to 115,635 kilograms (254,703 pounds).

The number of different species has also diminished along with destruction of the natural river environment. The once-prized lake sturgeon has virtually disappeared; the unique paddlefish has declined in numbers; the once-abundant blue catfish now makes up only a small percentage of the catch. The catch is, in fact, now dominated by carp, an introduced species.

I have often heard that the wild, braided Missouri River once offered excellent waterfowl hunting. It was a special kind of sport that, along with pursuing game on extensive wooded islands, is today limited to only a few isolated sites. Now, in places, agricul-

The Corps of Engineers is now being pressured to loosen the river's straightjacket, with the hope that some wildlife habitat and fisheries will be restored.

tural levees have made cultivation possible within a stone's throw of stabilized banks, and what were formerly islands are now fields of corn and soybeans. Lewis and Clark would never recognize their avenue in the wilderness if they saw it today.

RECENT ATTENTION

Environmental awareness has recently brought before the public the demise of a once great, natural river. The governor of Missouri was prompted to proclaim 1980 "The Year of the River" to publicize its potentials for recreation and esthetics, which have long been neglected. The *Missouri Conservationist* magazine devoted its entire January 1980 issue to the Missouri River; numerous activities were planned to give the proclamation some impetus.

Perhaps the most exciting activity was performed by the "Company of the Lower Missouri." Twelve men costumed as 19th-century mountain men traversed the state in an 8-meter (26-foot) replica of a northwoods birchbark canoe. They embarked at Kansas City in April 1980, in the midst of a late-season snowstorm, stopped at every town along the river, and finished a week later at the famed Gateway Arch to the West at St. Louis.

One day in June, a flotilla of 150 canoes, accompanied by a Corps of Engineers barge crowded with spectators, travelled 34 kilometers (21 miles) of the river. This assemblage of self-proclaimed "river rats," 600 strong, brought additional publicity to the Missouri. Interest has also been generated by a series of educational workshops, devoted to historical, cultural and recreational aspects of the river.

TOO LATE? YES AND NO

But is all this attention too late? What can actually be done for a mighty river that is already dammed and channelized?

Obviously, what has been covered by dams and their impoundments is irretrievably lost. Yet there are certain possibilities that may help the lower Missouri. The Corps of Engineers is currently being pressured to loosen the straitjacket it has imposed, with the hope of restoring some fisheries and wildlife habitat. One way this is done is by blasting 15-meter (50-foot)-wide notches in certain wingdikes. This is a self-maintaining technique to restore small chutes and backwaters for fish life and aquatic birds. Another step is to create small ponds, or potholes, from borrow pits where dirt has been removed for levee construction. These, however, tend to fill with sediment when the river overflows its banks. Both of these proven methods are inexpensive, but they provide only token restoration of habitat.

To attempt major restoration of habitat would require reopening of major chutes behind islands. But many islands are no more. They have been joined to the mainland and have become the legal property of adjoining landowners. Just to reacquire such lands would likely necessitate purchase by eminent domain. (Eminent domain is the term given the right of a government to appropriate private property for public use, usually with compensation to the owner). Yet in some opinions there would be justification for this. The Fish and Wildlife Coordination Act of 1958 implies authority for mitigation—the equitable replacement of lost habitat—under a clause that states that wildlife resources "shall receive equal consideration." But a major flaw is that congressional authorization for Missouri River channelization predates the Act of 1958.

The laws are not clear enough; they conflict. If anything can be done in favor of mitigation, it will likely be done only by influencing Congress to restore a needed balance in river management—a balance ensuring just consideration for wildlife and recreation resources. In the meantime, the state of Missouri has been acquiring whatever land it can afford to buy from willing sellers along the Missouri. As one can imagine, such well-meaning action does not go far toward restoring wildness to a once-great river.

Occasionally I go and stand on one of the agricultural levees that closely skirt the Missouri River. I try to envision a reasonable way to restore some of its former wildness for people who value their natural heritage. I see the levee moved back from the bank far enough to allow a one-kilometer (approximately 0.5-mile) buffer zone for flood overflow, for a wooded greenbelt, for wildlife habitat, and for the kind of meandering chutes that harbor fish and waterfowl. Then I try to envision the river as George Fitch described it in 1907, and the vision blurs. It will never again be as wild and restless as a traveling man. But it would be a shame to kill it completely ☐

📖 SELECTED READINGS

"Good way to save a river" [minimum flow legislation for western rivers] by B. Schneider. *Outdoor Life,* January 1981.

Across the Wide Missouri by Bernard De Voto. Houghton Mifflin Company, 1947.

At one time the Missouri's abundant islands made for excellent waterfowl hunting. Now most of the islands have been joined to the mainland for agriculture.

Missouri Department of Conservation

IBM

Scientists have recently developed a method for computer simulation of the complex electrical and chemical changes brain cells undergo before a certain type of epileptic attack.

HEALTH & DISEASE

HEALTH & DISEASE
REVIEW OF THE YEAR

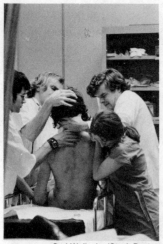

Carl Wolinsky/Stock Boston

Immediate access to emergency medical care is critical during life-threatening situations, as was highlighted by the shootings of Reagan, Brady, and Pope John Paul II.

New devices and X-ray techniques used by radiologists are saving many patients from surgery. For example, these physicians can now ream arteries and snare gallstones nonsurgically.

Centinela Hospital Medical Center

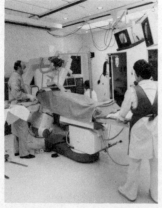

Emergency Medicine. Nothing brought home the importance of emergency medicine and the urgency of getting an injured person to a hospital as fast as possible as the shootings of President Reagan and Press Secretary James Brady in Washington, and Pope John Paul II in Rome.

President Reagan was shot as he was leaving the Washington Hilton Hotel, but the injury was recognized only when a Secret Service agent noticed blood around the President's lips as he was being rushed back to the White House. The limousine turned to George Washington University Hospital and by the time the President arrived he was severely short of breath. His blood pressure was so low that it signalled impending shock. In the emergency room a trauma team put needles in his veins to give fluids and blood transfusions. The doctors also put a tube in the President's chest to drain blood and to relieve air hunger from the collapsed lung. When the doctors noted that the bleeding was continuing at a brisk rate, they whisked the President to the operating room where Dr. Daniel Aaron removed the bullet in a two-hour operation. The President lost 3.7 quarts (3.5 liters) of blood, or about two-thirds of the total amount in his body. But because the blood was transfused as fast as it was being lost, he did not go into shock and risk the potential fatal complications of that condition. Mr. Reagan was discharged after a 12-day stay and recuperated at the White House. No one can say for certain what would have happened if his emergency care had been delayed. Chances are that the President would not have survived.

James Brady's head wounds were obvious at the scene of the shooting and he was rushed directly to George Washington University Hospital where doctors initially were pessimistic about his chances for survival. Nevertheless, they applied standard emergency measures as well as those for head injuries. They tried to reduce the amount of brain swelling by injecting mannitol, a drug that reduces brain pressure, as well as steroids and other drugs. They also connected him to a mechanical respirator. Those steps bought time while a team of neurosurgeons, headed by Dr. Arthur I. Kobrine and guided by CAT scans, performed microsurgery to relieve the pressure. Dr. Kobrine ranked "overwhelming luck" highest in the list of circumstances that helped Mr. Brady survive. Among the other factors: the critical time saved by not having to wait for an ambulance and having the Secret Service drive him to the hospital; a brain surgeon present in the emergency room when he arrived; the time of day when a full team was ready and an operating room vacant. Mr. Brady's recovery was complicated by further surgery—to stop leaks of air and spinal fluid and to trap potentially fatal blood clots from travelling from his legs to the lungs—and by seizures. He went home in late November and is continuing to receive rehabilitation therapy.

Pope John Paul II was shot in St. Peter's Square on May 13 and rushed by ambulance to Gemelli Hospital where he had an operation lasting 5 hours and 25 minutes to repair several areas of his bullet-torn bowel. The doctors made five repairs to the small intestine, including the removal of two segments. They also repaired a damaged area of the large intestine and made a temporary colostomy to help the wounded area heal. They also filled with wax a hole made by a bullet that had gone through the sacrum, the bone at the bottom of the vertebral column that protects the spinal cord. The Pope narrowly missed being paralyzed. The Pope had virtually his entire volume of blood replaced by transfusions. He remained on the danger list for 10 days, largely because of the risk of peritonitis. However, antibiotic drugs helped prevent this life-threatening complication. He was discharged after a three-week stay only to return 17 days later because of a persistent mild fever. The symptoms were attributed to cytomegalovirus, presumably acquired as a complication of the blood transfusions. After an eight-week hospital stay, he was pronounced "clinically recovered."

These three cases dramatically showed the importance of emergency care and the great advances of medicine within the past several years. Not even sophisticated medical techniques or fast emergency care could, however, save President Anwar Sadat of Egypt. Bullets fired at him while he was reviewing a military parade in Cairo caused irreparable, lethal damage. According to one account, one of the bullets tore a blood vessel connecting the heart and a lung.

Ulcers. For more than 25 years physicians in the United States and some European countries have been noting a pronounced and puzzling decline in the incidence of peptic ulcers. More recently studies have shown an even sharper drop in the number of operations on ulcer victims.

In the United States about one person in ten will suffer, at some time, from a small, usually sharply circumscribed sore that appears in the stomach (gastric ulcer) or the first section of the small intestine (duodenal ulcer). Duodenal ulcers are about four times as common as gastric ulcers. No one knows what causes these ulcers, which can cause gnawing pains and which can lead to potentially fatal complications. However, some things are clear: the once popular notion that hard-driving executives are especially prone to peptic ulcers is now considered a myth. In fact, many studies have failed to show a connection between peptic ulcers and type of job, emotional stress, or diet.

All the possible reasons for ulcers and their decreasing incidence are now being overshadowed by the dramatic success of a drug called cimetidine. The Smith Kline Corporation began marketing this drug as

Dan McCoy/Rainbow

Patients with severe burns are being successfully treated with artificial skin made from cowhide, shark cartilage, and plastic by doctors at Massachusetts General Hospital.

Montefiore Hospital and Medical Center

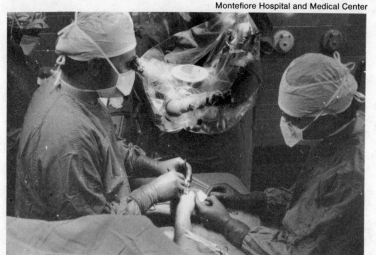

Dr. Berish Strauch at Montefiore Hospital and Medical Center in New York uses a microscope while performing microsurgery to reconstruct a patient's severely damaged hand.

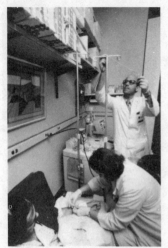

Ken Sherman/DISCOVER © Time Inc.
1980

Stuart Saal (in background), of New York Hospital, administers treatment to a patient for a commonly fatal blood disorder that now responds to plasma-pheresis, or plasma exchange.

Mrs. Judith Carr gets a first look at her newborn baby girl, Elizabeth, the first baby born in the United States as a result of "test-tube," or in vitro, fertilization.

UPI

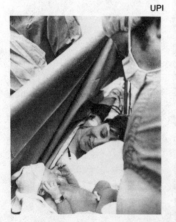

Tagamet in the United States in 1977, almost one year after it was sold for the first time anywhere in Great Britain. Cimetidine belongs to a new class of drugs called histamine H2 receptor antagonists that are power-ful suppressors of the stomach's production of hydrochloric acid, which is thought to play a major role in the production of duodenal ulcers. Ci-metidine is not a cure but it can produce rapid and sustained relief of ulcer pain, and it hastens healing of ulcers after about two months of therapy.

Because the introduction of cimetidine in the United States followed a 30 per cent decline in the number of operations done for ulcers in this coun-try over the preceding 12 years, doctors are not certain if the further de-cline is due to cimetidine or to some other unidentified factor. The recent trends are just part of the mysteries of ulcers. No one knows why, over the past 150 years, peptic ulcers have shifted from primarily a disorder of the stomach in young women to a disease of the duodenum in middle-aged men.

Interventional Radiology. Radiologists are changing their image. Tradi-tionally these physicians have been diagnosticians who have looked at images on film to detect a myriad of disorders. Now by harnessing new X-ray techniques with other devices they are working more directly with patients and saving many from surgery. Among the newer things radiolo-gists are doing:
• Reaming arteries clogged by fatty deposits (atherosclerosis), thereby relieving obstruction to blood flow. In some cases the technique, called angioplasty, has avoided the need for coronary-artery bypass surgery, operations on the arteries feeding the legs to save limbs, and to treat, even cure, some cases of high-blood pressure caused by narrowing of one of the arteries that feed the kidneys.
• Snaring gallstones that surgeons have accidentally left in bile ducts. (One example was the case of the exiled former Shah of Iran.)
• Mapping the location of cysts and abscesses deep in the belly and then draining them by inserting tubes and long, thin needles—less than 0.75 millimeters (0.03 inch)
• Threading tubes through arteries to inject drugs, gels, and other sub-stances to stop uncontrolled bleeding from the bowel.
Many of these techniques were overlooked in the United States for sev-eral years after pioneering work by European doctors. The techniques involve significant risks, but when performed properly they are improving patient care in the United States.

Artificial Skin. Artificial skin made from cowhide, shark cartilage, and plastic has been successfully used by doctors at Massachusetts General Hospital in Boston to replace skin destroyed by burns. The new skin successfully performs many of the functions of real skin.

Unlike other substances that are used temporarily to cover the skin of burned patients, the newly developed artificial skin avoids the need for drugs that suppress the body's immune system. These drugs, which must be taken if skin from a relative or other donor is used for skin grafts, increase the patient's chances of getting a serious infection—and infec-tion is a common cause of death among burn victims.

The artificial skin was developed in a ten-year collaborative effort be-tween a hospital team of researchers headed by Dr. John F. Burke and another group headed by Professor I. V. Yannas at the Massachusetts Institute of Technology. "We needed their engineering knowhow and

TWO PRENATAL TREATMENTS

These drawings illustrate the techniques used for treating fetuses found, after prenatal tests, to have life-threatening conditions. Corrective surgery is done though the mother's abdomen.

HYDRONEPHROSIS: A
blockage in the urinary tract causes a backup into the fetus's abdomen. A drainage tube must be inserted.

ABDOMEN
UTERUS
NEEDLE — AMNIOTIC FLUID
NEEDLE
CATHETER IN BLADDER — KIDNEY

The catheter, put in place with a needle, remains in the bladder.

HYDROCEPHALUS:
Buildup of fluid in the fetal brain prevents development of nerve cells, causing retardation or death.

ABDOMEN
UTERUS
AMNIOTIC FLUID
NEEDLE
VENTRICLE SYSTEM — CATHETER
NEEDLE

A brain shunt, inserted by a needle, drains fluid into the amniotic sac.

Robert Conrad/The New York Times

they needed our medical expertise,'' Dr. Burke said. Because the artificial skin is still made only in the laboratory, it has had only limited use—for patients with severe burns. However, Dr. Burke believes that the prospects for commercial application and for stockpiling in hospitals for immediate and more widespread use are very good.

Leeches. Leeches are an ancient remedy that fell from favor as specific therapies were introduced into medicine. Now, at least one serious new application for leeches has been found. French doctors in Bordeaux, Nancy, and Strasbourg have used leeches as an adjunct to microsurgery—specifically for certain plastic surgery patients in whom blood clots and congestion jeopardized the operation's success. Leeches have been used to help save fingers amputated in accidents. Surgeons, aided by microscopes, can restore blood circulation by sewing together tiny arteries severed in such accidents, but when microsurgeons cannot reconnect the delicate veins in the fingertips, blood can accumulate beneath the fingernail. The pressure of this accumulated blood can then cause clots in the arteries, stopping the flow of blood and depriving cells in the affected area from receiving oxygen and other vital nourishment carried by the blood. Yet if blood congestion can be avoided long enough the body can form new blood vessels that will drain the blood and allow the reimplanted finger to survive. Leeches, by sucking the blood in the fingertip area, prevent the accumulation of blood so that new vessels have time to form. Some U.S. microsurgeons have credited leeches with saving several fingers and contributing to the success of other plastic-surgery operations.

A Rare Cancer. A rare and often rapidly fatal form of cancer was detected among homosexual men, mostly in New York and the San Francisco Bay area, during 1981. The sudden appearance of the cancer, called Kaposi's sarcoma, prompted an investigation by federal and other epidemiologists because it could have scientific as well as public-health importance, because of what it may teach about the causes of more common types of cancer.

Kaposi's sarcoma appears as one or more violet-covered spots anywhere on the body. The spots generally do not itch or cause other symptoms and often can be mistaken for bruises. They do, however, sometimes appear as lumps and and can turn brown after a period of time. The disease often causes swollen lymph glands and kills by spreading throughout the body.

Lawrence K. Altman, M.D.

Bloodsucking leeches, once used as an ancient remedy, fell from favor as a curative long ago. But now leeches are being used in microsurgery for finger reimplantation.

Dr. Croy/Black Star

Rich Clarkson/Sports Illustrated

In a magnificent performance, English track star Sebastian Coe (254) races to victory ahead of Steve Ovett (279), winning the 1980 Moscow Olympics 1,500 meter final.

SPORTS SCIENCE

by Natalie Angier

HIS lungs ballooning and his heart furiously pumping almost twice the normal blood volume, English track star Sebastian Coe broke the tape in August 1981 in a mile run at Zurich in 3 minutes 48.53 seconds. It was a new world record, beating the 1980 mark—3:48.80—set by Coe's countryman Steve Ovett. One week later, in Koblenz, West Germany, Ovett returned the compliment, running the mile in 3:48.40 and recapturing the championship. Only two days elapsed before Coe got back on the track. In a stunning performance in Brussels, the 24-year-old running machine blazed yet another mile record, this time in 3:47.33, or 1.07 seconds better than Ovett's still fresh mark.

That incredible two-man, ten-day international spectacle surprised fans and raised some provocative questions among sports physiologists. How much faster can mere mortals run the mile? How much higher can they leap? How much more weight can they lift? How much farther can they jump, or hurl a javelin, or put a shot? Are there limits to athletic performance? And if so, what are they, and when will they be reached?

YESTERDAY, TODAY, TOMORROW

Since the golden days of Greece, when athletes paid homage to their sporting deities in the Olympic games, people have sought to outrace the wind, outleap the deer, outdo their opponents—and outfox their own bodies. With competitive spirit, strict discipline, and hard training, dedicated athletes have shown their disdain for limits. Today, in virtually every kind of sport, they continue to pit themselves against both competitors and the apparent constraints of their own muscles and organs in order to break record after record. These continuing assaults on the record books have confounded the physiologists who try to understand the limits of human physical endeavor. No sooner do they believe that they have seen the impossible in athletic performance than the sports pages send them back to the laboratory to review their data.

It was long thought that no one could run a mile in less than four minutes—until Roger Bannister broke that barrier in 1954. The time that won swimmer Mark Spitz a gold medal in the 1972 Olympics for the 100-meter freestyle would not even qualify him for a medal in that event today. Today's athletes are simply stronger, faster, and more efficient than yesterday's, and tomorrow's will be even better.

Much of the improvement in performance can be traced to improvements in training techniques, nutrition, and equipment. Moreover, renewed interest in physical fitness has led to greater participation in all sports, and consequently to a greater pool of talent from which record breakers will naturally emerge.

ANY LIMITS?

Still, scientists remain convinced that the body does have its limits, and they wonder how far human muscle, bones, and sinew can be pushed. When does the advantage of having a great coach no longer matter, and when do the ultimate biological limitations of muscle, the skeletal structure, and the cardiovascular system come into play? In a handful of laboratories across the United States, scientists have reached some tentative conclusions suggesting barriers that body and will cannot surmount. Weight lifters in the lightest body-weight categories, for example, may reach their limits some day soon—unable, finally, to set new records. High jumpers, milers, and certain other track athletes will also have to accept the fact that their record-breaking days are numbered.

To assess the factors that explain athletic prowess and define its possibilities, scientists analyze human muscle fibers, study enzymes, and even crush bones to test resil-

Rica Reinisch, a top-notch swimmer for East Germany, won three gold medals in the 1980 Moscow Olympics, and set a new world's record in the 100 meter backstroke event.

Lehtikuva/Photoreporters

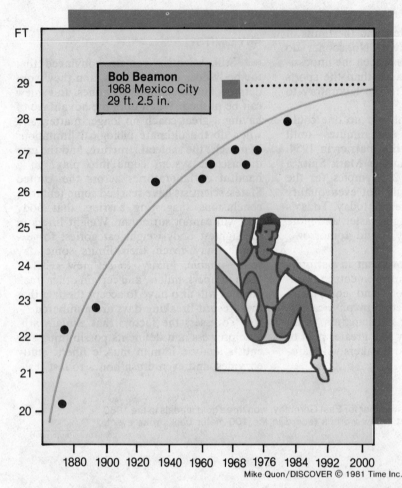

Bob Beamon
1968 Mexico City
29 ft. 2.5 in.

FT

29
28
27
26
25
24
23
22
21
20

1880 1900 1920 1940 1960 1968 1976 1984 1992 2000

Mike Quon/DISCOVER © 1981 Time Inc.

The dotted line shows that Bob Beamon's astounding, "superhuman" long-jump feat should not have occurred until the 21st century.

ience. Living specimens—top athletes—are run on treadmills, worked out on Nautilus machines, wired, tapped, probed, and poked from toe to top. But, as neurologist Ernst Jokl, of the University of Kentucky, has said, "the real laboratories for studying the limits are actual world-class competitions."

THE BODY MACHINE

Whether the athlete is strapped into a padded chair or is flipping dolphinlike over the pole-vault bar, the physiologist must study the body as a machine that operates according to mechanical and chemical laws. The human body requires a certain amount of energy to move, and the efficiency with which it can convert food into energy is limited by its own internal mechanisms.

That conversion system involves two distinct yet interacting processes—aerobic and anaerobic—that produce energy for the muscles. In aerobic metabolism, the muscle cells rely on oxygen, delivered to them by the blood, to convert fats and carbohydrates into energy at a relatively slow rate. In anaerobic metabolism, the muscle cells use no oxygen but make the conversion from carbohydrates into usable energy much faster.

Different physical activities make different demands on the two processes. During marathon running, in which an athlete must pace himself to run for hours, the muscles depend almost entirely on the slow, steady form of aerobic conversion. By contrast, a weight lifter who heaves more than 500 pounds overhead for only a few seconds needs the quick energy that the anaerobic process provides. Other sports, like swimming and running, use both processes in roughly equal proportions. Says Robert

Chuck Muhlstock/Focus on Sports

Physiologists are studying the fine details that explain the biological differences between weight lifters, like Soviet Olympic champion Vasily Alexeyev (above), and marathoners like Alberto Salazar (at right), to determine the body's outer limits.

Fitts, a muscle physiologist at Marquette University in Milwaukee, "The body knows just when to depend on one or the other."

INTERACTING PROCESSES

In past decades, scientists have measured the efficiency of the two metabolic systems. They have discovered how the body switches them on and off. They have found that the anaerobic process, though speedy, is extremely inefficient. Muscle cells that function without oxygen discard carbohydrates after only a small percentage of the available energy has been extracted from them. Moreover, the cells tend to rebel in these circumstances. Through a complex mechanism, they release hydrogen ions into the muscle tissue, causing fatigue.

At that point, the body's aerobic machinery steps in to take up the slack. With the help of oxygen, the muscle cells turn the by-

© Steven E. Sutton/Duomo

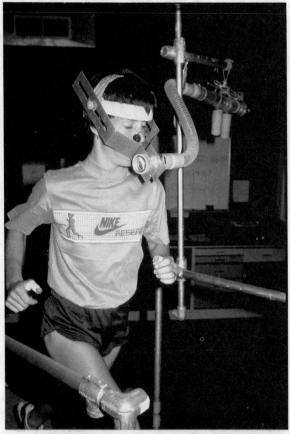

© Gale Constable/Duomo

At the Nike Research Center in Exeter, New Hampshire, athlete Joan Benoit is monitored to determine how well her body metabolizes foods.

products of anaerobic metabolism, along with additional fats snatched from pockets in obscure corners of the body, into carbon dioxide, water, and finally energy. The oxygen delivered by the blood helps to clear out the fatigue-producing hydrogen ions embedded in the muscle cells.

HEART-LUNG LIMIT

Although the general picture of the body's power-train system is understood, physiologists are examining the finer details that explain the biological differences between, say, a marathoner like Bill Rodgers and a weight lifter like the Soviet Olympic champion Vasily Alexeyev. Such compari-

sons are crucial in determining the body's outer limits. The scientists must also learn how much energy can be spent before the body collapses from exhaustion. They consider the details of enzyme reactions as well as the different muscle types and body proportions. Certain features, like long legs, are genetically determined. Other factors, like the amount of blood the heart can pump, change with training, and here researchers try to extrapolate the limits by working athletes to utter exhaustion.

Physiologists David Costill and William Fink, at Ball State University in Muncie, Indiana, have calculated the maximum volume of oxygen that certain athletes are able to consume per pound per minute. This would be an approximate measure of the best aerobic performance that can be expected from those athletes. Costill experiments with champion runners. He plugs up their noses, stuffs a tube in their mouths, and runs them relentlessly on treadmills. He measures the volume of air that is breathed in and out, as well as the ratio of carbon dioxide to oxygen in the expired air. The percentage of carbon dioxide tells him how well the body metabolizes its deposits of fat and carbohydrates.

These metabolic processes, in turn, depend on the ability of the heart to deliver oxygen and the ability of the muscles to use that oxygen. Fink reckons that top runners like Bill Rodgers use roughly 80 milliliters (4.8 cubic inches) of oxygen per kilogram (2.2 pounds) of body weight per minute (an average male Sunday jogger uses about 45 milliliters, he thinks). He has now concluded that "the upper limit is probably in the eighties or nineties," because the heart would not be capable of delivering any additional oxygen.

In another experiment, Swedish researchers injected radioactive dyes into the blood stream of a cross-country ski champion who had an exceptionally large build and heart, and monitored him at rest. They discovered that his heart could pump about 36 quarts of blood per minute. (The heart of a typical man delivers about 18 quarts.) It is doubtful whether any athlete could surpass 36 quarts: the hearts of the average-sized Coe and Ovett pump about 30.

PRESSURE ON LEGS

Another figure that is not likely to improve, and one that affects sprinters and weight lifters, is the amount of pressure that a human femur (thigh bone) can withstand. At the University of California at San Diego, orthopedic surgeons subjected the thigh bone of a human cadaver to the jaws of a compression device. They found that the femur can tolerate 1,600 pounds per square inch before it splinters. At present speeds, the leg bones of a 160-pound sprinter in action withstand forces up to five times his body weight, or 800 pounds. As sprinters get faster and weight lifters stronger, the forces will increase accordingly and approach the breaking point.

ENTER GENETICS

Another element in athletic performance is the genetically determined quality of muscle fiber. Sports scientists divide this fiber into two types, depending on the speed with which muscles move. So-called fast-twitch fibers are stronger and larger and are most suited for anaerobic activity; slow twitchers are best for aerobic work. Physiologists Costill and Fink have examined these factors in athletes. After anaesthetizing volunteers, they take out a bit of muscle, "anywhere from the size of a grain of rice to a pea," says Fink.

The fibers are then examined under microscopes, and compared with those of other athletes. Fink has found that a Rodgers-class marathoner seems to possess 80 to 90 per cent slow-twitch fibers. (Marathoners, remember, depend mostly on slow, aerobic processes.) Top men and women sprinters (who depend more on the faster anaerobic processes of energy production), like AAU champions Carl Lewis and Evelyn Ashford, have about 70 per cent fast twitch. But physiologists do not rule out the possibility that evolution could produce marathoners with far greater potential. Fink sees no reason why a genetic fluke could not turn out somebody with more than 90 per cent of either fast- or slow-twitch muscles. So equipped, a person might surpass currently accepted limits on performance.

After measuring the upper and lower legs, upper and lower arms, backs, feet, shoulders, and hips of hundreds of athletes, Marvin Clein, of the University of Denver, has defined the ideal physical proportions for various sports. Sprinters, he says, should have narrow hips and narrow shoulders for a streamlined profile, short upper legs and long lower legs for a greater stride, and small feet to free the legs for maximum swing. Swimmers should have big hands to plough through the water, broad shoulders to accommodate the necessary large muscles, and narrow hips for straight-line efficiency. Clein does not expect ever to see a sprinter with upper legs three inches long, but he concedes the possibility that two ideal sprinters might produce children with characteristics of even greater athletic benefit than those of either parent.

ENZYME SPURTS

Some of the most definitive biological limits to athletic performance can be found on the subcellular level. At Washington University in St. Louis, Missouri, scientists are

Dr. Ernst Jokl, a neurologist at the University of Kentucky, assesses factors of athletic prowess.
Courtesy of Ernst Jokl, M.D.

Focus on Sports

Bruce Jenner, shown here practicing for the shot-put event, trained heavily for four years to win the men's decathlon in the 1976 Montreal Olympics.

studying molecules like adenosine triphosphate (ATP), the major energy-storing molecule in the body. They have found that ATP provides periodic spurts to drive the metabolic machinery in both aerobic and anaerobic energy conversions. When a muscle is in motion, ATP is ignited by a collection of metabolic enzymes. According to John Holloszy, an exercise biochemist at Washington University, some world-class (world-class denotes the highest caliber in the world) athletes may have up to three times as many of these enzymes for aerobic work as do nonathletes. This provides swifter and more effi-

cient ATP activity, hence more energy per muscle cell.

Improved training apparently leads to the creation of more enzymes, but Holloszy suspects that enzyme production is reaching a plateau. Three times the average amount, he says, "seems to be the upper limit."

PROJECTIONS AND LIMITS

The biological information that emerges from these experiments can be applied to projections and even limits in a wide range of sports. Experts at the Soviet Union's Research Institute of Physical Education have worked out models for ideal performance. The most efficient sprinter in the 100-meter dash, for example, would be 23 years old, stand 5 feet 10 inches tall, and weigh 160 pounds. Competing against today's 100-meter record of 9.95, that model athlete should break the tape at 9.84 by 1984, 9.81 by 1988, and 9.75 by 1990. Jokl disagrees; he thinks that the absolute limit is probably 9.8.

Breaking records in the mile and beyond requires considerably more than ideal height, weight, and age. Clein and John Keefe, one of his colleagues at Denver, say that the main limiting factor in such events is the heart. Only hearts larger than the ones that now exist in human beings will be able to pump more than 36 quarts of blood per minute. But bigger hearts demand bigger lungs, a fuller rib cage, and a larger, stronger spine. This means added weight, which requires more energy to propel the body.

Since nothing short of an evolutionary breakthrough is likely to produce bigger human hearts, it is not probable, they say, that a miler will ever run faster than 3:34.00, which is 13.33 seconds faster than Sebastian Coe's new record. High jumpers, too, may be nearing their upper limits. Again, the Soviets have produced models. Their ideal high jumper should be 20 to 26 years old, stand 6 feet 3 inches tall, and weigh 160 pounds. He should be able to leap 8 feet 2 inches by the year 1990 (today's record is 7 feet 8¾ inches, set by Gerd Wessig of East Germany). Again, Jokl differs; barring major changes in shoe design or jumping technique, his ultimate jumper would probably soar no higher than 8 feet.

SWIMMING AN EXCEPTION

Of all sports, perhaps the one that has not yet begun to confront its limits is swimming. For one thing, the effects of gravity on the heart are diminished in water. Thus in swimming, the heart has a far greater potential for work than in, say, running. Furthermore, the body releases enervating heat more efficiently in a pool. In fact, the unusual conditions that water presents are a particular boon to women swimmers. Their higher percentage of body fat provides greater buoyancy, enabling them to devote less energy to staying afloat and more to propelling themselves. Clein expects that in the next century the gap between the men's and women's world swimming records will narrow to less than 10 per cent in all events. In the 400-meter freestyle, the gap is already only 6.9 per cent—3:50.49 for men (by Peter Szmidt of Canada), 4:06.28 for women (by Tracey Wickham of Australia).

UNPREDICTABILITY

As the physiologists probe the limits, they must also consider the occasional superhuman performance that goes off their charts. In the 1968 Mexico City Olympics, America's Bob Beamon shattered credulity as well as the world record with an unbelievable long-jump feat of 29 feet 2½ inches. The previous record was 27 feet 4¾ inches, set by Igor Ter-Ovanesyan of the Soviet Union in 1967. Beamon benefited slightly from the thinner air and lower pull of gravity in mile-high Mexico City. Nevertheless, his great leap forward was so spectacular—previous long-jump records had usually been lowered by mere fractions of an inch—that Jokl will only describe it as a "mutation performance." Says he: "Beamon's jump is the greatest single feat in the recorded history of athletics. It is unlikely that it will ever be surpassed."

It is perhaps just as well that sports science was unprepared for Beamon. Says Jokl: "The wonderful thing about sport is that it is unpredictable. The arrival of geniuses like Bach and Mozart in the world of music could never have been predicted. And the same is true for genius in athletics. Unpredictability

Tom Sobolik/Black Star

Allison Roe, shown here crossing the finish line in the 1981 New York City Marathon, ran the fastest marathon that has ever been run by a woman.

is an element of sport at its best." And, he might have added, the best sort of challenge to science □

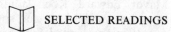 SELECTED READINGS

"Computers are helping coaches to train athletes by analyzing tiny details of their performance" by William M. Bulkeley. *The Wall Street Journal,* August 14, 1980.

"Drug that builds Russians" by Stephen Fulder. *New Scientist,* August 21, 1980.

"Medicine catches up with the sports boom" by James C. G. Conniff. *The New York Times Magazine,* October 5, 1980.

"Sports scientists train athletes to defy old limits" by Jay Stuller. *Smithsonian,* July 1980.

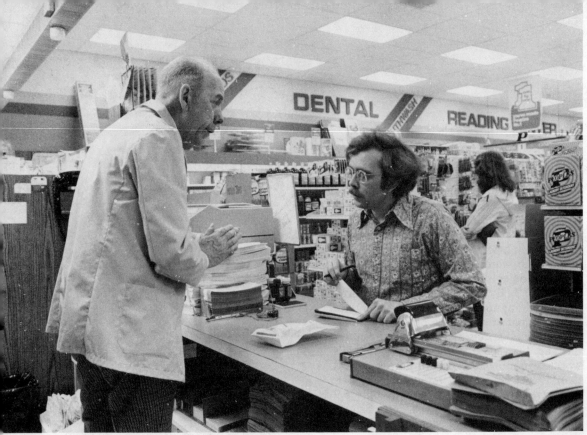

Sygma

Robert Randall, a 31-year-old glaucoma patient shown here at a pharmacy, is the first American legally authorized to smoke marijuana. He claims the drug aids his vision.

MARIJUANA:
BAD NEWS AND GOOD

by Natalie Angier

IT is as commonplace as a pitcher of beer. Adolescents stroll along city streets with joints casually cupped in their hands. Advertising executives discreetly light up after a tough day of brainstorming. New York Mayor Edward Koch admits to having turned on in the past, and some 15,000,000 people in the United States smoke it regularly. In fact, *Cannabis sativa,* or marijuana, is second only to alcohol in popularity.

Marijuana has only a slightly addictive effect on those who smoke it, but scientists studying its characteristics find it almost irresistible. They are increasingly intrigued by the potential—for bad and good—in the chemical compounds of the cannabis leaf. They are generally more cautious than the scientists who in the mid-1970's concluded from sketchy data that smoking pot led to a breakdown of the body's immune system, demasculinization, and permanent intellectual impairment. They do, however, suggest that frequent use of the complex drug may have other harmful effects. At the same time, they are finding that some of the ingredients of marijuana, used properly, perform wonders in medicine.

VERY SUBTLE AND COMPLEX

New tests show that cannabis interacts with the body in subtler ways than alcohol, morphine, and many other substances. Research on animals and human beings indicates that marijuana may affect ovulation, sperm production, and adolescent hormonal balance. Because tampering with these functions is risky, some scientists are deeply worried. Says Dr. Reese Jones, of the Langley Porter Psychiatric Institute in San Francisco, "Not long ago I wouldn't have guessed just how complicated marijuana is. Now we're finding out, and it could be only a matter of time before the dangers become known. After all, it took sixty years of steady cigarette smoking in the United States before doctors realized that there was a connection between lung cancer and cigarettes."

Other scientists view marijuana's complexity differently. They see in the plant a therapeutic potential that has only begun to be exploited. Today about 12,000 cancer patients use tetrahydrocannabinol (THC)—the active ingredient in marijuana—to relieve the terrible nausea and vomiting that accompany chemotherapy. Glaucoma victims smoke joints to ease intraocular pressure. The plant is also being studied as a possible aid to people stricken with epilepsy, acute migraine, or multiple sclerosis. Recognizing its promise, the U.S. Food and Drug Administration in September 1980 classified THC as a Class C drug, one with clinical applications. By mid-1981, 27 states had approved the distribution of THC for medical purposes, and a drug company has applied for a license to market it in capsule form. Laboratories that manufacture the pills and researchers who want to test raw marijuana get their supplies not from street peddlers but from a crop grown under government supervision at the University of Mississippi.

Scientists are only beginning to understand the chemistry of cannabis. The plant yields more than 400 chemicals, including some 60 cannabinoids unique to it. However, only THC is known to have an important psychoactive effect. When consumed, THC turns into about 25 other compounds, which can react differently with each user's metabolic system. Says Raphael Mechoulam, of Hebrew University in Jerusalem, who first isolated and described THC, in the late 1960's, "This could partly explain why some people seem to get high from very small amounts of cannabis, and others have no reaction even to large doses."

BINDING SITES IN THE BRAIN

Researchers do not know precisely how THC interacts with the brain, any more than they know how most other drugs affect the brain. But they have some intriguing clues. Dr. Louis Harris, of the Medical College of Virginia, has preliminary data from studies on rats that indicate specific binding sites, or receptors, for THC in the brain. These are protein molecules on the surface of the nerve-cell membrane that are shaped as though they were tailored to hook up with the THC molecule. Says Harris, "This implies that there may be naturally occurring compounds like THC in the brain. Why would the brain make specific binding sites for some strange substance in a plant?" In earlier studies, the finding of brain receptors for morphine led to the discovery of endorphins, natural opiates produced by the brain. To Harris this suggests the brain also makes some substance akin to THC.

In another experiment on rats, Mechoulam, Erminio Costa, and their colleagues have shown that THC reduces the rate at which acetylcholine, an important neurotransmitter, is produced and broken down in the hippocampus section of the middle of the brain. A neurotransmitter is a chemical involved in the transmission of impulses between nerve cells. Because the hippocampal area controls emotions, which THC strongly affects, Mechoulam suggests that the lower acetylcholine production could be a reason for the marijuana "high."

EFFECTS ON MALES

The thing that most concerns scientists who view marijuana as dangerous is that THC and the compounds produced from it do not dissolve in water, and so are not flushed out of the body as easily as, say, alcohol or caffeine. Instead, the compounds mix with internal fat deposits, and may linger in their plump pockets for as long as two weeks. These fat deposits are found in some chemically sensitive areas—the brain, the adrenal glands, the ovaries or testes, and the placenta of a pregnant woman.

The first hint that THC could damage these parts of the body came in the early

1970's, when scientists found that chronic marijuana smoking lowers the level of testosterone, the male sex hormone, in the blood. At first this caused alarm. Now, having found that the level never dips below the normal range, and quickly rises again once a man stops smoking, many scientists no longer think that THC endangers the health of an average adult male.

But some doctors fear that smoking pot during adolescence—and preadolescence—may be harmful to boys. Says Carol Smith, of the Uniformed Services University of Health Sciences in Bethesda, Maryland, "In adolescence, a boy's body is going through many changes—it grows taller, it gets hairier, the voice deepens—and these changes are controlled by testosterone. Marijuana could very well block the normal growth process. There have been case reports of boys who use marijuana having a delay in the onset of puberty."

In an investigation of the impact of marijuana on the male reproductive system, Gabriel Nahas, a pharmacologist, and Wylie Hembree, an endocrinologist, both at Columbia University, studied 16 apparently healthy men who smoked five to fifteen joints a day for four weeks. After the men stopped smoking, their sperm counts were low and many sperm cells were abnormal in shape—effects that lasted for weeks. These findings could mean that smoking may keep marginally fertile men from becoming fathers.

AND FEMALES

Because it was assumed that women and girls did not smoke nearly so much as men, they were generally ignored during the early days of marijuana research. But now that pot smoking is so common, especially among the young, scientists have turned their attention to its effects on women, whose hormone levels are more delicately balanced than men's.

Carol Smith has been studying the effects of THC on the menstrual cycles of rhesus monkeys, which are almost identical to those of human females. For two weeks of their cycles, 22 monkeys were given THC in doses equivalent to what would be consumed by a heavy marijuana smoker. The results were unequivocal: menstrual cycles in all the monkeys were disrupted—even to the point of stopping ovulation—for about five months following the doses of THC.

Says Smith, "Nothing we have ever tested, not even oral contraceptives, has as radical an effect on the menstrual cycle as marijuana does." Smith's findings seem to agree with those of a study of a small group of marijuana-smoking college women, done by the Masters and Johnson Institute in Philadelphia. A number of the women turned out to have defective menstrual cycles; their hormone levels were irregular, and they sometimes failed to ovulate. Says Smith, "The female reproductive system appears to be much more disturbed by marijuana than the male's."

Adding to the fears is the discovery that marijuana is present in the placentas of pregnant women who are chronic smokers, and that the drug readily passes through the placenta to the developing fetus. Baby monkeys whose mothers had been given THC were unusually small, and often failed to thrive. While no human birth defects have yet been attributed to marijuana, doctors are now unanimous in advising pregnant women to avoid the drug.

EFFECTS ON THE BRAIN

Some researchers think that marijuana causes physical damage to the brain. Echoencephalograms—ultrasonic pictures of the brain—and computerized brain scans of chronic smokers in the United States and in Greece show no evidence of physical brain damage. But using monkeys, Robert Heath and Austin Fitzjarrell, at Tulane University, have looked deeper into the brain than researchers studying humans have, and they have found ominous results.

In a six-month study, the monkeys were placed in incubators for as long as 45 minutes each day, where they smoked one to three marijuana cigarettes a day through a hole in the incubator wall. Fitzjarrell says that "the monkeys would take a drag on the cigarettes and hold the smoke in their lungs as if they were trying to savor it." Electrodes were implanted in the monkeys' brains to record their interior brain waves. The brain wave patterns were found to be abnormal both during the six-month period and up to one year afterward. Biopsies of the brains revealed major structural changes and early indications of the breakdown of nerve cells.

PSYCHOLOGICAL EFFECTS

How far animal research can be applied to human beings is hotly debated. Animals and people have some significantly different physical reactions to marijuana. For example, marijuana speeds up the heart rate in human beings, whereas in most other animals it slows the heart rate down. Therefore animal studies would not necessarily provide a warning of the potentially disastrous effect of marijuana on people with severe heart problems. Such discrepancies make researchers cautious. Says Louis Harris, "The problem is, if we cry wolf once too often, then nobody listens when we talk about real dangers."

The worst dangers of marijuana, most doctors think, are the psychological ones. Says Harris, "What we should be saying to young people who are turning on is not that they shouldn't smoke grass because it may stunt their growth, or some such thing, but that they shouldn't be using *any* drugs at that age. They're simply not emotionally developed enough to cope with the psychological effects."

That chronic marijuana use has devastating effects on the personality is undebatable. When a smoker is high, his intellectual abilities—particularly his memory—plummet. Recent studies indicate that marijuana impairs the connection between short-term memory and long-term memory. Lists of words or numbers that a person learns while he is stoned are forgotten once he is "straight" again. Says psychologist Douglas Ferraro, of the University of New Mexico, "This means that a student should keep away from the stuff." Drivers too should avoid marijuana: the drug affects a user's response time and sense of spatial relations. Says Dr. Robert Petersen, of the U.S. National Institute on Drug Abuse, "Some people say they drive better while stoned. A lot of drunks say that too." What the kids mean by the word

Wide World

In Mount Sinai Hospital in New York, pharmacist Joanne Campbell prepares marijuana tablets to investigate the herb's clinical applications.

"pothead" tells it all. Observers ranging from psychiatrists to parents to disgusted peers have noticed that people who smoke several joints a day often lack motivation to work, study, exercise, or indeed do much more than sit around and listen to music. And today it is easier than ever to be a pothead; according to chemists at the University of Mississippi, street marijuana is now up to ten times as strong as it was in 1974.

Yet marijuana may not have a lasting effect on intelligence. An often cited study of veteran pot smokers in Jamaica showed that their average IQ, measured when they were not stoned, was equivalent to that of a non-smoking control group. Follow-up studies in the United States, Greece, and Costa Rica

Hank Morgan/Rainbow

In the marijuana garden at the University of Mississippi, chemist Carlton Turner stands beside a collection of *Cannabis sativa* and its derivatives.

pounds found in cannabis are a family of drugs with as much potential as the steroids or the penicillins. Says Hebrew University's Mechoulam, "I have great certainty that it will become an important force in medicine."

ANTINAUSEA TREATMENT

Marijuana's success in easing the side-effects of chemotherapy was discovered in quite an unscientific manner. Anecdotal reports by young patients who had previous experiences with pot began drifting around cancer wards, and soon even older patients were surreptitiously lighting up in hospitals. Doctors could not help being impressed with the initial results, and official clinical trials were soon underway.

In the year following the FDA classification of marijuana as a drug with clinical applications, the National Cancer Institute mailed out 600,000 tablets, each containing about five milligrams of THC (there are 10 to 20 milligrams in the average marijuana cigarette), to doctors and hospitals across the country. Although it is one of the best anti-nausea treatments known, THC is no miracle cure. Only about 60 per cent of the people suffering from nausea find it effective. Many patients, especially young ones, argue that a cigarette works better than a tablet, and request marijuana in that form. Many doctors disapprove, because doses cannot be controlled when smoked rather than swallowed. Some older people find the marijuana "high" anything but pleasurable. Says Petersen, "The so-called euphoric sensations may scare the devil out of them."

In an effort to accommodate these patients, pharmacologists are working to separate THC's anti-nausea agent, which scientists believe works on the vomitting control center of the brain, from its psychoactive ingredient. Several drug companies are testing experimental subcompounds.

HELP FOR GLAUCOMA AND SPASTICITY

A THC-like drug without side-effects would also be appreciated by glaucoma victims who are taking THC tablets—or smoking marijuana—along with standard medication, to reduce intraocular pressure. Glaucoma, a poorly understood affliction, is

have yielded similar results. Nevertheless, insists Fitzjarrell of Tulane University, "My advice to both social and chronic users of marijuana is to quit."

AS THERAPY

It is perhaps because marijuana still has a reputation for being a killer weed that it has had such a hard time winning acceptance in the United States as a therapeutic drug. Marijuana as medicine is nothing new. In 2737 B.C. the Chinese emperor Shen Nung tried it as an anaesthetic, and since then it has been used the world over as a treatment for rheumatism, leprosy, gonorrhea, impotence, and virtually every other human malady. Most accounts are mere folk tales, but some researchers today claim that the coma leading cause of blindness in the United States, incentive enough to find a cure for it. In this disease, THC seems to act both locally, either by reducing the production or promoting the outflow of excess ocular fluid, and centrally as a sedative that somewhat decreases intraocular pressure. Experimental THC eyedrops have been disappointing; they act locally only. Besides, the insoluble THC molecules irritate the eyes.

Glaucoma patients may soon be helped by another chemical in the cannabis plant. Dr. Keith Green, of the Medical College of Georgia, and Leon Zalkow, of the Georgia Institute of Technology, have been testing a water-soluble protein that they obtain from marijuana. Tiny quantities of the substance are a thousand times as effective in lowering intraocular pressure in rabbits as any other known drug, including THC. The pressure may be reduced by as much as 85 per cent, and the effect can last as long as 15 hours. Says Green, "We've never seen anything like it. We're trying to find out exactly how it works, and when we do, we'd like to start testing it on humans, perhaps in another two years or so."

Spasticity in some people with multiple sclerosis has been reduced by doses of THC smaller than those necessary to produce psychological effects. Drugs like phenobarbitol and valium, currently used to treat the involuntary muscle spasms associated with this disease, are not very effective. In an experiment at Pennsylvania State University conducted by Carl Ellenberger and Denis Petro, THC lowered the incidence of spasticity in six patients out of nine. Other people who might benefit from the antispastic properties of THC are those suffering from stroke, cerebral palsy, paraplegia, or spinal cord injuries.

CBD—EVEN BETTER?

Another promising constituent of the cannabis leaf is cannabidiol, or CBD, now under study as an anti-epileptic drug. Epilepsy can be a desperately debilitating disease, and for 30 per cent of its victims the standard medicine, dilantin, is ineffective. Researchers at the University of Utah have studied the effects of CBD on rats that have been electrically or chemically stimulated to

a state of artificial epilepsy. In all the rats, CBD lowered the intensity and frequency of the epileptic seizures. At the Paulist School of Medicine in São Paulo, Brazil, CBD has been tested on human epileptics. In four patients out of eight, the number of seizures declined dramatically during the 18-week trial. The number of seizures in two of the other epileptics was markedly reduced, and somewhat reduced in one more.

Because even in large doses CBD has no psychoactive effect, Mechoulam considers it the most promising chemical yet discovered in marijuana. "If CBD works so well in epileptics," he says, "then it could work well to cure chronic migraine—another neurological disorder."

IT'S JUST A DRUG

Marijuana is thus slowly finding its way out of the little plastic bag and into the medical repertory. This progression disturbs those who fear that young people will have a new supply of marijuana easily obtainable through a faked prescription, and pleases those who have been crusading for its therapeutic use. Says Petersen, "Grass has this crazy mystique about it. Some say it poses the biggest moral crisis since original sin, some say it's the greatest thing that's happened to the human race since the invention of the bed. But it's just a drug. Like any drug, it has the potential to do either harm or good, depending on how it's used." So far the balance seems tipped toward the harm. But the ultimate answer is still locked up in marijuana's complex, largely unknown chemistry □

SELECTED READINGS

"Alcohol, marijuana, and memory" by E. F. Loftus. *Psychology Today,* March 1980.

"Marijuana: hints of medical uses" by J. Greene. *FDA Consumer,* March 1979.

"Marijuana use and abuse" by M. J. Nicar. *Chemistry,* January 1979.

"Medicinal marijuana" *SciQuest,* September 1980.

"New look at marijuana" by D. Gelna and others. *Newsweek,* January 7, 1980.

"Cognition and long-term use of ganja (cannabis)" by Jeffrey Schaeffer and others. *Science,* July 24, 1981.

Karen Chernsh/DISCOVER © Time Inc.

Drs. Teruko and Kimishige Ishizaka made a significant breakthrough in scientists' knowledge of how the allergic reaction works.

ZEROING IN ON ALLERGIES

by Denise Grady

AT the age of 36, a man suddenly becomes allergic to fish. A woman who has always been allergic to cats is given a kitten, and her sneezing and itching mysteriously diminish. Some people are allergic to soft-boiled eggs but not hard-boiled eggs. Hay-fever victims occasionally react to cantaloupe as well as to ragweed.

Some 37,000,000 people in the United States know firsthand the quirks and miseries of allergy. As many as 15,000,000 of them have hay fever, the annoying sensitivity to tree, grass, or weed pollens that can last from May until the first frost. Many others are plagued by year-round itching, wheezing, coughing, sneezing, swelling, and hives. The offending substances, or allergens, range from food dyes and preservatives, to "natural" foods such as nuts, fruits, milk, and chocolate, to molds and mite droppings in household dust.

Doctors, drugs, and hospital care for allergies and related illnesses cost Americans more than $1,500,000,000 a year. Lost wages total hundreds of millions more. Repeated attacks are costly in another way. They leave allergy victims prone to respiratory infections and sometimes scar the respiratory tract. Allergies can even be fatal. Each year 2,000 to 4,000 people in the United States die of asthma, a respiratory disorder that is often caused by allergy, and at least 50 die from insect stings that bring on anaphylactic shock, a massive allergic reaction.

Doctors are still puzzled by certain aspects of allergy. Injections of dust, mold, or pollen extracts gradually help 80 per cent of allergy victims build some tolerance to those substances, but just how is not known. The shots are rarely given for allergies to foods or animals. Although antihistamines often help relieve symptoms, their effectiveness varies from one person to the next. And, sad to say, medical science has yet to find any cure. But in recent years scientists have learned much about the cellular and molecular mechanisms that cause allergy. Before the end of the 1980's, their research may yield drugs that will prevent the allergic reaction entirely or at least relieve the symptoms better than anything now available to unfortunate sufferers.

HISTAMINE RELEASE

Much of the current research is based on a landmark discovery made in the 1960's at the National Jewish Hospital/National Asthma Center in Denver by two Japanese doctors, Teruko Ishizaka and her husband, Kimishige. When the Ishizakas began their research, scientists already knew that pollen and other allergens cause certain cells, called mast cells, in the skin and in the mucous membranes of the respiratory and gastrointestinal tracts to release histamine and other chemicals. These substances aid healing and help fight infection when injury occurs, but in allergic reactions they act as irritants. When an allergen penetrates the skin, histamine turns the area red by dilating capillaries and causes swelling by making them leak fluid into surrounding tissues. The chemicals can also make breathing difficult by stimulating the secretion of mucus and constricting the involuntary muscles that control the flow of air to the lungs.

What scientists did not know was how allergens made mast cells spill their contents. Earlier research had shown that the immune system was involved. One type of antibody, or immunoglobulin (a complex molecule made by the immune system to defend the body against foreign substances), was somehow crucial to the allergic reaction. But researchers did not know what the antibody was or how it worked.

IgE

The Ishizakas set out to isolate that antibody from the blood of allergy victims, using themselves as guinea pigs. Since neither had any allergies, extract of ragweed pollen injected under their skin produced no reaction. But if they injected first a minute amount of an allergy victim's serum (the fluid, non-cellular part of the blood), then the pollen extract in the same place, itchy welts appeared. Separating the blood serum of the allergy victim into different components, they repeated the skin test with each, discarding those that produced no reaction and purifying those that caused welts.

Four years of experiments with human serum (and scratching) passed before the Ishizakas found their elusive substance, in 1966. They named it immunoglobulin E (IgE). It is one of five classes of antibody churned out by the cells of the immune system.

The immune system can produce a virtually infinite array of antibody molecules, each designed to link up with a specific foreign particle. Most classes of antibody circulate freely throughout the body and help destroy trespassers or sweep them from the body. This is the fate of pollen and animal dander that find their way into non-allergic people. But IgE behaves differently from other antibodies. Instead of floating freely, its Y-shaped molecules are embedded, tail first, in the membranes of the mast cells—as many as 500,000 of them to a cell. When an allergen particle—grass pollen, for example—comes along, it combines with the upper regions of two adjacent IgE molecules, bridging them and drawing them together.

Adolf Brotman/DISCOVER © 1981 Time Inc.

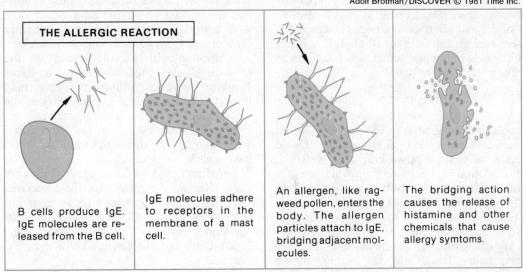

THE ALLERGIC REACTION

B cells produce IgE. IgE molecules are released from the B cell.

IgE molecules adhere to receptors in the membrane of a mast cell.

An allergen, like ragweed pollen, enters the body. The allergen particles attach to IgE, bridging adjacent molecules.

The bridging action causes the release of histamine and other chemicals that cause allergy symtoms.

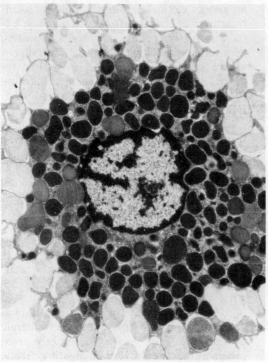

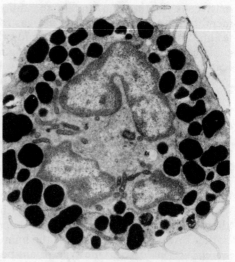

These electron micrographs show the changes that occur in a mast cell when an allergen is introduced. The cell at left has been stimulated to discharge histamine, which flows from tiny granules. The mast cell seen above is at rest.

The resultant tugging changes the mast-cell membrane, causing the cell to release histamine and other powerful chemicals. The severity of the reaction depends on the amount of allergen and IgE present, and on how prone the mast cell is to discharge. All allergies to pollen, house dust, and other airborne substances, as well as many cases of asthma and allergies to drugs, food, and insect venom, can be blamed on IgE. Allergy victims have ten and sometimes 100 times as much IgE as other people.

FRONT-LINE DEFENSE

When IgE was discovered, scientists could not imagine why the body produced such a troublemaking substance. Dr. David Katz, of the Scripps Clinic and Research Foundation in La Jolla, California, used to think there was no useful purpose for IgE. "Now I think it's one of the most important antibodies we have. It provides front-line defense against invaders at the layers of tissue exposed to the environment—the skin, the respiratory tract, and the lining of the gastrointestinal tract." Sneezing, for instance, may be touched off by IgE to expel unwanted substances.

In addition, IgE levels rise in parasite infections, and most researchers think the antibody helps prevent parasites from taking hold. It may do this by causing the gut muscles to contract and expel parasites. People with high IgE levels suffer less frequently than others from certain parasite infections.

Immunologist David Marsh, of the Howard Hughes Medical Institute at Johns Hopkins University, thinks that allergy may in part reflect a general hyperactivity of the immune system and a tendency to resist infectious diseases. During the past 5,000 years, people with this high immunity would have survived epidemics and, since the trait is hereditary, passed it along to their children. This may explain why the associated trait, allergy, is so common today. Says Dr. Gregory Siskind, of Cornell University Medical College in New York City, "People who lack IgE are extremely rare, so it must be important."

B CELLS AND T CELLS

Thus an allergy treatment that eliminated IgE production might dangerously weaken the patient's natural defenses. But lowering IgE levels might be useful, and both Katz and Kimishige Ishizaka are trying to do this. Their research groups have found substances that enhance or suppress the immune system's production of IgE, and now they are trying to learn what controls the formation of these substances.

Two types of white blood cells, T cells and B cells, are involved in the production of IgE. The B cells produce IgE, and the T cells make substances that can turn this production on and off. In rats and mice, a parasite infection leads to a great increase in the number of T cells, which then produce a substance that stimulates the formation of the B cells that spew out IgE. But if the infected animals are given steroid drugs, which suppress the entire immune system, the T cells produce a substance that turns off the IgE-producing B cells. Under certain conditions, the scientists have found, IgE itself can also lead the T cells to make the suppressor. This suggests a feedback system: the buildup of IgE may signal the T cells that enough IgE has been produced. If there is such a feedback system, something has gone wrong with it in allergy victims.

Both the Katz and Ishizaka groups are studying the structure of the suppressor and the enhancer. The molecules are similar. Both are proteins, and the researchers think they may work by competing for access to the same control sites on the membrane of the IgE producing B cell. The molecule present in greater numbers assumes absolute control.

Allergists are naturally more interested in the suppressor. Each research group seems to have isolated a different form of the suppressor, but both forms appear to have simular biological action. Each team has also extracted from human cells substances that they believe could possibly be IgE suppressors.

This work has great medical potential, says Katz, because "ideally, it may be possible to make a drug that can regulate the production of the patient's own IgE suppressor."

Treatment would not have to be tailored for individual allergies. One drug would work for all involving IgE. Katz thinks that such a drug could be ready for use within ten years. In the meantime, he says, "it might even be possible to use suppressor from human cells for therapy." Ishizaka is not so sure. Normally, the suppressor is made where it is used. But since it is a small protein, he says, if it is injected elsewhere it might be broken down in the body before reaching its destination.

ALLERGIC BREAKTHROUGH

Finding IgE suppressors and enhancers has inspired Katz and his colleagues to formulate a new theory of allergy, called allergic breakthrough. It helps explain some peculiarities of the disorder. It is known that the allergy victim, once exposed to an allergen, is "primed" to poduce large quantities of IgE against that substance. Katz suggests that IgE levels are regulated by a damping mechanism that reflects the balance of suppressor and enhancer. IgE production should usually be low. When the damping mechanism is disrupted—perhaps by a huge blitz of allergen—IgE production soars, and allergic breakthrough and a full-blown attack occurs. Changes in this system may cause allergies to appear and disappear mysteriously.

The breakthrough concept may explain why not every brush with pollen or danger results in an attack: the allergen may be insufficient to cause the production of enough IgE. Similarly, it may explain why skin and other diagnostic tests for allergy can be misleading. A positive result means that IgE is there, but it cannot reveal whether enough is there to cause a reaction under normal circumstances or whether the mast cells are sensitive enough to spill their contents. Consequently, many people with positive tests for certain allergens never react to those substances in the real world.

AND SHOTS?

Allergy shots—small doses of allergen, gradually increased to a maintenance level—may work on the damping mechanism. They may depress IgE levels. How they may do this is unknown. The injections supply enough allergen—a small amount but more than would be inhaled—to stimulate production of non-IgE antibodies. Researchers think these outnumber the IgE molecules and swoop down on the offenders to destroy them or hustle them out of the body before they can trigger IgE production. The success of a new type of injection appears to bear out this theory. It uses polymerized allergen—large complexes of partly purified allergens that stimulate the immune system but are too large to interact fully with IgE and mast cells.

Some people think they can achieve the same effect as injections by even more exposure to the things that cause their allergies. This is a favorite fantasy of animal lovers. Katz says it may work, but others are skeptical. Animals are walking dander bombs that inundate the mast cells with so much allergen that most specialists will not even try injections; the shots usually fail.

NEW CURES COMING?

What happens to the mast cell when an allergen links up with the IgE coating is Teruko Ishizaka's main interest, and one shared by Dr. K. Frank Austen, of the Harvard Medical School. Both research groups are studying the changes that occur within seconds after an allergen collides with a mast cell. A long chain of biochemical reactions take place, eventually letting the cell contents rush out. Since enzymes keep the chemical processes going, Ishizaka hopes to find an enzyme unique to the allergic reaction. Then she could develop an enzyme inhibitor that, by breaking the chain of reactions, would reduce allergy symptoms without disrupting other cell functions. She has found one enzyme that looks promising, but it needs further study.

Austen and his colleagues have taken a different approach. They hope to identify the two dozen chemicals inside the human mast

House dust, magnified 1,800 times its actual size, causes many allergy victims to sneeze year-round.

© David Scharf

Plant pollens, like this magnified grain of marigold pollen, makes millions of people suffer.

© David Scharf

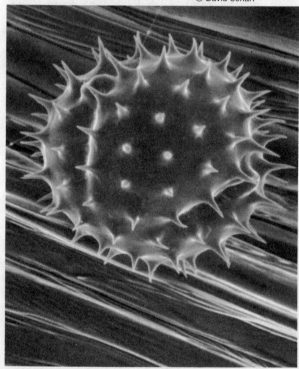

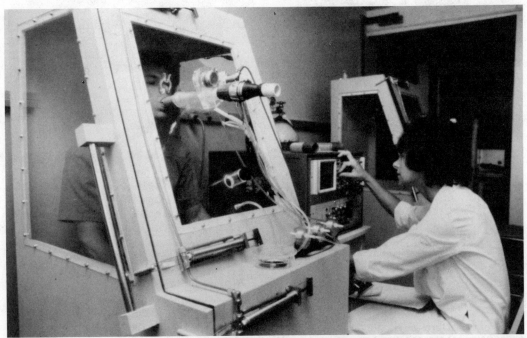

National Jewish Hospital/National Asthma Center

After inhaling an allergen that is a suspected cause of this man's asthma attacks, he is placed in a "body box" where changes in his airway resistance are monitored.

cell, to identify others that form when IgE and allergen attach to the mast cell, and to prevent the cell from releasing them in response to an allergen. A drug called cromolyn sodium can make the mast cells resist spilling their contents. However, because those contents, even histamine, also serve useful functions, it would be a mistake to cut off their release entirely.

Antihistamine drugs were developed in the late 1930's to thwart histamine at the cell surfaces, where it acts. But when antihistamines failed to relieve many allergic conditions, especially asthma, it became obvious that other mast-cell chemicals must have a role.

These were identified in the 1970's as leukotrienes—unusual sulfur-bearing compounds. They are a hundred times as potent as histamine in producing inflammation and swelling and in contracting involuntary muscles. They play a major role in asthma and anaphylactic shock, and their effects last longer than those of histamines. Research at

Harvard is aimed at developing antileukotrienes, which Austen considers the most promising approach to allergy today.

AGE HELPS

What to do in the meantime? The answers are standard: get rid of the cat, vacuum up the dust, buy an air conditioner, try antihistamines. For short, intense attacks, a steroid nasal spray or inhaler may be helpful, but long-term use of steroids may be dangerous. For the truly miserable, allergy shots are worth a try. But if they do not help within three years, doctors advise quitting.

One last bit of hope: after age 40, the immune system becomes less energetic, and allergies may simply go away □

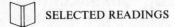 SELECTED READINGS

Allergies and You by Sheila Burns. Messner, 1980.

Understanding Your Allergy by Herman Hirshfeld. Arco, 1979.

Courtesy of American Heart Association

A diet of cholesterol-lowering foods may reduce the risk of heart disease. But recent studies suggest a connection between low cholesterol and an increased risk of cancer.

LOW CHOLESTEROL AND CANCER

by Gina Bari Kolata

WATCH your diet! Not too many eggs; limit fatty meats. Remember you want to keep your cholesterol level low.

Standard good advice?

Well, maybe.

There is accumulating evidence for a connection between low blood serum cholesterol concentrations and an increased risk of cancer. This has led researchers to pursue the question more vigorously, especially in light of other data that point to a clear relationship between high cholesterol levels and heart disease. Jeremiah Stamler of Northwestern University Medical School, who strongly supports cholesterol-lowering diets, says "there certainly seems to be something there, but the relationship between low serum cholesterol and cancer is by no means clear, consistent, and unequivocal."

In an attempt to resolve the issue, the U.S. National Heart, Lung, and Blood Insti-

tute (NHLBI) contacted about 100 researchers who have been studying cholesterol and heart disease and asked them to reevaluate their data to see if they show an association between low cholesterol concentrations and cancer.

CONFLICTING EVIDENCE

As long ago as the early 1970's evidence suggesting a low cholesterol—cancer connection was reported by M. L. Pearce and S. Dayton of Veterans Administration Hospital in Los Angeles. They noted an increased incidence of cancer in men on a cholesterol-lowering diet. But other researchers could not confirm this result when they looked at data from similar studies.

Then in 1976, Geoffrey Rose of the London School of Hygiene and Tropical Medicine accidentally came across a relation between low cholesterol and colon cancer.

Rose hypothesized that colon cancer might be associated with high cholesterol concentrations. He reasoned that the populations with high rates of colon cancer were those with high rates of heart disease and high average cholesterol concentrations. He reviewed data from a number of large, prospective studies of heart disease and came up with an unexpected finding. He found that those who got colon cancer tended to be those whose cholesterol was low—less than 190 milligrams of cholesterol per 100 milliliters of serum. The serum cholesterol concentration of the average person living in the United States is 215 per 100 milliliters, and until recently it was 230 milligrams per 100 milliliters. Only 10 per cent of Americans have cholesterol concentrations below 190 milligrams per 100 milliliters.

But Rose's study was retrospective; it looked back, reviewing the past history of those with colon cancer. One of the first prospective studies was that of Robert Beaglehole and his associates at the University of Auckland, New Zealand. They reported in 1980 that in an 11-year study of 630 New Zealand Maoris, men and women with serum cholesterol concentrations below 190 milligrams per 100 milliliters had a higher rate of cancer. Similar results were then reported by Curtis Hames, director of the Cardiovascular Epidemiology Study in Claxton County, Georgia. Hames's group studied 3,102 people for 12 to 14 years.

In the meantime, researchers with the Framingham study, a prospective NHLBI-supported study of 5,200 residents of Framingham, Massachusetts, were looking at their data, which go back to 1948. Manning Feinleib, an NHLBI epidemiologist in charge of analyzing Framingham results says, "We found to our surprise and chagrin that people who were at the lowest end of the cholesterol spectrum had an increased cancer mortality." The association, however, held only for Framingham men, not for women. It was especially strong for colon cancer but also held for all cancer combined. Men with cholesterol concentrations below 190 milligrams per 100 milliliters of serum had three times the incidence of colon cancer of men with higher cholesterol concentrations.

Data from two other NHLBI prospective studies that involve only men—the Puerto Rico Heart Health Study and the Honolulu Heart Study—also show an association between low cholesterol and cancer. In Honolulu, the association was with stomach, colon, liver, and lung cancers. In Puerto Rico, it was with stomach and esophageal cancers.

However, four other prospective studies do not show any such association. These studies included deaths from all types of cancer.

RESULT, NOT CAUSE?

The picture became more complicated when two other groups found an association between low blood cholesterol concentrations and cancer, but an association that disappeared with time. Rose and M. J. Shipley of the London School of Hygiene and Tropical Medicine followed nearly 18,000 men for 7½ years. In the first two years of follow-up, those who had low cholesterol concentrations on entering the study had higher cancer death rates, but in subsequent years the rela-

People with low cholesterol levels tend to have more sterols in their intestines, which intestinal bacteria like these can convert to carcinogens.
© David Scharf

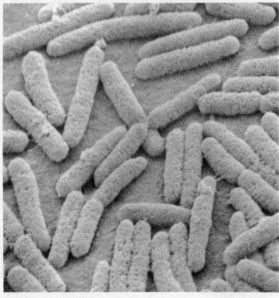

tionship disappeared. This finding led Rose and Shipley to propose that the men who died of cancer in the first two years of the study may have had undetected cancer when they entered the study. This cancer may have caused their cholesterol concentration to drop. Thus the low cholesterol concentrations in those who died of cancer in the first two years may have been a manifestation of the cancer, not a cause.

F. Cambien and J. Richard of Equipe de Recherche de Cardiologie INSERM in Paris together with P. Ducimetiere of Unité 169, INSERM in Villejuif, France, came to a similar conclusion after noting that an association between low cholesterol and cancer in their population of 7,603 middle-aged men disappeared after seven years of follow-up.

DATA INADEQUATE

In 1980 the NHLBI held a conference to review the available data on low cholesterol

Dr. Jeremiah Stamler recommends eating plenty of fiber with foods low in fat and cholesterol to move the cholesterol out of the intestines.

Courtesy of Dr. Jeremiah Stamler

and cancer. "We agreed that there is weak but suggestive evidence that low cholesterol may be in some way associated with cancer risk," NHLBI director Robert Levy says. "But the association still seemed inconsistent."

One reason why existing data are inadequate to determine whether there is a relation between low cholesterol and cancer is that heart disease is much more common than cancer. Therefore, even the largest of the studies of cholesterol and heart disease have relatively few cancer deaths. And when it comes to breaking down the data into cancers of specific types, there are even fewer deaths. It remains possible that low cholesterol may be associated with cancers in general, yet, says Stamler, "Everything we know about cancer tells us you must be very careful about treating all cancers as a group."

POSSIBLE EXPLANATIONS

Several explanations have been considered for the association, if any, between low cholesterol and cancer. First is the possibility, raised by the French and British studies, that low cholesterol results from, rather than causes, cancer. Levy is a bit doubtful of this, because if it were true, the Framingham cases would have had low cholesterol concentrations for more than 10 years before their cancers were detected. "It would be strange, although not impossible, for low cholesterol to be a marker for cancer so long ahead of time," he says.

It also may be that low cholesterol levels are linked to another factor that makes people susceptible to cancer. One possibility is that some people absorb less fat, and so absorb less of the fat-soluble vitamins, especially vitamin A. A deficiency in vitamin A has been associated with an increased risk of cancer. Hames finds that those people in his study who had low cholesterol concentrations and cancer also had lower blood concentrations of vitamin A.

Stamler suggests that people whose serum cholesterol is naturally low may either absorb dietary cholesterol inefficiently or excrete it efficiently. In either case, they would tend to have more sterols (products of fats in the diet) in their intestines than do people

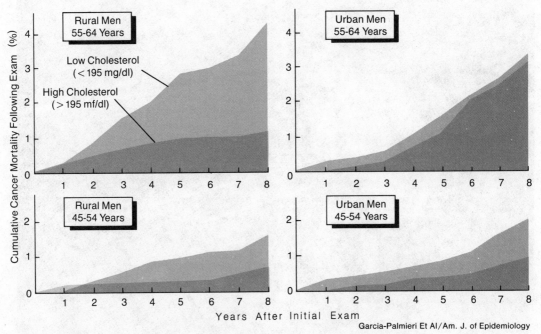

The Puerto Rico Heart Health Study found a low cholesterol–cancer association.

who eat the same diet but have higher cholesterol levels. Intestinal bacteria can convert sterols to carcinogens, or cancer-producing agents, which may explain why those people with low cholesterol are at a higher risk at least for colon cancer—if indeed they are. "If this hypothesis is true," says Stamler, "the way for people with naturally low cholesterol concentrations to protect themselves against cancer may be to eat a diet low in total fat and cholesterol and also to eat plenty of fiber to move the cholesterol out of their intestines."

CAUTION FOR NOW

It is not yet clear what this information means to anyone who is concerned about diet. Levy says that the NHLBI still recommends that those whose cholesterol concentrations are high try to lower them by dieting. But, he says, "To those who have suggested that the lower the [serum] cholesterol the better, the data on low cholesterol and cancer doesn't silence them but it should make them a little more cautious."

Although the American Heart Association recommends diets low in saturated fats and cholesterol, Scott Grundy of the Veterans Administration Hospital in San Diego, who heads the Heart Association's nutrition committee, says he thinks that for those whose serum cholesterol is below 200 milligrams "the reasons for changing the diet are not as compelling as for those whose cholesterol is 250, where the risk of heart disease is 4 to 5 times as high. There is no proof yet that lowering your cholesterol from 200 to 160 is beneficial. I'm not advocating that people push their cholesterol as low as possible." But, he explains, since diet can lower cholesterol concentrations by only 10 to 15 per cent, no one with elevated cholesterol is likely to lower his cholesterol to anywhere near the range that may be associated with cancer.

At present, the NHLBI and the Heart Association are awaiting additional information on low cholesterol concentrations and cancer □

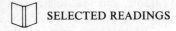 SELECTED READINGS

"Cholesterol dilemma" by E. C. Naber. *Bio Science,* September 1980.

"Low fat diet poses little or no cancer risk" by R. J. Smith. *Science,* May 29, 1981.

H. Armstrong Roberts

STROKES

by Jane E. Brody

True or false?
- *Strokes happen only to older people.*
- *Strokes occur without warning.*
- *There is nothing you can do to prevent a stroke.*
- *Few who survive a stroke are ever normal again.*

ALL the above statements are, as you may have guessed, false. The very myths that surround stroke—the third leading cause of death in the United States—contribute to its disabling of so many thousands of people annually.

The truth is that stroke can occur at any age, though it is far more common after age 60; that many, perhaps most, strokes are preventable, and that to be most effective prevention should start while you are young.

Furthermore, strokes often give warnings that can alert you and your physician to the need for treatment that can head off a potentially crippling attack.

Of the 500,000 people in the United States who suffer strokes each year, two-thirds survive. Even after a major stroke all is not lost. Though most victims suffer some lasting disability, about one-third recover fully or nearly so and can return to their usual activities. Those who do not can often regain much of their abilities through modern rehabilitation programs. About one-half remain partly handicapped and 15 per cent are incapacitated. Nearly 3,000,000 people in the United States alive today have suffered strokes.

Louis Pasteur suffered a stroke at age 46 that nearly killed him. Through determined effort he returned to work and, despite lasting paralysis on his left side, continued his pioneering work in establishing the livesaving science of immunology.

WHAT IS IT?

A stroke is a sudden disruption of the blood supply to a part of the brain, which in turn disrupts the body function controlled by that brain area. Without a source of fresh blood, brain cells are deprived of oxygen, which can paralyze or kill them, depending on how long the deficit lasts. Though cell paralysis is often reversible and the lost function is regained after a while, the death of brain cells is permanent, usually leaving lasting disability. Sometimes, however, uninjured cells can take over the lost functions.

Strokes are of three major types, as follows:

Thrombotic. The most common type, thrombotic stroke, it arises in arteries supplying the brain that have become partly closed by the fatty deposits of atherosclerosis. Blood flow around the obstructions is slowed so clots can form and lodge in the clogged vessel, blocking the blood supply to a part of the brain. (An identical process in the coronary arteries is the primary cause of heart attack.)

Embolic. In embolic stroke a wandering clot becomes lodged in a cerebral artery and, as in the thrombotic stroke, blocks the blood flow.

Hemorrhagic. Sometimes, because of a weakness present from birth or as a result of uncontrolled high blood pressure, a "blowout" occurs in a cerebral artery and a leakage of blood or a hemorrhage results. The fatality rate from this type of stroke is extremely high and the chances of complete recovery are poorer than with strokes caused by clots.

RISK FACTORS

With or without full recovery, a stroke and the damage it can induce are usually a devastating experience. Though little progress has been made in reducing the death rate among the victims of strokes, much is known about how to prevent them. The main clues to prevention reside in the factors known to increase the risk of having a stroke. Since most of these factors are identical to those that increase the chances of a heart attack, preventing one may prevent both.

High-blood pressure. This silent health problem is the single most common factor associated with strokes, both the clot and the hemorrhagic types. More than one-half of strokes occur in people with high-blood pressure. Even mild hypertension (high-blood pressure), if not adequately treated, increases the risk. Elevated blood pressure promotes clogging of the arteries and puts abnormal pressure on the blood vessels' walls, possibly causing a rupture at a weak spot. Blood pressure should be checked regularly, and consistently high pressure should be treated with a low-sodium diet, weight control, and, if necessary, drugs.

High-fat diet. The diet typical of many people in the United States is rich in saturated fats and cholesterol. This promotes atherosclerosis, the accumulation of fatty de-

A team of emergency medical technicians prepare a stroke victim for transport to a hospital. Prompt care can prevent functional loss and death.

H. Armstrong Roberts

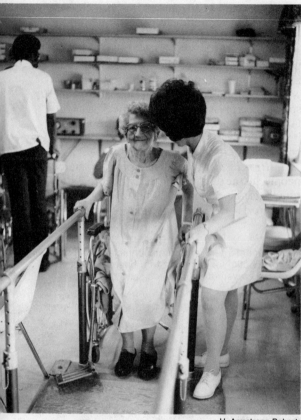
H. Armstrong Roberts

Engaging in a program of special rehabilitation exercises soon after suffering a stroke is a vital factor for many patients in making a major recovery.

posits in arteries throughout the body, most critically in those arteries that nourish heart and brain. Lowering blood-cholesterol level by eating less fat and fewer cholesterol-rich animal foods may reduce the risk of brain-damaging clots.

Stress. A stroke often seems to be precipitated by stress, perhaps through a direct effect on circulation in the brain or because stress raises blood pressure. Various relaxation techniques or professional counseling may help improve the quality of life as well as ward off a stroke.

Inactivity. Though the link between sedentary living and stroke is not firmly established, the potential benefits of exercise to the circulation—less atherosclerosis, larger

and more numerous blood vessels—should benefit the brain as well as the heart. However, exercise should be regular and moderate; occasional bursts of vigorous activity can precipitate a stroke.

Smoking. Again, though the evidence is not conclusive, most researchers believe that, for men at least, stroke should be added to the list of life-threatening disorders that may be increased by tobacco smoke, probably because of nicotine's adverse effects on blood vessels. Men who are heavy smokers have nearly three times as many strokes as non-smokers with the effect of smoking most prominent in men aged 45 to 54.

Obesity. This all-too-common health problem increases the likelihood of developing high blood pressure, heart disease, and diabetes, all of which in turn increase the risk of stroke.

Oral contraceptives. Women who suffer migraine headaches while taking birth-control pills that contain estrogen face an increased risk of stroke. The pill is also a stroke hazard to women in their 40's, especially those who smoke.

Of course, other factors linked to stroke, such as being male, black—there is a higher incidence of strokes among blacks than among whites—or genetically prone to atherosclerosis, are not under your control. But even here greater attention to life habits and underlying diseases that are also linked to stroke can reduce risk substantially.

WARNING SIGNS

One such problem, called transient ischemic attacks, or T.I.A.'s, actually serve as a warning sign of an impending stroke.

Recognition and prompt treatment can avert a serious stroke. A T.I.A. is actually a ministroke caused by a temporary loss of blood supply to a part of the brain. It usually lasts only a few minutes and nearly always less than an hour, with complete recovery within a day.

Symptoms are often vague and confusing, and because they are temporary, people tend to brush them off. However, any of the following symptoms, even in people as young as 30 or 40, should be brought to a doctor's attention without delay:

- Weakness of or numbness in an arm, hand, leg or facial muscles, usually only on one side of the body.
- Difficulty speaking, understanding speech or swallowing.
- Failing or blurry vision in one or both eyes.
- Deafness or ringing in the ears.
- Clumsiness or mild loss of balance; dizziness or fainting, often with double vision.
- Sudden, unexplained headache; abrupt personality disturbances (irritability, impatience, suspiciousness), impaired judgment or forgetfulness.

PREVENTION

Four out of five stroke victims have a history of transient ischemic attacks, and 35 per cent of them suffer a stroke within five years unless treatment intervenes. Effective

After three severe strokes rendered her unable to speak, read, or walk, actress Patricia Neal worked relentlessly in therapy and now leads a normal life.
UPI

treatment includes the use of special drugs to prevent blood clot formation; small daily doses of aspirin, also believed to have an anti-clotting effect; or surgery.

Stroke-preventing operations include bypass surgery to improve circulation to areas of the brain supplied by damaged arteries and surgery to clean out the carotid arteries, blood vessels in the neck that are the main source of the brain's blood supply. Other risk factors would also be treated.

SOME AMAZING RECOVERIES

In 1964, while pregnant with her fifth child and in the middle of shooting a film in Hollywood, Patricia Neal suffered in quick succession three massive hemorrhagic strokes that nearly killed her.

Thanks to emergency surgery to repair the ruptured blood vessel in her brain, Miss Neal, then 38 years old, survived, only to emerge two weeks later from a coma to find herself with double vision and unable to speak or walk.

"I wanted to die," she recalled four years later. Instead she began the long struggle back to life and health. Aided by her husband, the author Roald Dahl, and by friends, neighbors, and professional therapists, Miss Neal learned to speak, read, and walk again. Six months after her strokes she gave birth to a healthy daughter and immediately resumed seemingly endless and exhausting rehabilitative exercises and speech lessons. They paid off. Three years later she was able to return to the demanding job of acting as the star of the movie "The Subject Was Roses."

Miss Neal's recovery after such severe strokes is an inspiration to all, but especially to the 300,000 or so people in the United States who each year suffer a stroke and live.

Nearly 3,000,000 alive today have survived one or more strokes. Though about 30 per cent of the survivors recover fully and return to normal activities, 55 per cent are left partly handicapped and 15 per cent totally handicapped.

REHABILITATION

The extent of brain damage incurred determines the outer limits of recovery.

However, how close a patient comes to reaching the limits is determined as much by the attitudes and efforts of the patient and the patient's family as by the timing and quality of special rehabilitation exercises.

For some patients, tests that delineate the cause of the stroke can lead to delicate brain surgery or other therapy that may head off a recurrence. But for most the main task is a struggle to adjust to and regain lost abilities.

The rehabilitation effort must start almost immediately to keep joints from becoming frozen and to take advantage of the responsiveness of the brain to speech therapy during its period of spontaneous recovery. The exercises must be vigorously pursued even when the effort is exhausting and seems hopeless, since most patients do improve significantly through rehabilitation.

As a rule, whatever major recovery is going to take place happens during the first year after the stroke, although slight gains can still be made through continued exercises and practice.

Within the limits imposed by any permanent damage to the brain, the more highly motivated the patient and the more understanding and cooperative the family, the more successful the rehabilitation and adjustment will be.

COMMON DISABILITIES

It is most important for all involved—the stroke victim and his or her family and associates—to know what can happen after a stroke and to respond in a way that will help rather than hinder recovery. Among the disabilities that are common after a stroke are these:

Speech and language difficulties. About one-half of stroke victims lose all or part of their linguistic facility at least temporarily. The difficulty may involve an inability to form intelligible words or sentences, understand spoken or written language, write, name objects and express what they mean. Often the patient will indicate understanding when the message did not really get through or was garbled.

Speech therapy should start as soon as the patient is allowed up. In speaking to a stroke victim with language problems, stand on the "good" side, keep sentences short and limited to one or two ideas, use your natural voice, speak slowly and distinctly and do not shout, use everyday words and phrases, do not interrupt when the patient tries to speak, do not talk down to the patient or correct mistakes, and give instructions one at a time and in simple phrases.

Partial paralysis. It is usual for a stroke patient to be partly or completely paralyzed on one side of the body—the side opposite the brain hemisphere in which the stroke occurred. Nine of 10 patients who cannot walk in the aftermath of a stroke will recover that ability, though some may have to use a cane or walker. When an arm is paralyzed, however, full recovery is much less likely. Here again, starting rehabilitation as soon as possible is crucial, as is devotion to the prescribed exercises.

Visual disturbances. About one in five stroke victims experience such problems as double vision, rapid eye movements (nystagmus), total blindness in one eye or a loss of peripheral vision in both eyes, making it seem as if blinders are on. Patients may totally ignore objects on the side where vision is impaired, not even turning their heads. Eyeglasses cannot help in such cases.

Spatial perceptions and the sense of balance may also be impaired. This results in "navigation" difficulties—bumping into doorways and not knowing left from right or sitting from standing. A patient with visual or spatial problems should not be allowed to drive.

Fatigue. Though the reasons are not clear, extreme fatigue is virtually a universal occurrence in the aftermath of a stroke, sometimes lasting a year or more. Everything seems to require an enormous effort, and once-active people may find this extremely distressing.

While it is best that the patient give in to the body's demand for additional rest, care must be taken that the fatigue is not being perpetuated by depression that should have professional attention.

Personality changes. This effect of a stroke is probably harder for loved ones to take than physical disability. For weeks or

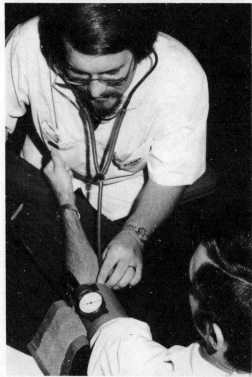

American Heart Association

High-blood pressure, the most common risk factor associated with strokes, should be treated and checked on a regular basis.

months after a stroke the patient may be extremely irritable and demanding, resistant to assistance, given to unreasonable anger and rapid mood swings. Sudden, unexplained crying jags, inappropriate bursts of laughter and streaks of cursing are common. These nearly always disappear with time.

If the patient is apathetic and uninterested in living, it is up to family and friends to try to stimulate interest and reignite the spark of life, which is essential to successful, rehabilitation. Excessive self-pity, depression, and resistance to therapy should receive professional attention.

Stroke patients should not be treated like helpless children and waited on hand and foot but should be encouraged to do more and more by themselves. It is important to be reassuring and sympathetic, but not pitying. To help rebuild a sense of worth, let the patient know he or she is still loved and worthwhile. Be encouraging about all progress, giving positive feedback immediately after something is done correctly. But do not nag about errors. The patient is already frustrated enough.

Learning problems. Though there is no loss of basic intelligence after a stroke, attention span and the ability to reason, render sound judgments, and remember things from moment to moment may be seriously impaired. Something learned in one setting may be quickly forgotten in another.

Most patients do better if detailed instructions, appointments, or other important messages are put in writing. Written reminders around the house about where things are and how to use them are also helpful.

A TEAM EFFORT

Stroke rehabilitation is a team effort. Professionals on the team include a physiatrist (physician trained in rehabilitative medicine), physical therapist, speech therapist, occupational therapist, recreational therapist, psychologist or psychiatrist, and social worker. Most large community hospitals and medical centers have special rehabilitation teams; in addition, some cities have free-standing rehabilitation centers.

If no rehabilitation facility exists in your area, you may be able to do a great deal yourself, with the assistance of friends and relatives, to aid a stroke patient's recovery, especially in the matter of speech therapy.

In addition, family and patient support may be available through "stroke clubs" organized under the auspices of the Easter Seal Society or the American Heart Association. Both organizations can provide much valuable information about strokes □

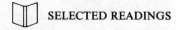 SELECTED READINGS

"Family works a miracle" by D. H. Melhem. *The New York Times Magazine,* March 11, 1979.

Stroke: A Guide for Patients and Their Families by John E. Sarno and Martha Taylor Sarno. McGraw-Hill, 1979.

What Every Family Should Know About Strokes by Lucille J. Hess and Robert E. Bahr. Appleton-Century-Crofts, 1980.

© 1982 Ira Berger

THE PLACEBO EFFECT

by Robin Marantz Henig

THE placebo effect has for years been considered a medical joke, proof of the amusing gullibility of the masses. In the 19th century, Sir William Gull, a noted physician, published a satirical report of the usefulness of mint in the treatment of rheumatic fever. He had meant to mock the many purported cures for rheumatic fever that were bandied about at that time, but to his dismay mint-water treatment soon became one of the most popular of these cures. To his greater dismay, even though he had thought of mint at random, the treatment worked. Gull's mint water, like so many nostrums and potions of his day, worked because patients and physicians believed it would. It worked because of the placebo effect.

SERIOUS MEDICINE

Placebos, we now know, can be serious medicine. A placebo is a pharmacologically inactive drug, usually in the form of a salt water injection or a milk sugar pill dressed up to look like the real thing. In recent years, the benefit of the placebo has been documented and studied around the world.

Contrary to folk wisdom, a response to a placebo does not prove that a patient is either a fool or a hypochondriac. Persons who respond to placebos may be well-read, well-educated, and indeed sick. Inactive "drugs" have been shown to cure certifiable physical ills ranging from allergies to warts. They have produced physiological changes in such hard-to-fake readings as blood cell counts, pupil size, respiratory rate, and blood pressure. Scientists studying it now view the placebo effect as a window on the mind-body relationship, and hope to learn from it just how the mind stimulates the body to mount an internal attack against the things that ail it.

The placebo's clinical clout comes not from chemistry, but from conviction. Belief in the pill—and in the doctor prescribing it—has been shown to lead to some rather astounding cures. In one patient, an impressive-looking sugar pill was able to lessen dramatically the tremors associated with Parkinson's disease—but when the same substance was mixed with milk and given to a patient without his knowledge, the tremors returned. Placebos need not be inert substances. They may be drugs with known pharmacological properties that simply are not appropriate for the condition for which they are prescribed, as when antibiotics are given to treat a cold. Dr. Stewart Wolf of the Cornell Medical Center in New York City demonstrated this when he treated a group of patients with nausea with a drug he assured them would make them feel better. All the nauseated patients improved, even though Wolf had given them syrup of ipecac—which is normally used to induce vomiting.

The placebo effect is activated not only by drugs, but by other interventions as well. Certain surgical procedures, such as those used to treat angina and the hearing disorder called Meniere's disease, have been compared with sham surgery (skin incision but no real surgery) to see which is more effective. The result: both real and fake operations were equally successful. This finding led researchers to conclude that the fuss and attention of surgery, rather than the procedure itself, may have caused the improvement. The placebo effect also has been shown to play a major role in the benefits of psychotherapy.

FAITH IS THE KEY

Faith is essential in mobilizing a placebo effect. Faith in the drug, faith in the doctor, and faith in the doctor's faith in the drug. For example, in a study by Dr. Thomas C. Chalmers of the Mt. Sinai Medical Center in New York City, designed to see whether vitamin C helped prevent colds, a belief in the vitamin was found to be the best cold preventative. The group of subjects given vitamin C was told they were the placebo group, and they developed more colds than did the real placebo group, who were told they were being given vitamin C. In another study, two groups of patients with bleeding ulcers were given placebos under different conditions: either by a nurse, who told them they were to receive an experimental drug with uncertain effects, or by a physician, who presented the pill enthusiastically and said it was sure to improve the patient's condition. In the nurse's group, 25 per cent of the ulcer patients improved with the placebo. In the enthusiastic doctor's group, the improvement rate was 75 per cent.

Despite the incredible power of the placebo, many physicians hesitate to prescribe it. Some think its use violates medical ethics, involving as it does the deception of the patient. Some believe it denigrates the patient, since the placebo (which in Latin means "I shall please") is usually used to placate rather than to search for the cause of the patient's complaints. And some, perhaps, fear that an acknowledgment of the effectiveness of placebos is a tacit admission that much of what doctors do—from psychotherapy to drug treatment to surgery—entails a little bit of voodoo.

THEY DO WORK

However much they may resist it, doctors can't escape the fact that placebos work about 30 to 40 per cent of the time. A classic literature review by Dr. Henry K. Beecher, a

Dr. Arthur K. Shapiro poses with a narwhal tooth—an ancient nostrum which supposedly restored youthfulness to old men.

Evelyn Floret/PEOPLE WEEKLY © 1981

In a remote village where most people depend on witch doctors for cures and potions, one of Ghana's most respected witch doctors performs a ritual healing ceremony.

John Moss/Photo Trends

Harvard anesthesiologist, reported in 1955 that of more than 1,000 patients treated in 15 clinical studies, an average of 35 per cent had improved on placebos. These patients had suffered from conditions including severe postoperative pain, seasickness, headache, cough, hay fever, and anxiety.

A lot of poetry and not much hard science has been invoked to explain the placebo effect. As journalist Norman Cousins phrased it in *Anatomy of an Illness:* "The placebo ... works not because of any magic in the tablet but because the human body is its own best apothecary and because the most successful prescriptions are those filled by the body itself."

Doctors are often equally vague in their descriptions. "The placebo mobilizes the doctor within," says Dr. Arthur K. Shapiro, a psychiatrist at Mt. Sinai Medical Center, paraphrasing Albert Schweitzer. "The placebo effect is an instinct; it's a built-in, genetically determined will to live. If you think about it in terms of survival of the species, you can see the adaptive value in developing a placebo effect, a rationale for living. Gods, religion, doctors—they're all placebos."

BUT HOW?

But this leaves us wondering just how the body goes about filling its own prescriptions, just how a pill—either active or inert—can help turn the will to live into a physiological healing force. The search for the placebo mechanism has been undertaken by only a few researchers, and it has taken them inside the human brain.

"The mind is located in the brain," says Dr. Jon Levine, a neurologist at the University of California at San Francisco. "If you make that assumption, then the changes that occur when no active intervention is involved must be a manifestation of the intrinsic healing systems in the body. The most logical place to look for these systems is in the brain."

Levine and his co-workers have demonstrated that the placebo effect may be related to the brain chemicals known as endorphins. These "natural morphines," several times more powerful than the drug itself, are released in response to pain. Their release has been shown to be stimulated by acupuncture, certain drugs, and, Levine theorizes, by placebos as well. Studying patients experiencing pain following extraction of impacted wisdom teeth, Levine showed that the administration of naloxone, a drug known to inhibit the effectiveness of endorphins, worsened the pain in those subjects who previously had responded to placebos. Naloxone had no effect on the pain levels of patients who had not responded to placebos, presumably for the same reason that the placebos themselves had no effect: because the internal painkilling systems of these patients were not switched on.

Scientists are intrigued by Levine's findings, which have since been replicated by researchers at the National Institute of Dental Research. But some have criticized his methods, especially his categorization of subjects as either placebo responders or placebo nonresponders. This, they say, falsely implies that response to nonresponse is a fixed trait determined by an individual's physiology or personality. But the placebo response seems to depend more on the situation in which a placebo is given than on the quirks of the individual who receives it.

NOT FOR DUMMIES

Placebo scholars now know that there is no such thing as a placebo responder. The 30 to 40 per cent of subjects consistently found to respond to placebos are not the same 30 to 40 per cent time and again. Any individual, given the right context, can be a placebo responder. Traditionally, physicians have held an image of a placebo responder as a gullible, uneducated, hypochondriacal patient, who invents distress and really needs only a pat on the hand and a harmless prescription.

Scientists say otherwise. "It's just not true that only dumb people react to placebos," says Arthur Shapiro. "Over the past 10 years, we've conducted studies on more than 1,000 patients. And our studies say that with any class of people, no matter what their IQ, educational level, cultural background, or academic achievement, we can, if the stimulus is appropriate to that class, elicit a placebo effect." The most important factor, he says, is the patient's attitude toward the physician. The more the patient likes the doctor, the more competent, attractive and compassionate the doctor seems, and the more likely the patient is to respond positively to a pill the doctor says will work.

A placebo response tends to indicate a healthy doctor-patient relationship, one in which the patient and doctor like and respect each other. Most placebo responses have been noted among patients who are well-educated, cooperative, and resourceful—just the kind of patient that doctors most appreciate. Studying cancer patients, Dr. Charles G. Moertel and his colleagues at the Mayo Clinic found that those who responded best to placebos for pain relief had one thing in common: they were fiercely independent, either by choice or by circumstance. "To be forced into a condition of severe dependency was something they would not tolerate," Moertel says. "They reached out for any kind of help."

Courtesy of W. W. Norton & Co., Inc.

Norman Cousins, author of *Anatomy of an Illness as Perceived by the Patient,* believes that the placebo effect is an instinct of adaptive value.

The men in Moertel's study were more likely to respond to placebos than were the women. Persons who were widowed, divorced, or separated were twice as likely to respond as were those who were married or never had been married. Women with children were twice as likely to respond as were women without children. And professionals and farmers—who are self-motivated and independent in their work—were more likely to respond than were unskilled laborers or housewives.

OLD MYTHS DIE HARD

But old medical myths die hard, and one of the slowest to die is the myth that placebos help only those whose complaints were imaginary all along. Despite the evidence, doctors continue to use placebos, if they use them at all, as punishment, not therapy. "Placebos are used with people you hate," notes one medical resident in New Mexico, "not to make them suffer, but to prove them wrong."

Ironically, even though a placebo effect depends upon a healthy doctor-patient relationship, it often is built upon the one thing that can shatter that relationship: deception. Many bioethicists say placebo therapy almost always infringes on the patient's rights. "A placebo can provide a potent, although unreliable, weapon against suffering, but the very manner in which it can relieve suffering seems to depend on keeping the patient in the dark," Dr. Sissela Bok, a Harvard University philosopher, wrote in a landmark article in *Scientific American* in 1974. "The dilemma is an ethical one, reflecting contrary views about how human beings ought to deal with each other, an apparent conflict between helping patients and informing them about their condition."

DECEPTION NOT NECESSARY

Some scientists, though, point out that placebo therapy works even when patients are told they've been given a placebo. Studies have shown that deception need not be a part of the placebo package. At Johns Hopkins University, for instance, 14 subjects reported improvement in their anxiety after receiving pills that they knew were placebos. Some of them, despite their doctors' honesty, had to provide their own deception. Even though eight patients believed they had indeed been given placebos, six patients—also told their pills were inert—believed the pills must have contained some active drugs. Two of the six were quite certain of it.

Shapiro points out that not only does honesty not wipe out the placebo effect—it sometimes heightens it. "I tell my patients what I know," he says, "including the results of our studies on psychotherapy [which show that much of psychotherapeutic success comes from the placebo effect]. But because I believe in the value of the placebo effect, I can state this information with integrity and treat my patients intelligently. So I get the placebo effect no matter what."

SOME RISKS

Another argument against overuse of the placebo, quite apart from ethical concerns, is that placebos, like their pharmacologically active cousins, carry certain risks.

Side effects from placebos can be as serious as those due to active drugs, including headache, nausea, dizziness, rash, severe clinical shock, and drug dependency. Adverse effects may be so severe that one researcher, Dr. Steven F. Brena of the Emory University Pain Clinic, invented a new label for it: the "nocebo" response (from the Latin for "I shall hurt"). Dr Brena says that this effect is more noticeable and lasts longer in patients receiving disability payments during the time they are sick.

In addition, the widespread use of placebos to treat the otherwise untreatable can perpetuate our false belief in the magic of medication. Many patients do not feel satisfied until a visit to the doctor is sealed with a prescription, even for conditions for which the only cure is time—or hope. When placebos are prescribed merely to please, the patient's reliance on drugs is reinforced.

THE DOCTOR WITHIN

Norman Cousins says that to focus on the pills, rather than on the placebo response itself, diverts us from the true wonder of the placebo effect—its mobilization of our incredible will to live. "The placebo," he writes in *Anatomy of an Illness,* "is only a tangible object made essential in an age that feels uncomfortable with intangibles, an age that prefers to think that every inner effect must have an outer cause. . . . The placebo, then, is an emissary between the will to live and the body. But the emissary is expendable. If we can liberate ourselves from tangibles, we can connect hope and the will to live directly to the ability of the body to meet great threats and challenges." We can, he says, learn that the most remarkable thing about the placebo effect is what it shows us about the powerful doctor within ☐

 SELECTED READINGS

"Placebos: cheapest medicine in the world" by Mary Gribbin. *New Scientist,* January 8, 1981.

"Deception or potent therapy" by Reginald W. Rhein Jr. *Medical World News,* February 4, 1980.

Anatomy of an Illness by Norman Cousins. W. W. Norton, 1979.

"Ethics of giving placebos" by Sissela Bok. *Scientific American,* November 1974.

"TAXI!"

Drawing by S. Gross © 1981 The New Yorker Magazine Inc.

PAST, PRESENT,
& FUTURE

PAST, PRESENT, AND FUTURE
REVIEW OF THE YEAR

Banoun/Caraociolo/FAO

Sacks of corn donated by the United States are loaded onto a barge for transport to Gao in eastern Mali, which is just one area where many people are in dire need of food.

Food and Population. Total world grain production was up in 1981, but only marginally more than population growth. The world harvest was slightly in excess of 1,600,000,000 metric tons of grain, with abundant crops in North America. However, there was a slight falling off in south Asia; and in sub-Saharan Africa, per-capita food production actually decreased. The Soviet Union imported more than 30,000,000 metric tons, about one-seventh of global trade in grains. The United States continued to be the major supplier of imports, maintaining about 55 per cent of the market. Reserves increased to about fifty days of consumption. Despite the gain in total grain production the number of malnourished and hungry people did not significantly diminish, even though in some parts of the developing world crude birth rates were down slightly. The distribution of food was still very uneven, and the World Food Council estimated that about 440,000,000 people remained at risk, more than one fifth of these children under five years of age. UNICEF estimated that 17,000,-000 children died of malnutrition or of diseases to which it made them vulnerable.

Although no progress was observed in international grain negotiations, the question of world food security remained high on the agenda of the Western economic summit in Ottawa, Canada, and this topic emerged at the first North-South summit conference in Cancun, Mexico, as the subject of greatest attention and broadest consensus. It is expected to be at the top of the agenda for whatever global negotiations ensue in the wake of Cancun and the efforts of the U.N. General Assembly to launch a new round.

Several important reports published during the year dealt with the food situation and in particular with the U.S. role in the international-food system. Food is the largest U.S. business, accounting for 20 per cent of the gross national product and 15 per cent of export value, and employing nearly 20,000,000 Americans in supplying, growing, processing, marketing, transporting, and regulating. Agricultural exports earned more than $23,000,000,000 net for the United States, the 13th consecutive year in which exports increased in value. Since the international-food system is so dependent on U.S. farmers, the findings of the reports—the National Agricultural Lands Study (NALS), the Structure of U.S. Agriculture, and the Global 2000 Report to the President—have great significance for whether the U.S. system can continue, on current trend lines, to play the central role it has played for years. The NALS report noted that the United States is losing land to erosion and non-agricultural uses at a much faster than tolerable rate. The Structure report pointed out that U.S. farms are decreasing in number and increasing in size, that farm debt has doubled in the past five years, and that it is increasingly difficult for younger persons to enter farming. The Global 2000 Report predicted that unless there are basic changes in the global patterns of production and distribution, real food prices could double, at least, by the end of the 20th century.

Martin M. McLaughlin

Recent fossil finds studied by Dr. Richard Kay of Duke University Medical Center, indicate that human ancestors may have been tree-living much later than previously believed.

Duke University News Service

Anthropology and Archaeology. Recent fossil finds have cast doubt on some widely held notions about human origins. The fossils—8,000,000 and 13,000,000-year-old skull and jaw bones—were discovered in Pakistan by anthropologist David Pilbeam of Harvard's Peabody Museum. They have been classified as *Sivapithecus*, a close, if not identical, contemporary of *Ramapithecus,* traditionally viewed as the oldest known hominid (in the human family). Analysis of the fossils indicates that *Ramapithecus* was not a hominid after all, but rather an ancient indirect ancestor of the orangutan. The two fossil specimens reveal facial specializations identical to those the orangutan has derived from its ape ancestors. The find also indicates that the man-ape evolutionary split took place at least several million years later than generally believed. According to Pilbeam, "this new material from Pakistan really clarifies and crystallizes what we've been thinking"—namely, that the hominids and apes did not diverge some 14,000,000 years ago as widely held, but rather some 7,000,000 to 9,000,000 years ago, according to his "best estimate."

Archaeologists have long been searching for clues to many old civilizations, including the Mayan and early Easter Island civilizations. Now they are competing for clues—competing with art thieves. In a recent example of how looters and art thieves are destroying archaeological sites and damaging important evidence, the Naj Tunich, or "stone house," cave of the Petén region in northern Guatemala was vandalized. This cave system, discovered in 1980, contains 1,200-year-old hieroglyphs and limestone wall paintings dating from the Classic Maya period. The Maya tamed the Central-American jungle, erected monumental cities, developed sophisticated art and mathematical concepts, and invented a complex—and still undeciphered—language. They reached their peak between A.D. 250 and 900 and then, for reasons still unknown, faded away. In hopes of unraveling some of the mysteries of the Maya, archaeologists, including George E. Stuart and his son David, an expert on Mayan hieroglyphs, have studied the cave, finding "some of the most beautiful examples of Maya art." Now they must compete with thieves, who, in this case, stole pottery and defaced paintings. ■ Questions about the earliest inhabitants of Easter Island may also have to be answered quickly: archaeological remains are vanishing at an alarming rate as this once remote area becomes more accessible and tourist-filled. The earliest inhabitants of Easter Island left 600 gigantic statues and ruins of vast masonry walls. Now George W. Gill of the University of Wyoming at Laramie believes he may have evidence about who these early builders were. He and colleague Sergio Rapu Haoa, an Easter-Island archaeologist, have analyzed skeletons from 19 sites on the island. They believe that continued skeletal analysis will reveal a Polynesian heritage. Gill also thinks that further study of his finds will substantiate an early theory, proposed by Thor Heyerdhal, that South-American Indians first settled the island and were overthrown by later-arriving Polynesians.

The oldest religious shrine has been found. A sculpted stone face—half-animal and half-human—presided over a sanctuary at El Juyo Cave in northern Spain 14,000 years ago. Anthropologists Leslie G. Freeman of the University of Chicago and colleagues Richard G. Klein of the University of Chicago, J. Gonzalez Echegaray of the Altamira Museum and Research Center in Santillana, Spain, and I. Barandiaran of the University of Santander, Spain, discovered the shrine in 1978–79 and announced the find in 1981. The complex they found is large, the construction of which probably required the cooperation of many people; has an enigmatic quality with features not needed for daily living; and is associated with a supernatural being—all features that archaeologists use to identify a sanctuary. It is the first intact religious sanctuary found from Paleolithic times.

Barbara Tchabovsky

George Stuart

An archaeological treasure trove of ancient Mayan hieroglyphs and wall paintings at the Naj Tunich cave in Guatemala are being stolen and destroyed by vandals.

The northernmost-known shipwreck, of the *H.M.S. Breadalbane,* undisturbed for 128 years, was discovered thanks to a new underwater vehicle developed by Benthos, Inc.

Courtesy of Benthos, Inc.

Don Normark/West Stock Inc.

This abundance of fruits and vegetables in a village market symbolizes a significant change in agricultural practices in much of the Third World.

THE FOOD GAP

by Richard Critchfield

GHUNGRALI village, India, 1959. As the bullocks strain forward, the carts they are pulling groan and creak, their iron-rimmed, wooden wheels digging into familiar dirt ruts. Turbaned, whiskered men coax the big animals ahead in harsh falsetto voices, *"Tat-tat-tat-tat, ta-hah, ta-hah!"* Ghungrali village, high on India's Punjab plain, stirs for another day. Cawing flocks of crows leave their nighttime roosts to scavenge from the rooftops and in the barnyards. Women in

saris churn milk and draw water. Old men chant prayers at the village temple. Through the haze of cooking smoke and the daily procession of bullock carts, the village seems made of dust.

Ghungrali looks like every other northern Indian village. There are the same camels circling the ancient waterwheels, the same stagnant malarial ponds, the same dark, curious Indian faces swathed in shawls. There is the familiar whiff of dried cow dung, *bidi* tobacco, pungent curry powder. There is the century-old banyan tree, roots dangling from its outspread branches like cobwebs. Except in the sowing and harvesting season, the village men often sit about in the tree's cool shade, passively waiting until it is time to get the crops in again. If you peer down Ghungrali's mud-walled lanes, except for the flies, dust and sense of stagnation, it might be picturesque. But, beneath a dusty sky, men and women struggle daily for subsistence inside a culture essentially cut off from the 20th century.

Ghungrali village, 1981. After dark, lights twinkle from 107 tube wells which supply irrigation water. Quick-maturing wheat and rice strains, plus a 60-day mung bean which takes nitrogen from the air, make possible a year-round crop rotation. Ghungrali now has 40 tractors and several combines. The last camel vanished with the waterwheels in the early 1970's. Fertilizer use has risen from nothing to more than 800 tons a year. Water is piped underground to prevent evaporation. Most houses have biogas plants, to supply both cooking fuel and fertilizer.

The bullock carts no longer make that satisfying creak. They have rubber tires and all the old dirt roads are paved. Idle men are gone from the banyan tree, which is now a stop for express buses to the Punjabi cities and Delhi. Several villagers now own cars and even the poorest have bicycles. A new vogue is to include a TV set in your daughter's dowry. The dust that hung like a permanent fog is gone for good and with it the age-old assumption that the future will merely repeat the past.

The change in Ghungrali has been revolutionary, and in many other villages in Asia, some in Latin America and fewer in Africa, much the same thing is happening. Since the mid-1960's, the world's post-1800 technological history has taken a dramatic turn. Better health and diets, longer life spans, plus the spread of contraception, education, and scientific farming are producing, at last, a great change in the general human condition.

For most of the time since 1959 I have been a journalist reporting on developing countries. Since 1969 I systematically observed change in villages in Egypt, Sudan, Mauritius, India, Iran, Bangladesh, Pakistan, Nepal, Sri Lanka, the Philippines, Thailand, Indonesia, South Korea, Taiwan, Morocco, Mexico, and Brazil. In all, I visited 50 countries, including China, and I lived in three villages for more than a year.

My conclusion, after going back to many of these villages recently is that much of the world, especially in Asia and especially in agriculture, may rather quickly challenge the supremacy the West won 200 years ago by harnessing technology first. This has already happened with Japan.

A WORLD OF VILLAGES

A "village" is a small community averaging 1,300 people, most of whom make their living cultivating land. There are about 2,000,000 villages and 2,700,000,000 villagers in the world. Three out of five people on earth live in them. The big difference between these villagers and the West is technology—power over nature, but not over human nature.

From the day people followed their cattle down onto the Mesopotamian plain and invented the plow, sail, wheel, and irrigation, there were no big changes aside from the invention of the moldboard plow, gunpowder, and the printing press, until about 1800. The people of 1800 used much the same energy resources as the people of 1800 B.C. Their travel was limited to the same tiny maximum distance per day. They used much the same materials for tools and fuel. They had much the same life expectancy. In summary, the life style of these people has been static.

Tilling land is a difficult, time-consuming job for this Egyptian farmer with his animal-powered plow. Antiquated methods of farming are the only ones he knows.

© David Burnett/Contact

RAPID POST-1800 CHANGE

But for those of us in the West, 10,000 years of technological stagnation ended after 1800. Today, thanks to western technology, world population has risen sixfold. Real gross world product has risen eightyfold. The distance a person can travel a day is up between a hundredfold and a thousandfold. The amount of energy that can be released from one-half kilogram (one pound) of matter has increased fifty millionfold.

Change has come so rapidly that anything can now happen, and in a very short time. This makes it hard to predict the future. Thomas Malthus, the English economist, went wrong in 1798 because he based his theory that population would outstrip food supplies on 1800 technology. Neo-Malthusians went wrong in the late 1960's because their forecasts of global famine were based on 1960's technology.

Well, it's 1982 and here we all are. Except for a few regional drought-caused famines in India and the African Sahel and man-made famines, as in Cambodia, food supply has kept well ahead of population growth. According to figures from the United Nations Food and Agricultural Organization and the World Bank, Third World economic output per head more than doubled between 1959 and 1975. Per capita grain production has gone up 40 per cent since 1950. The average person on earth eats more now than he did in 1960. Life expectancy has increased about 50 per cent in 20 years.

BIOLOGICAL TECHNOLOGY WINNING

Everywhere in the world, that gap between 1800 and 1982 technology has started to close. This change began in 1966–67. The breakthrough came after 30 years of research in Japan, Mexico, and elsewhere: scientists produced new short-stem, high-yield wheat and rice which grew faster and produced more grain, provided they got enough fertilizer and water. This was purely a genetic phenomenon related to two crops. But it acted as a catalyst for a worldwide acceptance of scientific farming.

The Indians, Pakistanis, and Mexicans planted the dwarf wheat first, almost doubling wheat production between 1967 and 1975. China took longer because it needed time to breed new varieties, crossing the Mexican wheat with its own and Korean cold weather strains. When it did, China doubled its wheat production, to over 60,-000,000 tons in 1977–79. In 1981 China suffered its worst droughts and floods in a quarter century, but that was a temporary setback. Norman E. Borlaug, the Iowa wheat breeder who won the 1970 Nobel Peace Prize for his work in Mexico, says, "China is about to replace the United States as, after Russia, the world's number two wheat producer."

This is just a start. Two years after the 1966–67 breakthrough, more than 14,000,000 hectares (approximately 35,000,000 acres) worldwide were planted in high-yield grain. By 1982 it was five to ten times that. In crop after crop, Japanese, Chinese, Korean, and Indian villagers are starting to get higher yields than U.S. and European farmers.

As a result, we can now give the term "Green Revolution" a new definition. It's the movement of scientific farming, from West to East, North to South, that ranks with the development of agriculture itself 10,000

The use of mechanized plows in many Third World villages represents a dramatic replacement of old agricultural practices with new technology.

Shostal Associates

© Jonathan T. Wright/Liaison

India is a largely untapped source of valuable resources. The Ganges River (above) could supply hydroelectric power and irrigation water, but most of it flows unused.

years ago, and the invention of irrigation and the plow in the Fertile Crescent 6,000 to 7,000 years ago.

This shifting tide of agriculture may have come just in time. U.S. farmers fed 2 per cent of the world's people in 1950, 11 per cent by the late 1970's and will soon feed 15 per cent. Even so, warns Howard H. Hjort, former chief economist in the U.S. Department of Agriculture, if the United States were to meet projected world demand by 1990 all by itself, it would have to produce 45 to 50 per cent more grain each year than it does now.

Can the United States respond? Since 1935, U.S. farmers have kept up with growing world demand with fewer, bigger farms—a drop from 6,800,000 to 2,700,000—and by farming more land—now up to 122,000,000 hectares from 95,000,000 hectares (about 301,000,000 acres from 235,000,000 acres) in 1970. The biggest production gains in the United States since 1935 have come from mechanical technology, such as combines and tractors. Now, warns Lester R. Brown of the Washington-based World Watch Institute, new constraints limit U.S. agriculture's capacity to grow: lower-quality land, lower returns on fertilizer, higher energy costs, and more competition for water.

Meantime, the biggest production gains in Japan, India, and China are coming from biological technology—improved crops and nitrogen. Biological technology works best with irrigated agriculture. India irrigates some 55,000,000 hectares (135,000,000 acres), is adding some 2,500,000 to 3,000,000 hectares (6,000,000 to 7,000,000 acres) more every year, and could irrigate as many as 110,000,000 hectares (270,000,000 to 275,000,000 acres). China irrigates nearly 45,000,000 hectares (110,000,000 acres) and possibly could expand. The United States—where dry land farming is based on rainfall and the plow—irrigates just over 16,000,000 hectares (just under 40,000,000 acres) and has no large untapped supplies of water.

POPULATION PEAK

The other side of the food equation is population. Though a steadily growing and prospering world population will demand vastly more to eat, including more meat and milk, demographers now agree that the rate of increase in world population growth has peaked. Estimates for population in 2000

Tom McHugh/PR

The advent of modern methods of irrigation in Africa, like this set-up on a Moroccan farm, means greater utilization of available land for agricultural cultivation.

have fallen since the early 1970's from 6,500,-000,000 to under 6,000,000,000. The planet's population is currently projected by the authoritative Population Reference Bureau to stabilize at just under 10,000,000,000 people, about 2¼ times more than now.

UNUSED RESOURCES

The leveling off of population coincides with the new food potential of villages. In China, where 24 per cent of the earth's people are fed on just 7 per cent of the world's cropped land, population is expected to peak at 1,500,000,000. But China's villagers never used chemical fertilizer until 1960. They apply only 7,000,000 tons a year now. Simply by using more, they can easily increase wheat and rice yields another 50 per cent.

India is a treasure trove of unused resources. Over 80 per cent of the Ganges and Brahmaputra river water flows unused into the Bay of Bengal. In neighboring Nepal, the Himalayas have six times more hydroelectric potential than all of North America, and it is largely untapped. India farms one-third more land than China but grows only one-half as much grain. It farms about the same amount as the United States but has three-and-a-half times more irrigated, multicrop-

able land and could have seven times more. What, then, holds countries like India back? Not technology, but people's failure to conquer their own human nature.

UNIVERSAL VILLAGE CULTURE

In my work, I've found that something of a universal village culture exists. In all small communities of people living off the land, there are certain shared habits and customs. For example, the basic institutions of all villages, at all times of history, have been marriage, family, and property. As I found out in a visit in 1980, this is even true in China, despite Mao Tse-tung's 27-year attempt to create a marriageless, propertyless communist society. Still there are variations. I have found six variations.

WITH VARIATIONS

First, Confucianism. Embracing East Asia, or about 1,200,000,000 people, it's a system of harmonious, subordinate relationships. Its confidence, esteem for education, and the placing of group over individual interests makes a potent combination for technological development. Japan's sci-fi farmers now grow rice with vinyl sheeting, concrete banked paddies, massive doses of nitrogen, helicopter spraying and an array of ingenious mini-machines designed for the part-time cultivator with a hectare (2 or 3 acres) or so. These allow the Japanese, who are increasingly eating more imported wheat and meat, to grow a large rice surplus on just 3,000,000 hectares (7,500,000 acres). The same practices have spread to South Korea and Taiwan. If China masters these techniques—and its common Confucian culture says it will—a huge economic powerhouse is going to rise in East Asia.

Second is Hinduism. The Hindu caste system affects about 880,000,000 people. It is based on the age-old custom of exchanging labor in return for a share of the harvest. Mukhtar, 35, an Indian laborer with whom I've harvested wheat several times, tells me, "It's better now. We get more money in town and we only work eight hours. And we are free. The landlords can no longer rule over us in the fields. They can no longer treat us like animals."

This breakdown of caste matters because low-caste landless or nearly landless field workers account for nearly 60 per cent of all families in India's 600,000 villages and just over one-half of the country's people. Higher caste landowners make up 15 per cent of village families, yet they own 75 per cent of all land. This badly skews India's income distribution. It will take land reform, and other redistribution of wealth and income before India can fully exploit its agricultural potential. If and when it does, it could quickly become the earth's number one food producer.

The third major village cultural variation is Malay-Javanese. It covers about 170,000,000 people in the nominally Moslem region of Malaysia, Indonesia, and smaller neighboring states. Until the mid-1970's, this culture was extremely resistant to modern technology. For years, Husen, a Jakarta pedicab driver whose fortunes I have followed since 1967, tried to get his father, now 70, to plant new high-yield rice and invest in fertilizer and pesticide. To the old man, the new money values brought by the new rice seemed like a curse. So it was a surprise to go back to Husen's village of Pilangsari in 1978 and find that Husen had come home to farm

for good, that everybody in the village was using the new rice technology and that nobody, including Husen's father, would admit that they had ever opposed it. Sometime in the mid-1970's, scientific rice farming, as well as contraception, suddenly became accepted.

SLOW IN SOME AREAS

In the other three main village cultures—Latin Roman Catholic, Islamic, and African tribal, embracing about 450,000,000 villagers—technological advance is coming much more slowly. Christian villages are held back by the Vatican's opposition to contraceptives, by the social inequality of Latin societies, notions of *machismo,* and the spiritual crisis and loss of confidence in Christianity's Euro-American heartland.

In many Asian villages, the use of high-yield crops, fertilizers, and irrigation has doubled food production. Scientific farming is now popular.

© Jack Fields/PR

Islam, too, is encumbered by medieval social customs. As with the Latins, the Moslem unwillingness to give women rights to equal work and education means 50 per cent of village people are denied their chance to be fully productive. There is also a deeply held Islamic belief that order and reason are limited, and no scientific or technical progress can enlarge them. As Shahhat, a young Egyptian *fellah* whom I have known seven years, has told me many times, "Everything is from Allah. I cannot decide anything."

In contrast, tribal Africans adjust rather easily to technology. Their problem is that modern science has yet to produce techniques to improve productivity in the environment of their slash-and-burn hoe cultivation of millet and sorghum. Africa is the only place on earth where food production actually declined in the 1970's, by 7 per cent.

THE FUTURE . . .
FOR THEM . . . FOR US

How should we perceive what is going on in the Third World villages?

In a 1964 book, *Transforming Traditional Agriculture,* Theodore Schultz of the University of Chicago took what was then an iconoclastic stand. Villagers, he argued, are rational. Economic growth, he went on, depends in large part on their education, health, and life spans. Since they are rational and their knowledge of technology is constantly expanding, he said, we must learn to deal with "disequilibria," or a highly dynamic, highly uncertain future. As each villager is forced to act, learn, and grow, his productivity grows, too, and so does the value of his time. This, in turn, makes it more expensive to have many children. Schultz predicted—correctly, it turns out—that as agricultural productivity rose, so human fertility would fall.

In the 15 years since technology really began reaching the villages, this is exactly what has happened. Not surprisingly, in 1979, when he was 77, Schultz won a Nobel Prize. I met him in Jakarta in 1980, and it was gratifying to discover that our village findings, drawn from entirely different experience, came out at nearly the same place.

Schultz felt that while Africa was doing badly and the picture in Latin America was mixed, a technological revolution was sweeping Asia.

For those of us in the West, the resulting challenge is not what it might seem. Will and Ariel Durant and other historians have reminded us that all civilizations, without exception, have begun with agriculture. They have prospered with commerce and industry, luxuriated with finance and then, cut off from the old agricultural moral code and work ethic, begun to decline. Perhaps we're reaching the end of our own technological petroleum-based rope while all those villagers are about to begin their technological climb.

Yet, western science and power over nature will keep on advancing, too. We may be able to successfully reorganize our increasingly post-agricultural, post-industrial society around electronics, biosciences, and other advances. The challenge will then be whether we can adjust our own human nature to a totally new way of living. And whether, as other nonwestern societies catch up, we can deal with them in a new spirit of cultural equality □

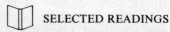 SELECTED READINGS

"Co$_2$, salt, and world food supply" by J. Mattill. *Technology Review,* May 1980.

"Food vs. fuel: competing uses for cropland" by L. Brown. *Environment,* May 1980.

"World food and nutrition: the scientific and technical base" by S. Wortman. *Science,* July 4, 1980.

"World food supplies down." *Americás,* May 1981.

Editor's Note

This article presents one opinion of the world food situation. Other observers are not as hopeful as our author. While conceding vast improvements in Asia, they cite many unsolved problems: inflation, energy costs and availability, continued population growth in some areas, and possible environmental dangers of modern farm technology.

This elaborate building is the Haida Tribe Community House. The spectacular structure stands in Totem Bight Park, which is north of Ketchikan, an Alaskan coastal town.

THE TOTEMS OF ALASKA

by Erwin and Peggy Bauer

IMAGINE for a moment that you are sailing aboard a Russian trading ship in the early 19th century. You have crossed the north Pacific to the New World, and now your creaking vessel glides to anchorage in a stony, sheltered cove of southeastern Alaska. All around you is a panorama of mountains, lingering snowfields, and black-green forests shrouded in soggy gray mists. But there is also human activity.

A few people are shuffling among the low rectangular houses that stand beyond the beach. Close by a fleet of ornate canoes is pulled out onto the gravel. Racks of red fish hang over dense, smoky fires. Then suddenly, through a brief break in the overcast, you focus on a row of tall, colored poles that

tower like a giant picket fence along the water's edge. Even from a distance it is a puzzling spectacle, a culture shock.

In time you go ashore with the rest of the crew. You inspect the poles at closer range and they become even more puzzling, if not actually grotesque. On one is carved the image of a grinning human face. Next to it growls a sharp-fanged bear or a toothy beaver or a crab. Wings project from some poles while others have whale fins or bird beaks. The colors are brick red, black, white, and aqua. Humans, birds, fish, and reptiles are stacked, one atop another, 15 meters (50 feet) high and more. What does it all mean?

Few of the Russian merchantmen saw any beauty or significance in the totems.

PAST, PRESENT, AND FUTURE **259**

Ernest Manewal/Shostal Associates

A tragic story is told by this vivid totem. It portrays a young man who drowned at high tide while his hand was caught in the grasp of a giant oyster.

Most were interested only in acquiring a cargo of furs, the only apparent riches of the American colony, and then hurrying homeward. Even the well educated officers barely mentioned the totems in their journals. Some simply reported that the natives—Tlingit and Haida—worshipped wooden idols. Others believed the totems to be pure ornamentation.

Even until fairly recent times—in fact, midway into the 20th century—relatively few, Indian or non-Indian, seemed to be interested in this compelling and distinctive art form. Unique in all the world, it evolved and flourished only in the lonely coastal villages of Puget Sound, British Columbia, and Alaska's panhandle. It also almost died there, totally unnoticed, as the old totems decayed and fell. Almost nobody carved new ones and carried on the art. Now, however,

there is a great interest in all native American cultures and with it a rush to rescue and study the few totems that survive.

CARVED NEWSPAPERS

The origin of totems and totem carving is almost as mysterious as the carvers themselves. Two hundred years ago, the Tlingits and Haidas were few in number and lived in a land of plenty. They could easily thrive on the bounty of the sea and forests that surrounded them. So these Northwestern coastal natives enjoyed a rare commodity—leisure time—and many became splendid craftsmen. From sedges and grasses they made exquisite baskets that could hold water. They also made durable fabrics from certain tree barks and wild animal hair. Many became expert carvers, first of ornate dwellings, or clan houses, later of seaworthy canoes, and eventually of the stylized totems that told the simple, interesting stories of their lives.

The earliest "totem poles" were structural interior house poles, and possibly the posts at the corners of the clan houses. The detached free-standing poles we see today were the last to arrive on the scene and reached their peak of quality and number in the late 1800's. They were always fashioned of western red cedar, trees native to that cool, damp climate. Largely because the natives lacked a written language, totems became the story, even the history, of their lives. Any Indian could read a totem as easily as we read a newspaper today.

EASY LANGUAGE

Most of the figures on totems can be identified rather easily by laymen. Claws, wings, and beaks, of course, are birds. The straight beak always signified the raven, the most important of the animals. The curved beak was the eagle. Often an entire fish is represented, but just fins or fluted tails can mean the same. Sharp teeth belong to a wolf or bear; look at its feet to see which—long, curved claws are the bear's, rounded paws belong to the wolf. Frogs never have teeth, and the flat halibut with both eyes on the same side of its head is easily identified. Beavers have recognizable teeth and lifelike scaled tails. Ears of humans are on the sides of the head, those of animals on top.

In some areas where the cedars were notably large, the totems were more massive than those carved where growth produced only small trunks. But no matter how large the pole, its cylindrical shape dictated the general outline of the finished totem.

Usually the carving was done on only one side, and often the center had rotted out, so the artist had to use, as economically as possible, a narrow, curved surface. If space did not permit carving the entire figure, only selected, identifiable parts were depicted. Each creature, unless an appendage was later added, had to sit or stand with arms and legs drawn up close to the body. Sometimes creatures were carved with the head down or in other unnatural positions to fit the allotted space.

CAREFUL DESIGN

When the Haida prepared for the carving of the totem pole, a search was initiated for a suitable tree close to the shore. It was felled, cut to the proper length, trimmed, and peeled on the spot. If the pole was large and not to be used as a house pole, it was hollowed out on what was to be the back side (the side with the most knots). That way, it was lighter and easier to move during the carving and raising processes. With the preliminary work completed, the pole was skidded into the water, floated to the village, and beached where the carving would be done.

In the early days the carvers used adzes with nephrite jade bits. Later steel tools brought by the white fur traders were used, including knives with curved blades resembling the Eskimo's mitlik, or thumb knife. The carving of a pole took many months, the actual time depending on the number of apprentices hired.

Poles were not lightly conceived or created. Only carvers of known skill were engaged to oversee the making of a new pole. Underlings did the basic work while the carver attended to the difficult details himself.

Fins, wings, and other pieces standing at right angles to the pole were cut outsize and fitted into a rectangular hole in the pole.

© S. J. Kraseman/Peter Arnold

A man sporting a bear-head hat marks the grave of a Tlingit chief. The bear's mouth displays bared teeth to show revenge for the murder of the chief.

Where glue was needed, it was made from boiling down halibut fins. The main carving job was done after the piece was mortised.

Totem poles were usually raised by the trench method. A trench 6 meters (20 feet) long was dug at a 30° angle and the pole was rolled into it, the top at the shallow end. The depth at the deep end was the depth at which the bottom of the pole would rest. This was often shallower than one would expect, due to the presence of bedrock close to the surface. This is why some poles lean to one side. A short log roller was placed under the upper end and was moved forward as a team of natives pulled on ropes.

HISTORY AND LORE

Totem poles served several purposes in the culture of the Northwest Coast Indians. There was a ridicule pole, for example. One wonderful ridicule pole holds up to derision a white trader who cheated the Indians in a fur exchange. It stands today at Saxman Park, Ketchikan. In a culture that had no written language, traditions and tribal lore were represented by a totem pole that guided oral transmission. Family histories were preserved in wood. Family crests topped the pole, and the rendering of two crests showed a marriage. Often, too, a pole was made as a memorial to one who had died. One famous totem features a top-hatted Abe Lincoln standing at the top.

PRESERVATION EFFORTS

Strangely enough, however, once the totem was put in place it was not kept in good repair. No wood preservatives were ever used, and when a village moved, the poles were left behind to the less than tender mercies of weather and vandals.

Few poles were carved after the early years of the 20th century, and the dignified old columns neared total ruin as years passed. In 1938 a U.S. Forest Service program of reconstruction was launched, and about one-third of those poles known to have been standing at the end of the century were salvaged.

This colorful eye belongs to an eagle on a sign for Sitka National Historical Park. The park is on an island that is located southwest of Juneau, Alaska.

Shostal Associates

However, the program was not a total success. The Civilian Conservation Corps (CCC) engaged the services of natives, many of whom had never seen a pole before and had no woodworking skills. Many valuable poles were sold to dealers, some were stolen, and a great number succumbed to the swift rot that accompanies the abundant rainfall and regrowth of wild vegetation in the area.

In many instances, however, the CCC work was carefully and conscientiously done. Although original native colors could not be duplicated, commercial paints of the same hue were used. A colorless wood preservative was applied, and native tools were used either to carve and finish duplicate poles or to repair the originals. In this way the original type and texture of workmanship was preserved.

THREE MAJOR SITES

There are three major areas in Alaska where totem poles can be seen today. One site that is seldom visited by tourists is Klawak (or Klawock) Totem Park on Prince of Wales Island. All the carvings there were made to contain ashes of the dead or as memorials. These totems are less complex than others, and the poles themselves are small and slender, since this is at the northern limit of the western red cedar. These poles are distinctive in that the uncarved areas have been squared off, as is the base. So it appears that the carver began with a square, rather than a round tree.

The Sitka National Historical Park displays 18 poles in a beautiful, natural setting along a hiking trail that winds among towering evergreens. Sitka is on a picturesque island southwest of Juneau. None of the poles are native to the area, but were brought in as early as 1902. Others first went to the World's Fair in St. Louis in 1903, and currently only 9 or 10 of the poles are originals. The origin of many of them is a mystery. At Sitka, as everywhere, a constant battle is waged to protect the poles from rot and deterioration while maintaining their original character.

But no doubt the best and easiest place to see many totems of different kinds is in and around the quaint Alaskan coastal town

Shostal Associates

In lieu of a written language, northwestern coastal natives carved totem poles to preserve the histories, legends, and traditions of their tribes for their Indian descendants.

of Ketchikan. In the center of the town is Chief Johnson's Pole, the only pole still standing in its original position. It was carved and erected there in 1901. Five other originals are housed at Ketchikan's Heritage Museum, where the visitors can also see restorations in progress and hear a short informative talk on the totems of Alaska.

South of Ketchikan on the Tongass Narrows lies Saxman Totem Park. This area, together with another to the north of Ketchikan, is the best place of all to enjoy the totem poles of Alaska in a natural green setting. A spectacular grouping stands in a flat semicircle of grass against the backdrop of deep green forest. On clear days the huge spires can easily be spotted from the decks of the ships approaching and leaving the busy dock area of Ketchikan.

North of Ketchikan is Mud Bight Village, or Totem Bight, the gem of totem collections. Here, on the exact spot where the Tlingit Indians traditionally had a camp, is a marvelous gathering of totem poles carefully placed where each can be appreciated individually. A wooden boardwalk guides the visitor from one to another. There is also a large Indian clan house built as an exact replica of those constructed previously. The area is in what is now the Tongass National Forest on the edge of a gravel beach. It is edged by a stream that salmons still ascend to spawn each year □

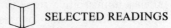 SELECTED READINGS

"Mute relics of Haida tribe's ghost villages" by Wilson Duff. *Smithsonian,* September 1976.

The Totem Poles of Skedans by John and Carolyn Smyly. University of Washington Press, 1976.

Lost Heritage of Alaska, The Adventures and Art of the Alaskan Coastal Indians by Polly Miller and Leon Gordon Miller. World Publishing Company, 1967.

SCIENCE FRAUDS

by

William J. Broad

Andrew Myer

THERE is little doubt that a dark side of science has emerged since the late 1960's. In ever-increasing detail, the scientific and general press have reported the pirating of papers and the falsification of data. Four major cases of cheating in biomedical research came to light in 1980 alone, with some observers in the lay press calling it a "crime wave." Two of these cases may end in criminal charges.

In a profession that places an unusual premium on honesty, the emergence of fraud has created something of a stir. Scientific societies are holding symposia on the subject. The National Institutes of Health (NIH) has taken administrative steps to cope with the rise in cheating. And Congress is preparing to hold hearings on the falsification of data in biomedical research.

Is the issue important? After all, reported cases of cheating are few, and NIH funnels U.S. government funds into nearly 18,000 extramural projects. When a dozen research directors, NIH officials, bench scientists, and sociologists were queried, one recurring observation was that fraud has always been around, but not always advertised. Changes in contemporary science and its interactions with society are making fraud in the labs more visible.

• John Long, a researcher with $750,000 in federal funds at Massachusetts General Hospital, forged data and for seven years watched over a cell line for the study of Hodgkin's disease that proved to be absolutely useless.

• Vijay Soman, a researcher at Yale medical school, plagiarized a rival's paper, fabricated data, and received for 1980 alone some $100,000 in NIH support. Eleven papers were retracted. He ultimately returned to his home in India, but left his coauthor and boss, Philip Felig, in an administrative and ethical tangle.

• Elias A. K. Alsabti, a young researcher from Jordan, pirated almost word-for-word at least seven papers and published them in obscure journals.

• Marc Straus, a Boston University researcher who in three years was awarded nearly $1,000,000 in cancer research grants, submitted reports containing repeated falsifications. He resigned under fire, insisting that he was the victim of a conspiracy by select members of his 20-person staff. More than two years later, after the Boston *Globe* ran a five-part series on the affair, the National Cancer Institute (NCI) initiated an investigation.

In response to these and a few other incidents, Congress has invited two witnesses to the falsification drama, Long and Felig, to come and give their views on what, if anything, is happening to U.S. biomedical research. Also invited are a bevy of NIH officials, research directors, and bioethicists. Cheating is also being discussed at various symposia and in early 1981 at the Harvard School of Public Health, the seventh national conference on Public Responsibility in Medicine and Research held a session on "How to detect and prevent fraudulent or unethical research."

TRADITION OF SELF-CORRECTION

Until recently, charges or even discussions of scientific fraud were seldom aired in public. Most scientists, conscious of their image and eager to avoid political interference, tried to stay out of the limelight. Control was an internal matter. An informal group of scientists could hold court and decide to ban an offender from the realm of research. More fundamentally, science was said to be self-correcting. If an experiment was important enough, other scientists would try to repeat it. This self-correcting mechanism would expose cheating and encourage honesty. It would detect and deter. Dubbed "organized skepticism," this view was originally set forth by Robert K. Merton, the father of the sociology of science. "Scientific inquiry," he wrote, "is in effect subject to rigorous policing, to a degree perhaps unparalleled in any other field of human activity." Initially propounded in 1942, this view has become the conventional wisdom. Donald Fredrickson, former director of NIH, puts it this way. "We deliberately have a very small police force because we know that poor cur-

rency will automatically be discovered and cast out."

A sterling example of such self-correction comes from a case involving a Nobel laureate. The incident unfolded at Yale in the late 1950's, with the arrival of a young graduate student in biochemistry. Working in the lab of Melvin Simpson, the student quickly made significant gains in the cell-free synthesis of cytochrome *c,* a key protein in cellular energy-releasing reactions. In early 1960, Simpson and the student coauthored a paper on the successful experiments that received wide attention because it was the first time such a single, highly purified protein had been synthesized outside a cell. The success carried the student, now equipped with a Ph.D. from Yale, to the lab of Fritz Lipmann at Rockefeller University. There he coauthored a paper with the Nobel laureate. The promising career, however, soon suffered a setback.

Simpson, back at Yale in late 1960 after spending several months on sabbatical in England, reassembled his lab and started trying to extend the successful experiments with cytochrome *c.* His efforts met with failure. "I had gone all around Europe giving seminars on our success," he recalls. "And now I couldn't repeat it. Imagine the agony."

A call from Lipmann at Rockefeller revealed that people in his lab were also having difficulty repeating the student's work. The student was called back to Yale and told to duplicate the cytochrome *c* experiment. He worked under around-the-clock supervision, and failed. He was subsequently told to leave research in general. Two retractions one from Simpson and one from Lipmann's lab, were published in late 1961. Sometime later it was discovered that the student's undergraduate college in Massachusetts had no record of his ever receiving a degree.

MORE REVELATIONS

Since that time, revelations of cheating—but not necessarily cheating itself—seem to have slowly but steadily increased. The cause? According to Robert H. Ebert, former dean of the Harvard medical school, part of the reason may be increasing pressure. Writing in *The New York Times* about the fabrication of data by John Long at Mass General, Ebert said "it would be a mistake to consider this an example of human frailty and nothing more. Medical schools and academic research centers have inadvertently fostered a spirit of intense, often fierce competition . . . There is intense pressure to publish, not only to obtain research grant renewals but in order to qualify for promotion."

The implication in this account of a rise in cheating itself is dismissed in many quarters. Pressure, say a chorus of commenters, has always been around. Moreover, many hold that the rate of finagling has remained roughly the same throughout the years, and cite the purported cooking of data by Mendel, Newton, and Ptolemy to back this up.

CHEATING ESSENTIAL?

A radical view comes from philosopher of science Paul Feyerabend, who holds that small-scale cheating is essential to the advancement of science. He argues that no theory, no matter how good, ever agrees with all the facts in its domain. A scientist must therefore rhetorically nudge certain facts out of the picture, defuse them with an ad hoc hypothesis, or just plain ignore them. A similar but less polemical view is expressed by philosopher Thomas S. Kuhn. Kuhn divides the history of science into periods of normal and revolutionary activity, arguing that during normal periods, anomalies observed by the scientist must be suppressed or ignored.

EXPOSURE TO OTHER SCIENTISTS

If finagling of one sort or another is endemic, what then causes increased exposure? Here it is necessary to make a distinction: exposure of fraud to other scientists and exposure to the public.

In the first instance, one mechanism that may bring cases of cheating out in the open is the denunciation of scientists by one another due to cutbacks in research funding, according to Ronald Lamont-Havers, a former NIH official who witnessed the Long affair from his position as director of research at Mass General. If this is indeed the case, troubled times may lie ahead: since 1979, NIH has had a drop in purchasing power.

The increasingly close scrutiny of research that has direct implications for public policy or public health is also a factor in inter-scientist exposure, according to Columbia University sociologist Harriet Zuckerman. This clearly seems to be the case in the Straus affair at Boston University. Data from about 200 patients studied by Straus and his team were kept in the computer files of the Eastern Cooperative Oncology Group. This was a 40-hospital consortium funded by the National Cancer Institute to conduct large-scale testing of new cancer treatments. In 1978, five members of Straus's team disclosed to officials at Boston University problems with the data. Falsifications ranged from changing a patient's birthdate to reporting treatments and laboratory studies that were never done and inventing a tumor in a patient who had none. Boston University says a detailed study of medical records found no evidence of patient mistreatment or inappropriate care. Disagreeing with this view is a Food and Drug Administration official familiar with an ongoing investigation of the Straus affair: "To say the least, some of this had serious clinical implications, both in the sense that the patient in the study was endangered, and that data generated would present conclusions that were poorly founded."

EXPOSURE TO THE PUBLIC

Concerning exposure to the public, one factor repeatedly singled out is the growth of a vigorous scientific press. Indeed, the National Association of Science Writers, founded in 1934 by 15 reporters, now has more than 1,000 members. And clearly, the NCI investigation of the Straus affair would never have materialized had it not been for the series in the *Globe*.

A general rise in social consciousness among scientists may account for some of the increasing public exposure, according to E. Frederick Wheelock. He is a microbiologist at Jefferson Medical College in Philadelphia whose work was pirated by Jordanian researcher Alsabti. "In the past," he says, "the system was much more closed. People were afraid to call attention to cheating." In his own case, Wheelock at first hesitated to

David Forbert/Shostal Associates

Scientific integrity is based on the careful accumulation and replication of experimental data. All researchers should always carefully monitor their experiments and maintain accurate records of their test results.

charge Alsabti with piracy. Wheelock had kicked Alsabti out of his lab after two young researchers came to him with proof that Alsabti was making up data.

Later, when Wheelock saw his work being published in the scientific literature by Alsabti, he discussed the problem with his program manager at NCI, who suggested that he alert the wider community. After first writing to Alsabti and demanding retractions (that did not materialize), Wheelock wrote letters to *Nature, Science, Lancet,* and the *Journal of the American Medical Association* and described ways for researchers to "avoid such episodes in the future."

RISING SUSPICIONS

The list of possible reasons for increasing exposure rambles on, most everyone having their own pet speculations. Lurking in the record of events, however, is an in-triguing contradiction. A review of the cases where cheating has come to light since the 1970's shows that the failure to duplicate experiments plays a relatively minor role in uncovering fraud. This self-correcting mechanism "worked" in earlier episodes: in the cases of Mendel, Newton, and Ptolemy (though it took two millennia), or in the case of the Nobel retraction. Recently, however, other means have predominated. The mechanism has often been the detective work of young lab assistants or young scientific rivals who have extra-experimental evidence of cheating, who have some independent reason for suspicion. This kind of extraneous sleuthing was the means of discovery in all four of the 1980 fraud episodes.

The gap between real and ideal ways of detecting and preventing fraud (what sociologists of science euphemistically refer to as the "social control of science") has helped

"DON'T FEEL BAD ABOUT FALSIFYING THE SOLUTION. I FALSIFIED THE PROBLEM."

Sidney Harris

fuel a heated critique of the conventional wisdom.

On the deterrence side of the debate, critics have argued that the self-correcting mechanism does not distinguish between error and fraud. In the published literature, an experiment is only found right or wrong. Given the ever-present academic pressure to succeed in a spectacular way, this chance of being found wrong may not deter a researcher from cheating. After all, guesses, fudging, and unconscious finagling that are correct go undetected.

Defenders of the conventional wisdom say that this weakness, by definition, does not make any difference. The only thing that matters is the accumulation of scientific "truth," and not whether a falsifying researcher is caught and punished.

It is here, on the detection side of the debate, that critics rail most vehemently. The acceptance or rejection of claims in science often depends not so much on "truth," according to such observers as philosopher Ian I. Mitroff at the University of Pittsburgh, but on who makes the claim and how well the claim fits prevailing beliefs. In short, the goodness of a reputation or the attractiveness of a theory often gives immunity from scrutiny.

LONG AND BURT

This immunity from scrutiny was probably a factor in why the problems with John Long's contaminated cell lines at Mass General escaped detection for so many years. He worked in a prestigious lab at one of the world's leading teaching hospitals.

Immunity from scrutiny was also clearly a factor in the case of Cyril Burt, the English psychologist whose studies of identical twins supported his theory that intelligence is determined partly by heredity, and whose work went unchallenged during his lifetime. According to Leon Kamin, a psychologist at Princeton, Burt's data remained unchallenged for so long because they confirmed what everyone wanted to believe. "Every professor knew that his child was brighter than the ditchdigger's child," he says, "so what was there to challenge?"

Burt's work was picked up by researchers in the United States, and figured prominently in the debates over whether heredity might underlie racial differences on IQ scores. Eventually, after a reign of nearly 40 years, his data were found to be riddled with internal implausibilities and basic methodological oversights. Some researchers concluded that Burt may have doctored or even invented his collection of IQ data.

Critics for the most part do not argue that the conventional wisdom is wrong, but rather, taken alone, it is inadequate to explain how science really works on a day-to-day basis. Perhaps the most troubling observation is that even when the self-correcting mechanism works, it addresses only experiments and observations that are "important" to pure science, to the accumulation of scientific truth. No one, after all, takes much time to repeat clinical trials of new drugs, therapies, or treatments. Replication of a multi-institutional clinical trial, such as the one at Boston University that Straus worked with, is financially and structurally impossible. In terms of the self-correcting mechanism, these are not applicable areas of research, although they may be important in terms of patient welfare.

Just as there was no scientific or institutional mechanism to detect or deal with fraud in the Straus affair, neither was there a government mechanism. When three top officials at Boston University medical center flew to Washington, D.C. to tell the NCI director about their rapidly unfolding problems, NCI told them there was nothing the government could do.

PREVENTING ABUSE

The slow response of the federal bureaucracy, the questioning of the self-correcting mechanism, and the emergence of a few graphic examples of fraud have combined to stir considerable activity concerning data abuse. At Boston University, the multihospital group that got stuck with the project's bad data has set up a system of random audits to ensure that the program will never again be vulnerable to such falsification. Congress is in the process of holding hearings. The President's commission on bioethics plans to hold a number of sessions at "sites of controversy involving the conduct of research."

Confronted with the increasing reports of fraud-related incidents, NIH has taken steps to prevent abuse in the future. In November 1980, debarment regulations went into effect that allow the government to cut off an entire institution from NIH grants if just one researcher is caught misusing grant money or falsifying reports. This sweeping mechanism was needed, says NIH associate director William Raub, in order to put the onus for prevention and detection of fraud on the institution.

No person or institution has yet been debarred, and NIH officials say they have no plans to make debarment retroactive. If it were, all of Yale University, for example, could well be cut off from the federal research-dollar pipeline. In addition to the threat of debarment, NIH officials say they have now built into their vast computer network an alert system so that NIH administrators are warned if an investigator applying for a new grant is himself under investigation for cheating.

HOW IMPORTANT IS IT?

Is it important? Perhaps the emerging issue of fraud represents a small, seamy side of science that warrants nothing more than a cursory glance before being tossed onto the pile of passed-over issues. One might argue that the major cases are few, and the minor ones are just that, minor. Science is above it all. Nobel Prizes are awarded and greatness is measured not on the basis of "honesty," but insight. Newton and Mendel may have finagled, but their theories are today committed to memory by every high school student.

In a sense, all this is correct. It is also true that fraud in the literature wastes the time and money of researchers who pursue leads only to find them wrong. Further, in a profession where "organized skepticism" is meant to be the rule, the emergence of a type of fraud not detected by the self-correcting mechanism may prove especially corrosive to community ideas.

The mechanism did not and could not deter data fabricators at Boston University, with the result that patient safety was probably jeopardized. And the fact that immunity from scrutiny often seems to supersede any kind of "organized skepticism" can only lead to the discouragement of the young, who tend to be far from immune.

No matter why they come forth, the recent cases illuminate much. They disclose a gap between the ideal and the real, between reliance on automatic self-policing and the fact that mechanisms such as immunity from scrutiny often prevail. They hint at support of philosophical views that say finagling of one sort or another may be endemic to the research enterprise. Perhaps further study of the dark side will disclose more about the structure of science. At the very least, the recent cases illustrate that "organized skepticism" and the self-policing nature of science need themselves be taken with a little more skepticism □

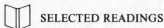 SELECTED READINGS

"Watching the watchers" by Susan Lawrence. *Science News*, May 23, 1981.

"Imbroglio at Yale (I) and (II)" by William J. Broad. *Science*, October 3 & 10, 1980.

Vernon Miller/Brooks Institute

An amazingly lifelike image is apparent in this photographic image of the Shroud of Turin, which suggests the shroud itself is a negative.

SHROUD OF MYSTERY

by Annette Burden

IN the great nave of the cathedral of San Giovanni Battista in Turin, Italy, Roman Catholic priests approached the Holy Shroud of Turin. They removed the relic from its bulletproof plastic shield and special nitrogen-filled atmosphere. They then carried it to a room in the adjoining royal palace where more than 25 scientists and photographers waited.

Shortly before midnight, the room grew silent. Under a frescoed ceiling and surrounded by magnificent paintings, black cloaked nuns carefully unwrapped the shroud from its red silk lining cloth and presented it to the scientists, members of the Shroud of Turin Research Project. The shroud was stretched over the long tilting table of aluminum and stainless steel designed specially for the shroud. The team gathered around, hands held self-consciously behind their backs. Soon they began to stir. They had only five days and nights to work.

ALL TECHNIQUES

Using fiber optics, photomicrography, ultraviolet and infrared light, low-energy X-ray radiation, and ordinary light, they captured every small section of the shroud on film with thousands of exposures. With spectral photoelectric equipment they measured the way light reflects from different areas of the shroud. They collected, with sticky tape and a special vacuum device, samples of tiny fibrils from the shroud as well as debris that had settled on it. For 120 hours around the clock the team worked in shifts. At every moment at least two, sometimes four, tests were going on.

The burned, soiled, tattered piece of linen on which they focused such inordinate attention is believed by many to be the burial shroud of Jesus of Nazareth. It has lain hidden for centuries in its sepulcher behind iron grilles. It is back there today, high above the black marble altar, rolled around a velvet staff, cushioned in silk and asbestos, and sealed in a wood and silver casket lying within an iron chest with three locks, which itself lies within a third wooden chest.

On this momentous occasion in 1978, after a rare exhibition held to celebrate the shroud's 400-year anniversary in Turin, the scientists dedicated to unraveling the shroud's true identity had gained permission to examine it. Consent came from its legal owner, Umberto II, the exiled former king of Italy and head of the Royal House of Savoy, and from Turin's Archbishop Anastasio Ballestrero, the official keeper of the shroud.

IMAGE WITH MANY MARKINGS

The Shroud of Turin is a 4-meter (14-foot) length of linen fabric, yellowed with age, bearing the faint image of the front and the back of an unclothed man laid out for burial. The markings on the linen depict a man who was powerfully built, bearded, about 1.8 meters (5 feet 11 inches) tall. The expression on the face is serene, yet from all indications he suffered torture and died an agonizing death by crucifixion.

The ghostly image seems to show swelling of the face as if from blows to the head, contusions over the body as if from a savage beating, and abrasions on the shoulders. Slightly darker, reddish areas suggest blood from wounds possibly made by nails pounded into the wrist and feet, and from a lance thrust between the fifth and sixth ribs. Other markings such as the scorches and patches along fold lines and symmetrical water marks are the results of a chapel fire, rescue, and repair in 1532.

MYSTERIOUS HISTORY

The shroud's whereabouts can be verified back only 200 years before that fire, to the 14th century when it surfaced in Lirey, France, in the family of a French knight known as Geoffrey de Charny. At that time forgery of religious relics was common, yet the de Charnys insisted the shroud was authentic. Cautiously, the church hierarchy allowed the family to exhibit the shroud to paying pilgrims on the condition it be described only as a representation of the burial cloth of Christ—a description the church has officially used for 600 years.

British journalist Ian Wilson, a member of the nonprofit British Society for the Turin Shroud, believes he knows something about the shroud's travels before it appeared in France and Italy. His hypothesis, constructed from legends, history, and art, traces the shroud from its tomb to Turkey, then to Constantinople, and on to France with the conquering crusaders known as the Knights Templar.

The detective work of Swiss criminologist Max Frei lends credence to Wilson's theory. In dust samples he collected from the shroud, Frei, former head of the Zurich Police Scientific Laboratory, found 48 samples of pollen grains under his microscope. He traced most of the samples to known locations of the shroud in France and Italy. But Frei found seven grains of pollen that came from plants that grow exclusively near the Dead Sea. Others were indigenous only to the Palestine area. To have picked up the pollen, Frei concluded, the shroud had to have been in the Holy Land at some time in its history. The Shroud of Turin Research Project, a nonprofit organization of scientists and photographers from the United States, is careful to point out that from their standpoint, Frei's small sampling was not statistically significant. They say the pollen might have been carried by the wind or deposited by the shroud's visitors. Its presence does not prove that the shroud was ever in the Holy Land.

FRAUD POSSIBILITY

The team came to Turin not to determine whether the shroud was the actual burial cloth of Jesus—there is no way to prove that—but to find out what mysterious process or processes created the image on it. That scientists and photographers of Catholic, Protestant, Jewish, agnostic, and atheistic beliefs might find the shroud to be a clever 14th-century hoax was an intriguing but incidental possibility.

To move ahead, however, the team had to deal with accusations of fraud from a former member of the project, Chicago microscopist Walter McCrone. The Chicago scientist believes he can substantiate the claim made in the year 1356 by a French bishop of Troyes, who insisted that he heard an artist confess to painting it. McCrone, who several years ago exposed Yale University's famous "Vinland Map" as a fraud, said he found "a great deal of artist's pigment" on the shroud. He based his statement on microscopic traces of iron oxide, part of the chemical makeup of red-earth pigments and organic binders used by artists.

Samuel Pellicori, an optical physicist with California's Santa Barbara Research Center, compared the spectral measurements of iron-oxide samples with data collected from the shroud and determined that the body image does not contain enough iron to contribute to its visibility. Other team members, Alan Adler, a professor of chemistry at Western Connecticut State College, and John Heller, a biophysicist with the New England Institute in Ridgefield, Connecticut, used fibril microchemistry and microscope magnification up to several hundred times and found no greater amounts of trace iron in the image than in the background.

Adler offers another explanation for the presence of iron. He says that during the ancient technique of fermenting flax in water to produce linen, the oxidation of cellulose (in the flax) would naturally have caused bonding with iron and calcium in the water. Others believe that since iron is an essential component of human hemoglobin, some of the iron-oxide particles may have come from the decomposed and abraded bloodstains.

On the team's third day with the shroud, the members took the first look at the underside since 1532. They found that unlike the body image, which is contained only in the topmost of the shroud's fibers, the apparent bloodstains had soaked through. After performing detailed microscopic analyses and chemical tests, Pellicori, Adler, and Heller concurred that the bloodstains do contain remnants of hemoglobin as well as serum protein. They also point out, however, that the presence of blood does not authenticate the shroud because the blood could have been applied artificially.

MEDICALLY CONSISTENT

According to Robert Bucklin, a forensic scientist with the Los Angeles County Coroner's office, the markings on the shroud are medically consistent with torture methods used by the Romans 2,000 years ago. Bucklin also pointed out that the shroud's markings depict an expanded rib cage and drawn-in hollow below it, which would be the case if the man died while hanging by the arms. Bucklin's practiced eye also noted an unmistakable sign of rigor mortis in one leg, stiff and slightly raised, as it would have been if both feet were fastened to the cross with a single nail.

In tracing the tool used to inflict the scourge marks that presumably covered the body, historians found that dumbbell-shaped lead weights used by the first-century Romans on their whips, or *flagra,* exactly fit the marks on the shroud. Moreover, excavated examples of the Roman *lancea,* or spear, mentioned in Biblical accounts match precisely the elliptical wound visible on the image's side. But contrary to Biblical accounts and to the event as depicted throughout the history of art, the markings on the shroud show nail wounds through the wrists, not the hands.

In the 1930's a French surgeon named Pierre Barbet of St. Joseph's Hospital in Paris investigated the discrepancy. He conducted experiments with cadavers and found that hands could not support the weight of a body upon a cross, but that wrists could. More verification surfaced in 1968 when archeologist Vasilius Tzaferis of Israel's Department of Antiquities and Museums discovered the first known remains of a crucified man buried on a rocky hillside outside Jerusalem. Examination of the radius bones revealed that this victim was also nailed to his cross through the wrists. One explanation for the discrepancy between Biblical accounts and physical evidence is that in the Bible's original Greek, the word for "hand" can include the wrist and forearm.

EXTREMELY DIFFICULT TO FORGE

Shroud scholars agree they cannot discount the possibility that an intelligent and

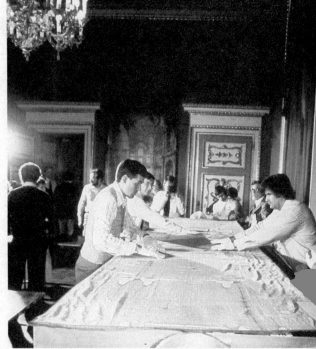

E. H. Brooks II, Brooks Institute

Physicist John Jackson, wearing gloves at left, helps smooth wrinkles out of the delicate shroud.

ingenious medieval forger created the shroud 600 years ago, but they find it hard to believe that a forger would have been aware of so many little-known historical details. They also point out the technical difficulty of painting an image that reveals no brushstrokes, that blurs if one approaches within arm's reach, that has no clearly defined edges except in the scourge wound areas, and that varies in darkness or intensity in direct three-dimensional proportion to the distance the covering sheet would have been from a body.

This three-dimensional information was discovered by two of the founding members of the Shroud of Turin Research Project, aerodynamic engineer Eric Jumper and physicist John Jackson. The two were intrigued by the turn-of-the-century discovery of an amateur Italian photographer, Secundo Pia, who found that on a photographic negative, the image of the figure appears far more distinct than on the shroud itself. What astonished Pia was that the image that appeared on the photographic plate was not a characteristic negative, in which the light and dark areas are reversed. Instead the negative showed all the qualities of a positive print, suggesting that the shroud itself is a negative.

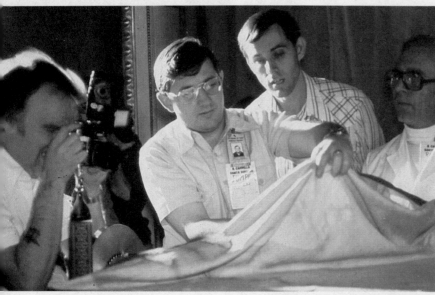

Scientists examine and photograph the underside of the shroud, exposing it for the first time since 1532.

E. H. Brooks II, Brooks Institute

NEGATIVE PRINT

Jackson and Jumper set out to discover why. They subjected photographs of the shroud to techniques developed to translate photographic images of the moon and Mars into three-dimensional relief. They found that unlike other photographs, contact prints of corpses, or artists' copies of the shroud, the colors in the shroud's markings are darkest where the body was close to the sheet and lightest where it was farthest away.

This suggests to them that whatever created the image must have acted at a distance rather than by direct contact. Jackson and Jumper constructed a lifelike relief of the body on a video screen. They could tilt the image to view it from all sides. At first they puzzled over unnatural bulges covering the eye areas until they learned about the ancient burial practice of placing coins or potsherds over the eyes of the deceased.

Later, at Baylor University Medical School in Texas, Jackson, Jumper, Bucklin, and another team member, Vernon Miller, head of the scientific and industrial department of Santa Barbara's Brooks Institute of Photography, draped a human model in a precisely marked facsimile of the shroud and subjected the person to a biostereometric examination. The test, originally designed to measure the volume of an astronaut for the precise fit of a space suit, produced a three-dimensional image identical with Jackson and Jumper's findings. Then Jackson and Miller conducted a simple yet vital experiment to see if a real body lying on a slab, as

in a tomb, would show the same slight deformation from gravity that the shroud indicates. They suspended a human model on a Plexiglas plate above them, then compared the distribution of the model's weight to the density of the shroud's dorsal image. Though final results are not yet in, the information from this test seemed to be a good match.

BUT HOW WAS THE IMAGE MADE?

None of this research conclusively proves the shroud to be authentic, of course. But authentication aside, an even more perplexing problem is how the image was made. One of the earliest theories was proposed by Yves Delage, a turn-of-the-century professor of comparative anatomy at the Sorbornne in Paris, and his assistant, Paul Joseph Vignon. They proposed that volatile components of morbid sweat would condense on the cloth and through chemical reaction with burial spices cause coloration.

More recent experiments, however, show that such vapors diffuse rather than travel in the straight vertical lines necessary to create an image on linen. Furthermore, vapors would saturate the cloth, so that any marking would permeate the fabric. The shroud's body image, however, is contained only in the topmost fibrils.

Some believe the colors of the shroud resemble those of a well-used ironing board cover, leading to the theory that the shroud's image was created with a heated statue or even an unexplained split-second burst of radiant energy from within the folded halves.

Experiments aimed at replicating the shroud by scorching failed. The tests could not achieve nearly the detail shown in the original. Finally the Turin team members laid the scorch theory to rest with a technique often used by museums on art treasures. Under ultraviolet light, the scientists watched scorches from the 1532 fire fluoresce reddish as expected, indicating the presence of complex organic compounds produced by high temperatures. But the body image itself did not fluoresce as it would if it too were made up of scorch marks.

LATENT IMAGE

Today the team's favorite hypothesis is the "latent image, cellulose degradation theory." Samuel Pellicori applied foreign substances such as body oils, sweat, olive oil, myrrh, and other ancient burial preparations to his hand, pressed it on pieces of linen, and then baked the samples at 150° Celsius (300° Fahrenheit) for four hours to simulate aging. The modern linen discolored to exactly match the shroud's spectral measurements, and contours of Pellicori's fingers, similar to those on the shroud, appeared. The same technique on his face, however, failed to turn up facial detail with the minimal amount of distortion of the original.

So even if Pellicori is right, he has solved only one part of the mystery: his theory may explain how the decaying cellulose in the shroud reacted with substances to form an image, but it does not explain the incredibly lifelike details, especially in the areas of the face where the cloth would not have touched the skin. Furthermore, it gives no indication of how relief information was encoded on the shroud.

KEY TEST REMAINS

A key test remains: carbon dating to determine the age of the linen. It used to be necessary to destroy a whole section of material to get a reliable date, a sacrifice the keepers of the shroud would not permit. But recently Harry Gove, at the University of Rochester in New York, offered a new carbon-dating method that would require the destruction of only a minute sample of material. Now several other groups also claim that

with a single thread they can pinpoint the age of the fabric to within 150 years.

In May 1981, team members John Jackson and Larry Schwalbe, a physicist with the Los Alamos National Scientific Laboratory, joined Fathers Adam J. Otterbein and Peter Rinaldi in Turin to present the team's preliminary report to Archbishop Ballestrero and the shroud's owner, Umberto II. The archbishop and the exiled king were satisfied with the team's findings and encouraged the men to gain support for carbon dating the shroud from Pope John Paul II.

On May 13, an hour before the scheduled meeting with the pope in Rome, the men gathered in St. Peter's Square. They saw the pope arrive and watched with 10,000 others as a Turkish terrorist shot the pope three times in a nearly successful assassination attempt. A few days later the U.S. scientists flew home.

Both the church and the scientists insist that if and when tests are held, they must be conducted by three separate agencies—using actual threads from the shrouds as well as "blind" or "fake" threads as a control. All agree there must be only one series of tests. No one wants to destroy the shroud thread by thread just to prove its age.

DOES IT MATTER?

But what if science eventually finds that the shroud is in fact old enough, and that the image was formed by some means that allowed people to say it could be an image of Jesus? Would that make a difference to Christianity? Or for that matter, what if the shroud is proved a fake? "It really doesn't make any difference," says Barrie Schwortz, a Turin team member. "People who have faith don't need a relic or an icon or an image. People who don't have faith aren't going to buy it even if we could prove that it was Christ, which no one will ever be able to do. It's still a matter of faith" □

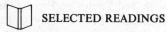 **SELECTED READINGS**

"Mystery of the shroud" by K. F. Weaver. *National Geographic,* June 1980.

"Shroud of scientific questions" *Science News,* April 25, 1981.

SCIENCE BOOKS OF THE YEAR

by Lansing P. Wagner

MANY books on science and technology are published every year. The titles below were selected by the editors for review because they seemed of particular significance, interest, or usefulness. The choice was not, however, restricted to books appearing within the last year, since the timeliness of their contents does not depend on their date of publication. Rather, the titles were chosen to represent the range of subjects that is provided within the various sections of this annual.

Disturbing the Universe *by Freeman Dyson. Harper and Row, 1981, 304 pp., $4.95.*

This diversified book details one scientist's ideas about what science is, how it works, and its effects on society. The author combines his skills—as a physicist, mathematician, philosopher, teacher, writer, political activist, and poet—in creating this quasi-literary work.

Each chapter is a beautifully-written essay. Frequently Dyson opens a chapter with a discussion of a book, a poem, or a movie. He uses these media to illustrate a connection between society and science. For example, Dyson uses Eliot's *Murder in the Cathedral* and Auden and Isherwood's *The Ascent of F6* to explain his feelings about the noted physicist J. Robert Oppenheimer.

Dyson calls himself a problem solver, rather than a creator of ideas. While Oppenheimer was struggling to understand the mysteries of nature through a grand unified theory, Dyson was active in nuclear engineering, space technology, pure math, and human concerns.

In one chapter we see the author as a member of a team developing a "safe nuclear reactor." In another chapter he is working with Ted Taylor on Project Orion, a nuclear spaceship. In the essay called "Peacemaking," we see Dyson as a member of the Arms Control and Disarmament Agency. In yet another essay, the author advises the town of Princeton, New Jersey, to let the university become involved in the controversial field of gene-splicing. "A Distant Mirror" and other chapters find Dyson exploring the future, as we ultimately explore the author's amazing versatility.

A Field Guide to the Birds East of the Rockies *by Roger Tory Peterson. Houghton Mifflin, 1980, 384 pp., illus., $15.00.*

The fourth edition of Peterson's famous field guide to bird identification is a completely new edition. Starting on page 33, every odd-numbered page contains a color painting of the birds described on the facing page. These beautiful, realistic illustrations have arrows that pinpoint the key field markings for identifying each species. Most of the descriptions of the 390 birds also have such headings as: *similar species, voice, range,* and *habitat*. Another aid to identification is the roadside and flight silhouettes of many birds on the insides of both covers.

Once you have studied the "Topography of a Bird" on page 30, you are ready to take the minicourse on "How to Identify Birds." Peterson lists 16 features for identification, such as "What is the bird's size? What is its shape? What are its field marks? Each one of these features is well-illustrated.

The bird guide covers North America east of the 100th meridian. Toward the end of the book are detailed, three-color maps that show birds' breeding and winter ranges, and where they are residential year-around.

The Soul of a New Machine *by Tracy Kidder. Little, Brown and Company, 1981, 293 pp., $13.95.*

This journal of the invention of a major, state-of-the arts computer is a masterpiece of science reporting. Tom West, of Data General Corporation (a super-competitive computer manufacturer), persuaded the company's president to let him direct the creation of a 32-bit computer. This new machine would be compatible in hardware and software with the successful 16-bit Eclipse already being used by the company.

To get the job, West promised to complete the project in a year—even though he had only a skeleton team of engineers and the sketchiest idea of the proposed machine's architecture.

West put together a team of the brightest electrical-engineering students that he could find. These young engineers, right out of graduate school, considered themselves very lucky to be designing a major computer. Their enthusiasm and involvement drove them to work late into many nights and through weekends.

Each engineer invented and solved his own problems in creating the new machine. There were many times when none of the team comprehensively understood how all the parts worked and fit together. But finally the project was successfully finished.

The author describes the engineers' backgrounds, personalities, conflicts, and responsibilities. In so doing, the reader learns what it is like to work at the cutting edge of a new technology and learns some of the technology itself. The reader is also introduced to the methodology of logic so integral to computer systems.

Dr. Frank Field's Weather Book *by Frank Field. G.P. Putnam's Sons, 1981, 210 pp., $13.95.*

If you have ever been intrigued by meteorology and the glamour of television weather reporting, this book is just for you.

Frank Field stumbled into meteorology while serving in the armed forces during World War II. He has managed to present this field of science in a most entertaining way. Field's descriptions of the atmosphere, weather conditions, and weather reporting are interesting and clearly written. The reader gets a fascinating, behind-the-scenes view of a weather bureau and a television studio. This book is certainly a fine primer on the subject.

Chapter 9, entitled "Toward Greater Accuracy," is especially well done. We discover that 20 per cent of the error in weather predicting comes from not having an adequate number of observation stations. This problem is greatest in the Pacific Ocean and throughout the Southern Hemisphere.

Field explains, however, that satellite coverage is rapidly reducing this source of error. He also claims that a substantial percentage of error in weather prediction stems from insufficient understanding of all the parameters that control the mechanics of the atmosphere. This error will probably be reduced when the results of the Global Weather Experiment have been analyzed.

Field also addresses and explores popular meteorological topics in his book. For example, after every heat wave or cold spell, weather forecasters are often asked if the country is undergoing a major weather and climate change. The author describes the theories of regular variations in the earth's orbit and in its inclination to the sun. He explains that these variations affect the earth's heat budget, and that heat is the major parameter governing the atmosphere.

The last few pages of the book contain comprehensive answers to the questions most frequently asked of forecasters. A useful glossary is also included.

Jane Brody's Nutrition Book *by Jane Brody. W.W. Norton, 1981, 552 pp., $17.95.*

Already this book is the bible for those who want to be serious about good nutrition. Not only does Ms. Brody present sound reasons for eating correctly, she also illustrates how it can be done with healthful recipes.

Ms. Brody says, "This book is designed to steer you between the profit-motivated food companies and faddism. It is meant to help you understand the why and wherefore of good nutrition and to put them into practice . . ."

The author believes that Americans must learn about good nutrition because our supermarkets and food processors present us with too many foods that have little nutritional value. For this reason we eat too much fat, too much sugar, too much protein, and ultimately consume too many unnecessary calories.

If you like using salt but wonder what excessive salt intake can do to you, the answer is provided here. You will even find a delightful recipe for saltless Beef Bourguignon.

Jane Brody has much nutritional advice to give on the special dietary needs of pregnant women and babies, small children and the elderly, and how to cope with "junk" food lovers. The author even discusses the positive and negative aspects of a vegetarian life style.

The God That Limps *by Colin Norman. W.W. Norton, A Worldwatch Institute Book, 1981, 224 pp., $14.95.*

This is a thought-provoking book about the effects of technology on society and on the economy. Most of the ills of the world, according to some people, can be blamed on technology. Think of the increased population it has spawned . . . our increased consumption of limited energy resources . . . our increased pollution . . . the dislocations of people.

The following statement seems to be Norman's chief message: "Current systems for generating and applying technologies were established in the political climate of the fifties and sixties . . . The world has changed fundamentally, and technological systems have changed little."

With new technologies must come new skills and jobs, precipitating the loss of existing jobs and causing dislocations. The effects of microelectronics, robots, biotechnology, and even the Green Revolution are just starting to impact our lives. What can be done on a worldwide basis? The decade-long discussions of the Law of the Sea regarding the use of technology to mine the ocean floor for everyone's profit is an example of the immense problems involved.

Even if the world were not fragmented into haves and have-nots, free nations and enslaved nations, people do not yet realize all the parameters that relate to a technological system. Norman writes, ". . . if the experiences of the postwar years have taught us anything, it is that there are no simple technological fixes for complex social problems."

A Country-Lover's Guide to Wildlife *by Kenneth A. Chambers. The Johns Hopkins University Press, 1980, 228 pp., illus., $8.95.*

Everything within this compact guide works well together—and the ultimate result is an excellent book. To be accurate, the title should specify that it is a guide to wildlife of the Northeastern United States. Wildlife covered in this book includes only amphibians, reptiles, and mammals—no birds.

Each of these three classes of animals is introduced by a few pages of basic, interesting information. Then each order within a class is prefaced by an essay concerning the author's own observations of one of its members. For example, under the order of shrews and moles appears the essay "A Monster in Miniature." This is followed by descriptions of ten different shrews and moles. The three most common are described in much detail. The following headings are used: *adult size; description; breeding; food; habitat; range in the Northeast; similar northeastern species.* All of the species described are illustrated in 20 full-color pages. There are also numerous black-and-white sketches.

Chambers believes that the better you get to know your wildlife neighbors, the more you become interested in how they are related. For that reason, he has included Appendix B, which describes the system of classification.

Appendix A is a collection of animal-distribution tables for each of the nine northeastern states. At the end of the book is a handy check list for recording the wildlife you have seen, which makes this guide complete □

IN MEMORIAM

by Barbara Tchabovsky

SEVERAL people important in science died during 1981 and early 1982. Among them were the pioneering anthropologist Carleton S. Coon; meteorologist and Mars weather expert Seymour Hess; two Nobel laureates: biochemist Hans Krebs and physicist Hikedi Yukawa; and noted bacteriologist and environmentalist René Dubos.

CARLETON S. COON

Carleton Stevens Coon, who made important contributions to many fields of anthropology, was born June 23, 1904 in Wakefield, Massachusetts. He received a bachelor's degree from Harvard in 1925 and a Ph.D. in anthropology in 1928. He then served on the Harvard faculty, both teaching and doing research, until military service during World War II. In 1948 Coon became curator of ethnology at the University Museum in Philadelphia and professor of anthropology at the University of Pennsylvania.

Anthropologist Carleton Stevens Coon

UPI

Coon contributed to social and physical anthropology and to related disciplines, often combining in his field studies and analysis of contemporary societies with archaeological and biological studies of ancient man. He pioneered in researching the transition of humans from a hunter-gatherer culture to the first agricultural communities. He also analyzed the physical adaptations of humans in extreme conditions, such as desert, high altitudes, and the Arctic, and studied contemporary tribal groups in Patagonia, the Middle East, and India. He spoke ten languages, including those of some of the tribes he studied.

Coon wrote textbooks in anthropology—among them *A Reader in General Anthropology* (1948)—and books for a general readership on the early development of humans. *The Story of Man* (1954) and *The Seven Caves* (1957) are probably his best known works. An autobiography *Adventures and Discoveries was published in 1982. Coon was also known to the public as a regular panelist on the 1950's CBS science program What in the World?*

Coon semi-retired in the 1960's and moved to Gloucester, Massachusetts. There he continued research and writing and maintained an affiliation with the Peabody Museum of Archaeology and Ethnology at Harvard. He died June 3, 1981, at his home.

SEYMOUR HESS

Seymour Lester Hess, noted meteorologist who studied Mars' weather, was born in 1920 in Brooklyn, New York. He studied at Brooklyn College and the University of Chicago. After serving as a research meteorologist at Lowell Observatory in Flagstaff, Arizona, he joined the faculty of Florida State University in 1950. There he spent most of his career teaching, serving as associate dean and head of the meteorology department, and since 1978 as Robert O. Lawton Distinguished Professor.

Hess gave the first weather report from Mars. He began his study of weather conditions on Mars in the late 1940's and continued this interest until his death. In 1976 he lead a team of meteorologists monitoring the data being sent back to earth from the Viking lander on Mars. He reported the temperature and wind conditions of Mars at the time of the landing.

The author of numerous scientific papers, Hess was perhaps best known as the author of *Introduction to Theoretical Meteorology,* a basic text used by students around the world.

Hess died on January 15, 1982 in Tallahassee, Florida.

HANS KREBS

Hans Adolph Krebs, renowned biochemist, was born in 1900 in Hildesheim, Germany. He received his M.D. from the University of Hamburg in 1925, becoming an ear, nose, and throat specialist. His primary interest was research, however, and he went to Berlin to assist Otto Warburg in his work on enzymes (Warburg was awarded the 1931 Nobel Prize for this research). He continued his career at the University of Freiburg, moving to Cambridge when the Nazis came to power in Germany. Krebs began his Nobel-winning work at Cambridge University and completed it at the University of Sheffield. In 1954 he moved to Oxford.

Krebs discovered how food is converted into energy by the body. In particular he described the citric-acid cycle, now known as the Krebs cycle, and the urea cycle, both basic biochemical chain reactions for the production of energy. Unraveling the steps in the chain reactions Krebs showed how the body burns fuel very economically. The citric-acid cycle, for example, can be considered self-perpetuating in the sense that chemicals are broken apart and then resynthesized. In the process chemical energy in the form of sugar is converted into energy for the body in the form of muscle power. In the urea, or ornithine, cycle, the metabolism of proteins leads to the formation of urea in the liver. For his research on these two biochemical pathways, Krebs was awarded the 1953 Nobel Prize in Physiology or Medicine.

Friedrich Rauch/Photo Trends

Biochemist Hans Krebs, a Nobel laureate

His work established many fundamentals of modern physiology and opened the present explosion in biochemical research.

In his later years Krebs studied certain congenital diseases known as "inborn errors of metabolism" and ways of preserving livers for transplantation. He died in Oxford, on November 22, 1981.

HIDEKI YUKAWA

Hideki Yukawa, one of the world's leading theoretical physicists, was born in Tokyo on November 3, 1907. He studied in Kyoto and became a lecturer at the University of Kyoto in 1932. Then, after spending six years on the faculty of Osaka University, he became a professor at Kyoto. He spent the year 1948 at the Institute for Advanced Study in Princeton, the guest of J. Robert Oppenheimer and then served on the faculty of Columbia University for a few years. In 1954 he returned to his alma mater, Kyoto, becoming director of Kyoto University's Research Institute for Fundamental Physics.

In 1935 Yukawa predicted, on the basis of a series of equations, the existence of a new type of subatomic particle. The new particle, he said, was intermediate in mass between an electron and a proton; it became known as a meson. Yukawa further theorized that mesons were responsible for the force that binds the nucleus together, preventing the similarly charged protons from repelling one another.

Confirmation of the existence of the particle came in the late 1940's. The particle predicted by Yukawa—called the pi meson, or pion—and its decay particle, the lighter muon were observed in cosmic rays raining on earth from space. Laboratory tests using high-powered cyclotrons subsequently provided further confirmation. In 1949 Yukawa was awarded the Nobel Prize in Physics, and earned the distinction of becoming Japan's first Nobel laureate.

Yukawa, in addition to his research, spent much of his career training "new faces" in his field—Japan when Yukawa began his career had few eminent physicists. He also worked for peace and nuclear disarmament, declaring at one time that "this is a problem of atomic energy versus mankind."

Yukawa retired from Kyoto University in 1970. He died at his home in Kyoto on September 8, 1981.

RENÉ DUBOS

René Dubos, bacteriologist and environmentalist, was born in Saint-Brice, France, on February 20, 1901. After studying at the National Institute of Agronomy in Paris, he moved to the United States (he became a naturalized citizen in 1938) and received his doctorate from Rutgers University in 1927. He then spent his entire professional career at Rockefeller Institute, later Rockefeller University, except for a brief period (1942–44) when he served as professor of tropical medicine at Harvard Medical School.

Dubos' early work concentrated on the study of soil bacteria, human fungus infections, and the microbes responsible for dysentery and tuberculosis. In the 1940's he showed the feasibility of obtaining germ-fighting drugs from microbes. This pioneering work paved the way for the later discovery of antibiotics.

From the early 1960's on, Dubos turned most of his attention toward environmental issues. With economist Barbara Ward, he wrote *Only One Earth,* a fundamental environmental text that served as the basis for the U.N. Conference on the Human Environment. Through endless speeches, interviews, essays, and lectures, Dubos addressed himself to environmental issues. He blamed overreaching technology for most pollution problems, and said, "In my opinion there is no chance of solving the problems of pollution—or of other threats to human life—if we accept the idea that technology is to rule our future." His philosophy was perhaps best summed up in the title of a column—"The Despairing Optimist"—he wrote for the magazine *American Scholar.* Dubos also wrote *So Human An Animal,* which won the Pulitzer Prize for nonfiction in 1969, and *Celebration of Life* (1981).

The recipient of numerous honorary degrees and awards, Dubos died in New York City on February 20, 1982 □

Bacteriologist and environmentalist René Dubos
Courtesy of Rockefeller University

Lawrence Livermore National Laboratory

A yin-yang pair of superconducting coils is welded together to form a gargantuan magnetic mirror that will plug one end of the tandem Mirror Fusion Test Facility in California.

PHYSICAL SCIENCES

Physics. Developments in physics during 1981 included continued work on the search for a unified force in nature, study of elementary particles, particularly protons and their possible decay, and the discovery of a possible new form of matter.

Within the past few years physicists have found support for the idea that two forces in nature: the weak force, and the electromagnetic force, are really expressions of the same phenomenon. There are four basic forces in nature: the weak force, which is responsible for the interaction of electrons with their nuclei; the electromagnetic force that binds atoms to one another and is the basis of chemistry; the strong force, which holds the nucleus of an atom together; and gravity, which makes all things fall toward a massive object like the earth. During 1981 physicists found further evidence supporting the Weinberg-Salam Model that unites the weak and electromagnetic forces into a single mathematical framework. The weak force was demonstrated to make a distinction between left and right, or, in other words, to show parity nonconservation. A beam of polarized (aligned) laser light was targeted at bismuth atoms. The dominant electromagnetic effect of the laser was modified by the much smaller, neutral weak interaction between the bismuth electrons and their nuclei, causing the laser beam to rotate. Support for the Weinberg-Salam model is a step toward a long-sought goal—namely, the unification of all known forces into a single model.

One of the dogmas of physics has been that elementary particles have electric charge such as $+1$, -1, 0, $+2$, -2, and so on. During 1981 studies at Stanford University showed that quarks may have a fraction of a charge. [Quarks—five of them: up, down, strange, charm, and beauty (bottom)—are thought to make up elementary particles.] This means that, under certain conditions, particles made up of quarks could have a fraction of a charge. That could happen if one of the quarks had a fraction of a charge. It could also happen if one quark were replaced by a neutral quark. Protons, for example, are made up of three quarks, and have a total charge of $+1$. If one of their quarks is neutral, the proton is left with a fraction of a charge. This new theoretical quark—with a fraction of a charge—imposes complications for theories of elementary-particle physics. For instance, it raises the possibility that protons could occasionally have a fourth quark. Or, neutral quarks might have to be incorporated into theories of particle interactions. Or, a more drastic possibility is that quarks might sometimes exist in isolation, an idea not now accepted.

Glueballs, etas, and anomalons—they may all exist. The existence of glueballs was postulated in 1981 following the interpretation of experimental data obtained in 1980 at the Stanford Linear Accelerator. Glueballs are a duet of gluons, the forces that tie together quarks to form protons, neutrons, and some other atomic particles. Evidence for the existence of glueballs is important since they fit nicely into the framework of quantum chromodynamics, the currently popular theory of nuclear interactions. ■ A new particle—eta—was discovered by Berkeley-Stanford and Caltech-Harvard-Stanford research teams. A variety of charmonium, a family of particles each made from a charm and an anti-

---

Univ. of Texas Health Science Center

Donald J. Hanahan, professor of biochemistry at the University of Texas Health Science Center at San Antonio, injects a phospholipid sample into a gas chromatograph for analysis.

Gynecological surgeons use a laser to remove scar tissue from a woman's fallopian tubes. This technique is used in an attempt to help restore her fertility.

Laser Research Foundation

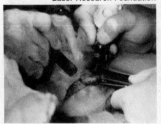

charm quark, eta differs from others of its family, such as psi, by having the spin of its two constituent quarks in antiparallel rather than in parallel configuration. ■ And evidence for a new form of matter, called anomalons, was obtained during the year. Anomalons are fragments of projectile nuclei that travel an unusually (anomalously) short distance following collision of the projectile nucleus with a target nucleus. During an experiment at Berkeley's BEVALAC accelerator, about six per cent of the fragments from projectile nuclei of ^{56}Fe (an isotope of iron) and ^{16}O (an isotope of oxygen) travelled anomalously short distances compared with the majority of fragments. This occurs following both the initial collision and subsequent collisions of the fragments with other nuclei. The extraordinarily short path of these anomalous fragments implies that they have a large size, larger than that of the largest naturally occurring nucleus known. One suggestion is that anomalons are made from quarks that have been arranged in a novel way, and thus represent a new form of matter.

Until now, protons were considered to have infinite lifetimes. In 1981, however, came evidence that protons decay. (See "Proton Decay," on page 296).

Chemistry. Advances in silicon chemistry, the war against insect pests, and energy conservation were among the developments in chemistry in 1981.

A whole new world of silicon chemistry may be opening. A breakthrough in silicon chemistry came with the synthesis by Robert West and colleagues at the University of Wisconsin at Madison of tetramesityldisilene, the first known silicon-silicon double bond-containing stable compound. Silcion is quite similar to carbon, the element upon which all life is based. Now that similarity has been found to be even greater: carbon atoms have long been known to form double-bonded chains with each other and in so doing to produce a large variety of organic compounds. Silicon is central to computer manufacturing and a family of compounds based on doubly-bonded silicon may be of great interest to that industry.

The war against insect pests continues. The East African plant *Ajuga remota* was found to contain natural substances—called phytoecydsones—that kill two major insect pests of cotton, the pink bollworm and fall armyworm, by interfering with their molting processes. ■ The spruce bark beetle is also being controlled—aggregation pheromone has been used to catch some 8,000,000,000 in Norway.

Chemists may also have found a new way to save some energy—by weaving a salt-containing hollow fiber into insulating drapes. The U.S. Department of Agriculture Textile and Clothing Laboratory in Knoxville, Tennessee, has found that the specific heat of polypropylene or rayon hollow fibers can be raised through melting of calcium/strontium chloride hexahydrate salts inside these fibers. Extensive use of drapes made with such fibers could moderate temperature changes and thus reduce the amount of energy needed to heat or cool a room.

There were several other significant findings. Dioxin, the ingredient of the Vietnam War herbicide Agent Orange, was found to suppress the immune system in mice. ■ At least one phospholipid has been found to be biologically active, not just a structural component of the body. This finding may help elucidate some of the mechanisms of biological reactions.

Marc Kusinitz

© Bettye Lane/PR

Vietnam veterans, who were exposed to the herbicide Agent Orange during the war, demonstrated in anger. It is now known that Dioxin suppresses the immune system in mice.

Substances called phytoecydsones, which are found in an East African plant, are being used successfully to destroy a major insect pest of cotton— the pink bollworm.

National Cotton Council

ELECTROMAGNETIC PULSE

by Janet Raloff

A NUCLEAR bomb detonates 400 kilometers (250 miles) above Omaha, Nebraska. A type of "fallout" most people have never heard of bathes the entire United States. Within a fraction of a second people coast to coast find themselves without power, without telecommunications, without computers—in a word, vulnerable. The fallout is called EMP, for electromagnetic pulse. EMP cripples or kills electronic equipment but leaves humans standing—very much alive and vulnerable.

It has been estimated that roughly 1/1,000,000 of the total energy of a nuclear explosion is emitted as an EMP. If the pulse from a high-altitude detonation were delivered in the opening salvo of a warring siege, the attacked population might spend precious minutes or hours reeling in chaos. Even if the defending military could respond, the civilian sector—unable to communicate well, if at all—would find recovery of vital services slow. But should the EMP shower down in "peacetime"—also a distinct possibility—a nation might find itself temporarily disabled industrially and crippled economically.

SLEEPING DRAGON

Nuclear-weapons-generated EMP is by no means a new phenomenon, though for years it has had an extremely low profile outside the defense-electronics community. In fact, since the detonation of conventional high explosives sometimes produces an EMP, similar signals were expected to accompany nuclear bursts. But the extent and particularly devastating nature of the nuclear-generated signals did not become obvious until several years after the United States began its program of above-ground nuclear-weapons tests. The signals left their imprint as a series of seemingly unexplainable failures or burnouts in equipment set up to monitor effects of the nuclear tests. Analysis ultimately pointed a finger at EMP as the cause when investigation showed that induced currents and voltages produced the failures.

Around 1960, several more graphic incidents drove home the possible vulnerability of electrical and electronics systems. One of the most famous was the simultaneous failure of 30 strings of street lights in Oahu, Hawaii, in 1962. The Hawaiian outages are now attributed to EMP from high-altitude nuclear tests nearly 1,300 kilometers (800 miles) away, near Johnston Island in the Pacific. That EMP is also held responsible for having opened power line circuit breakers and for setting off "hundreds" of burglar alarms in Honolulu.

But "EMP was just sort of a sleeping spook out there," says Bill Macklin of IRT Corporation, a firm that specializes in EMP work for the military. Then the electronics revolution and the related computerization of industrial processes and business functions ushered in a mushrooming escalation in our potential vulnerability to EMP disruption.

HIGHLY VARIABLE EFFECTS

The phenomenon wreaks its havoc by inducing current or voltage surges through electrically conducting materials. In some cases the surges merely trip circuit breakers, shutting down a piece of equipment or power line. In other cases, especially where semiconductor materials are involved, individual components or circuits are destroyed.

Vacuum-tube systems tend to be many times more resistant to permanent damage from EMP than are semiconductor systems, and 60-hertz (cycle-per-second) motors are even more resistant than vacuum tubes. "But even motors can be damaged if connected to a very large energy-collecting structure," warns the Defense Nuclear Agency. What's more, every system or electric complex must be evaluated individually to determine its potential vulnerability to EMP. Laboratory tests, for instance, have shown that the potential vulnerability of similar systems can vary widely depending on the type of components used, the way components are connected to

On the night of July 8, 1962, the U.S. detonated a nuclear bomb over Johnston Island, 715 miles southwest of Honolulu. The photo above, of Honolulu, was taken just before 11 pm. Seconds later, the blast over Johnston Island lit up the sky (below).

Both photos, courtesy of A.T. & T. Co.

Aerial lines of conventional telephone systems (above) make good antennas for picking up EMP surges. Fiber optics (shown on the right in photo below), are invulnerable to EMP surges.

one another, and even on the particular manufacturer of seemingly identical parts.

In a crude sense, EMP is similar to radio waves. However, it exhibits important differences. EMP waves include a broader range of frequencies and amplitudes than radio transmitters can produce. Electric fields associated with EMP can be millions of times greater than those associated with radio waves. Yet like radio waves, EMP energy is picked up by antennas and conducted to attached—or in some cases, adjacent unattached—equipment.

The actual energy raining down in an EMP pulse is not all that high, which explains why humans are not affected. In fact, EMP is presumed to be no more harmful to humans than is a flash of distant lightning. *Effects of Nuclear Weapons,* a book published jointly by the U.S. Department of Defense and Energy, adds that dogs and monkeys showed no adverse health effects after being exposed to single EMP's or pulses administered repeatedly over a period of months.

Contact with an effective EMP collector, though, such as a long wire, pipe, fence, conduit, railroad track or other large metal object, could impart a hefty shock. That's because, as a general rule, the amount of EMP that any antenna collects is proportional to its overall dimensions. And virtually every electrical conductor will serve as an EMP antenna unless it is adequately shielded.

ALTITUDE IMPORTANT

All nuclear explosions generate an EMP, although the intensity, duration, and area over which the pulse is effective varies with the altitude of the burst. Even the mechanism by which EMP is generated may differ with the altitude at which a bomb is detonated.

Gamma rays emitted by nuclear reactions and gamma rays produced by neutron interactions with bomb residues and other materials are largely responsible for the processes that create EMP. As the gamma rays interact with materials, they produce an ionized region about the detonation point. "The negatively charged electrons move outward faster than the much heavier, positively charged ions," say Samuel Glasstone and

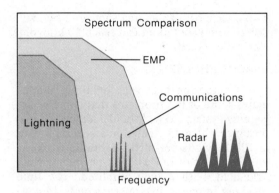

Spectrum Comparison

EMP

Communications

Lightning

Radar

Frequency

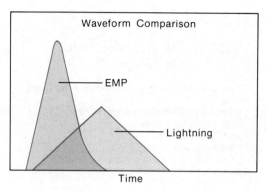

Waveform Comparison

EMP

Lightning

Time

Philip Dolan in their book, *The Effects of Nuclear Weapons.* This initially sets up a separation of charges, with regions nearer the blast point bearing a net positive charge while those farther away build a net negative charge. Charge separation creates an electric field that can attain its maximum value in about 1/100,000,000 of a second.

If the explosion occurred in an environment of perfectly homogeneous density, the electric field would be radial, symmetric and of equal strength in all directions, Glasstone and Dolan say. It would also fail to radiate electromagnetic energy—such as EMP. But for a variety of reasons (which can range from the detonation's proximity to the earth, to the configuration of the weapon, or the vapor content of the air) truly homogeneous environments never exist. The result of non-homogeneity is EMP.

In surface or near-surface blasts, the region of peak EMP hazard is restricted to a range of only about 3 to 8 kilometers (about 2 to 5 miles) from ground zero. For higher blasts—those occurring at altitudes up to 30 kilometers (19 miles) the EMP-hazard range will increase to a 14-kilometer (9-mile) ground radius.

True high-altitude blasts are another matter. For a blast 80 kilometers (50 miles) up, the affected ground radius on earth would be nearly 1,000 kilometers (600 miles). And for an explosion centered over the United States at an altitude of 320 kilometers (200 miles), the entire continental United States (including parts of Canada and Mexico) would be completely drenched in a bath of EMP.

PEAKS RAPIDLY

In these high-atitude bursts, gamma rays traveling upward enter an atmosphere of such low air density that they must go long distances before getting absorbed. Meanwhile, earthbound gamma rays encounter an atmosphere of increasing density. Their inevitable interaction with air molecules sets up an EMP source region. Roughly circular, this source region may climb 80 kilometers (50 miles) in its center. Horizontally it blossoms too. How far depends on the bomb's kiloton yield and altitude at detonation.

In this EMP-generating source region, gamma rays emitted by the blast collide with air molecules, creating what are known as Compton electrons. The earth's magnetic field deflects these electrons, forcing them to spiral about the magnetic-field lines. "This motion causes the electrons to be subjected to a radial acceleration, which results, by a complex mechanism, in the generation of an EMP that moves down toward the earth," Glasstone and Dolan say.

The pulse crescendos to a peak, then decreases. In fact, it's the nature of this radiation to peak rapidly and then to decay somewhat more slowly. Amplitude, or strength, varies widely over its broad frequency domain. The rise and fall of the signal occurs more rapidly than in an equivalent-size surface burst. Therefore, more of the electromagnetic energy pulsed by the high-altitude explosion falls into a higher frequency range. And for high-altitude bursts with yields of a few hundred kilotons or more, electric-field strength will vary by no more than a factor of two over most of the area showered by EMP. Maximum EMP fallout can reach 50 kilovolts per meter (yard).

UNIQUE PROBLEM

Comparing EMP with lightning illuminates some of the problems that come in designing systems to withstand a large EMP. For instance, the field created in association with a 100 kilovolts-per-meter lightning stroke is on the order of one kilovolt-per meter electric field, with a high amplitude rise time peaking in one to five microseconds. In contrast, for a large, high-altitude nulcear burst, the fields radiated onto the earth's surface peak roughly 100 times faster than lightning.

This fast rise time represents a double-edged sword. First, it means the energy will be distributed much more broadly throughout the electromagnetic band—including the lower microwave range. Second, the rise time is so rapid that an EMP can zip through a system—destroying sensitive electronics along the way—before lightning arrestors or other defensive power-shunting switches can respond to the surge.

In other words, EMP is different from any other electromagnetic environment usually encountered. Therefore, protection practices and components for non-EMP environments—radio-frequency interference, lightning, radar, and so on—are not directly applicable to EMP problems, explains the Defense Nuclear Agency's EMP Awareness Course Notes.

PROTECTION IS POSSIBLE

For systems whose continuous operation is deemed critical, such as military surveillance, communication, and attack units, EMP protection—known in the jargon as "hardening"—becomes essential. And not surprisingly, the military has attacked the problem of hardening more aggressively than has any other industry.

The public communications and power industries have been far less ambitious for a number of reasons, including the cost necessary to retrofit EMP hardening to their vast networks.

But the single most vulnerable segment of society—the electronics industry—has to

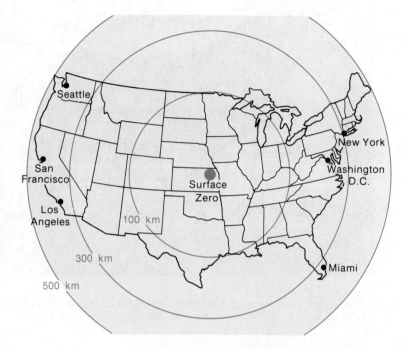

Inner circle shows area showered by EMP from blast centered over blue spot at altitude of 100 kilometers (62 miles). Outer circle shows coverage for blast 500 kilometers (330 miles) up.

date largely been overlooked, and its products are greatly increasing the U.S.'s vulnerability to EMP. IRT Corporation has begun a rough survey of the computer's role in society with an eye toward assessing EMP vulnerability. And based on preliminary data, IRT's Bill Macklin says, "We're awed by it." From automation of food processing to the computer control of fuel and power supplies, there could be a major civil defense threat brewing, he suggests.

LONG OVERLOOKED

According to Mike King, an EMP-shielding analyst who until July 1980 worked at the Defense Nuclear Agency in Washington, "I think, basically, that civilian industry per se has totally no regard for EMP. I guess their theory is, 'If we're going to be under a nuclear attack, why am I worried about my computer file?' " Interviews with several industrialists confirm that that view is one being used to justify ignoring the hardening—or protection—of equipment against EMP within the electric power industry.

In a paper issued in December 1980 Russell Clanahan of the Federal Emergency Management Agency (FEMA) attempts to

Portable EMP simulators, like this one in Maryland, are used to test the vulnerability of components and systems in warlike environments.

DNA

A Trestle EMP simulator feeds 1,000,000-volt pulses into transmission lines surrounding a B-52 plane. The simulator tests the "hardness" of the aircraft to EMP.

counter such attitudes. "Much of the destructiveness of a nuclear attack, in lives and property lost, depends on the unpreparedness of the one attacked. In a sense, ... the unwillingness to confront the situation and prepare becomes a self-fulfilling prophecy."

Perhaps if EMP protection were relatively inexpensive, there would be less resistance to hardening. But there is "a pretty impressive price tag" associated with hardening, notes IRT's Macklin. Estimates vary, but it could cost at least an extra 15 to 20 per cent to build EMP protection into a new facility. And the higher cost would go not so much for added or more expensive equipment, explains Ralph Sinnott, an electronics engineer with FEMA, as for "seeing that tradesmen do the construction differently." EMP-hardening an existing facility can be notably more expensive.

TWO APPROACHES

Perhaps the largest controversy in EMP-hardening—one Macklin describes as being almost "theological" in nature—has developed in response to the tackling of these potentially expensive retrofit cases. At issue is whether to shield all EMP-vulnerable components in a metal box, generically known as a Faraday cage, or whether to seek out and selectively shield only the most vulnerable components.

It may not sound like a big deal, but Macklin says that while the latter, tailored approach could involve more design analysis, it could also cost "almost an order of magnitude less" than installing a Faraday cage. That became an attractive selling point when the economy is undergoing a fiscal belt-tightening. In addition, tailoring in smaller, selective changes to an existing system usually proves less disruptive to its users—for example, no workers tearing out existing walls, ceilings or floors—during the hardening phase. And that's another strong plus.

But this tailored approach "is very configuration-dependent," notes King, a strong advocate of total shielding. He explains that the vulnerability of a particular system or facility is dependent on the exact layout of components and even the process used to manufacture seemingly identical parts. Any changes in the originally analyzed system could render a specific tailored hardening scheme "for naught." And it has almost become the rule, not the exception, for firms to upgrade electronic systems with minor changes or additions that inexpensively increase the productivity or capability of the existing system.

But there is an even more interesting aspect to the tailored versus Faraday cage debate. "While the tailored guys all agree that the [Faraday cage] approach will work," King says, "not everybody agrees that the tailored approach will." What's more, he says, even advocates of the tailored approach think that when building a new system or facility, it will cost less to shield it in a Faraday cage. So while shielding with a Faraday cage "is not only the soundest way to go," King claims, "it turns out—and I'm doing a lot of work in this area—that it appears also to be the cheapest way to go over the life-cycle" of a system.

NO ANTENNA, NO PROBLEM

One issue on which there is seemingly no argument is that technology now exists to EMP-harden any vulnerable system.

But just because something uses electronic parts doesn't mean that the system is vulnerable. And an impressive survey to narrow down when and why something is vulnerable has been conducted over the past 25 years, largely with Defense Department funding. Many of those studies are still classified, although their results are pouring into the open literature.

The general implication of these studies, notes the Defense Department in one of its manuals, is that mobile communications equipment—including walkie-talkies and the common transistor radio—are relatively survivable in an EMP environment. But radio-transmitting stations will be vulnerable unless expressly hardened for EMP.

"It sort of boiled down to," says Kerr, "if there's no antenna, there's no problem." For example, computers are one of the most vulnerable systems to EMP. But a computer "is not much more vulnerable than a piece of marble," unless and until it's attached to an antenna, the FEMA research director said. And every metal object represents a potential antenna to collect radiated EMP signals and focus them into more massive ones.

RADIO STATIONS HARDENED

That's one reason why FEMA has elected to EMP-harden radio-broadcast stations throughout the United States. Televisions, with their large rooftop antennas and power cords, are prime candidates for EMP damage. But transistor radios aren't, and it has been estimated that 80 per cent of the population has access to them. So if, and when, the Emergency Broadcast System (EBS) is called into use for warning the public about a nuclear attack, an EMP-hardened network of AM and FM radio stations could within 10 to 15 minutes broadcast the President or local leaders nationally. In mid-1981 roughly half of the United States was already within earshot of am EMP-hardened station. Completion of the network is expected by 1986 at the latest.

BUT POWER SYSTEMS?

Sinnott says that the EBS-network stations will be equipped with backup power-supply systems, usually diesel generators, and fueled to last several weeks. The anticipated need for that backup electrical power points to what is perceived as potentially one

A Vulcan flash X ray uses a pulse-radiation machine, to simulate the effects of gamma rays and X rays on electronic circuits and subsystems.

Courtesy of TRW-Quest Magazine

of the least prepared industries in the United States.

If a high-altitude nuclear blast bathed the nation in EMP, "my gut feeling is ... our power systems would probably not be available," says King. The Defense Nuclear Agency has run "EMP awareness courses" for electric-utility executives and engineers. Still there appears to be an attitude that lightning arrestors used throughout that industry are more than adequate to tackle the energy delivered by a nuclear EMP.

That's true, concedes King: "Some of the lightning arrestors are more than capable of handling the energy; but they are not fast enough." He explains that lightning arrestors—which short out circuits leading into sensitive power-controlled equipment—are designed to handle lightning pulses, which are about three orders of magnitude slower in their rise times than EMP. The result is that an EMP can flash through the circuit, wreaking havoc, long before the circuit can short.

The most likely result of an EMP exposure would be to trip circuit breakers across the United States. Companies with insufficient electric-load-shedding capabilities would be forced to shut generating stations down. "And you're talking 12 to 24 hours to get them back on line," King says. And the

How Likely Is a Rain of EMP?

Only a few years ago, nuclear war was depicted as the end of civilization. No more. Today, military strategists speak in terms of surviving a nuclear volley, and civil-defense planners are concentrating on postwar recovery schemes to restore vital services and government once the nuclear exchanges cease. Hence, a growing civilian interest in EMP.

While the radioactive contamination and explosive effects of nuclear warfare could prove massive, there has conventionally been reason to believe some hinterlands would escape relatively unharmed. But "EMP removes the possibility of an unscathed 'hinterland,' and thereby potentially adds an entirely new dimension of damage," explains a 1972 study by Oak Ridge National Laboratory.

It's this aspect that makes high-altitude detonations so awesome. While the searing heat, radiation and explosion will probably obscure any EMP effects in most ground blasts, it will be the other way around with high-altitude explosions; EMP effects will dominate.

And, "In a nuclear attack, a series of high-altitude bursts is likely," notes a July 1973 report prepared by the former Defense Civil Preparedness Agency. "The source of these bursts may range from an attacker's offensive missiles detonated explicitly to produce EMP effects, to our own defensive missiles deployed to intercept offensive missiles. It seems reasonable, then, to expect dozens or perhaps hundreds of high-altitude defensive and offensive bursts spread out over a period of a few minutes or an hour."

But Bill Macklin of IRT Corporation points out that there are other possible scenarios. For instance, a small terrorist group could seek ostensibly peaceful retribution against economic threats and political aggression by unexpectedly detonating one or a series of nuclear devices in the upper atmosphere of their enemy's territory. It needn't kill anyone, but it could certainly take an enormous economic toil.

Paul Fleming of the Defense Nuclear Agency tends to discount such hypothetical scenarios, asking, "Is that a creditable terrorist action?" He suggests that it's a costly and difficult gambit with no clear payoff and adds that it may also require more technological sophistication than most poor terrorists can muster.

What worries people like Macklin, however, is the existence of firms that might sell a launch capability to anyone with money. The West German firm Otrag (Orbital Transport und Raketen Aktiengesselschaft AG), for instance, is preparing to offer just such a service and has focused its marketing on the Third World. Otrag is now testing its equipment and by 1985 expects to be able to launch craft into orbit.

Explosive pulse can be clearly seen in this photo of a TNT blast. The expanding hot gas acts like a piston on the surrounding air, creating the high-pressure pulse.

net effect is that much if not most of the U.S. power grid would be shut down for hours to days, depending on the freqency with which successive EMP pulses arrived.

AN ACHILLES HEEL

"It is necessary to distinguish a rather striking contrast between civil and military approaches" to coping with potential EMP disruptions; explains a 1975 Defense Department study, *Electromagnetic Pulse and Civil Preparedness.* "While the nearly universal military approach has been to harden systems of interest, this is not a feasible civil measure." Military attack and communications systems cannot afford to shut down, even momentarily, during attack periods, whereas "civil preparedness systems can afford to be out of action for periods running from minutes to days." So while some attempt has been made to harden civil systems, such as the Emergency Broadcast Network, another common strategy has been to analyze likely damage should an EMP occur and then to develop contingency plans to cope.

These plans could include storing spare parts that would most likely need to be replaced or simply compiling directions for manually taking over formerly automated activities until repairs can be made.

A number of critics worry, however, that the electric-power industry has been too complacent to take even these measures. And it should be pointed out that the military is quite dependent on several civil systems that appear potentially still quite vulnerable to EMP—notably the nation's electric-power and telecommunications industries. As one EMP analyst points out—in the event of war, these military dependencies on non-EMP-hardened networks could prove an Achilles heel to national defense □

 SELECTED READINGS

"Nuclear pulse: awakening to chaos factor" by W. J. Broad. *Science,* May 29, 1981.
"Nuclear pulse: enduring delivery of doomsday sign" by W. J. Broad. *Science,* June 5, 1981.
"Nuclear pulse: playing a wild card" by W. J. Broad. *Science,* June 12, 1981.

Mort Tucker

Physicist William Kropp and engineer Dennis Hart inspect a powerful cutting head on a tunneling machine at an Ohio salt-mine experiment.

PROTON DECAY

by Peter Gwynne

DRESSED in coveralls, hard hat, and steel-tip boots, I slowly descended on a spider, the contraption that window washers use on the outsides of highrise office buildings. But this was no window job. I was dropping down the inside of a plastic-lined, five-story-high pit carved out of a salt mine nearly one kilometer (approximately one-half mile) beneath the shore of Lake Erie. Physicists and technicians there were preparing the pit for a watershed experiment that could reveal the true nature of the universe.

The experiment, one of many taking place in underground caverns around the world, seeks to confirm a theoretical prediction about protons, the positively charged components of the nucleus of an atom. Until recently, physicists thought that protons survive unchanging to eternity. The very fact that humans and other matter on earth do not glow with radioactivity is proof that the mass of most protons has not decayed into energy since the birth of the universe, an estimated 20,000,000,000 years ago.

Now, theorists working on the furthest frontiers of physical knowledge believe that the proton is not immortal. A typical one, they contend, splits asunder after about 10,000 billion, billion billion years—10^{31} years in mathematical language. As one prominent theorist, Nobel laureate Sheldon Glashow of Harvard puts it, "Diamonds may not be forever."

To the person in the street, 10^{31} years is hardly different from forever. Yet this extremely rare event, almost impossible to detect, could, if it is found to happen, have profound effects on the entire structure of theoretical physics that gives us some understanding of the universe. On the other hand, if experiments can conclusively rule out the possibility that protons decay, then physicists will have to throw out most of what they think they know and start all over.

"It's a very simple question that we're trying to answer," said John Vander Velde, a University of Michigan physicist who is one of the leaders of the salt-mine experiment I visited. "But it happens that the answer has very profound implications."

BIG-BANG FOSSIL

The scientists who come up with the first definitive evidence for proton decay will almost certainly earn a Nobel prize. And they will have brought science a giant step closer in its quest for a unified-field theory—a set of equations that would link the four known forces of nature.

Of these forces, electromagnetism and the weak nuclear force, which governs conventional radioactive decay, have been shown to be manifestations of the same force. Experts are now making spectacular progress in bringing into the scheme the strong nuclear force, which keeps atomic nuclei from tearing apart. Calculations by Howard Georgi, Helen Quinn, and Nobel laureate Steven Weinberg at Harvard suggest that those three forces become identical

GROUND LEVEL

2,000 FT.

EXISTING MINE

COMPUTER ROOM

PLUG

PROTON-DECAY DETECTOR

Artwork by Ray Pioch

An artist's conception of a proton-decay detector that is carved out of a salt mine beneath Lake Erie's shore. Physicists hope to obtain conclusive evidence that decay occurs.

at enormously high energies. (How the fourth force, gravity, could fit remains elusive.)

At these awesome energies, the Harvard trio asserts, particles such as protons that are influenced—specifically, kept in the nucleus of an atom—by the strong force can change into weak-force-influenced particles such as electrons. These awesome energy conditions would have actually existed in the universe only during the first few seconds of the Big Bang, the fireball that is thought to have started the cosmos. They would, however, have left a kind of fossil in the form of proton decay. This decay is predicted to occur so infrequently that detecting it poses one of the most stirring challenges experimental scientists have ever faced.

ELABORATE AND EXPENSIVE EXPERIMENTS

Thus, the experiments designed to detect proton decay are exceedingly elaborate and expensive. Not even the most dedicated researchers can wait 10^{31} years to spot the sudden collapse of a few protons. The alternative is to observe a great many protons for a shorter period. Proton decay, if it happens at all, happens a little bit at a time. Among a batch of 10^{31} protons, theorists expect that one solitary proton will decay in a year.

Looking for one decay a year would be a futile occupation, especially since the signature of such a decay would look much the same as some other events that are expected. For example, bombardment of protons by high-energy particles from space (cosmic rays) and other kinds of subnuclear decays would produce signals that could easily be confused with proton decay. Therefore, the experiments that are under way use samples containing 10 to 100 times that many protons and are performed deep underground to screen out the cosmic ray background as much as possible.

The cavern in the mine I explored, for example, will be filled with water containing 10^{33} protons—enough to yield 100 decays a year if the theorists are correct. Even so, the team of researchers from the University of Michigan, University of California at Irvine, and Brookhaven National Laboratory will have to be lucky as well as skillful to find positive evidence of proton decay. "We're trying to do an almost impossible task at the cutting edge of technology," co-principal investigator Larry Sulak says.

Experimental physicists find it hard to resist near-impossible challenges, and research teams around the world have joined the Michigan-California-Brookhaven group in a race to determine conclusively whether protons decay and, if so, to accurately measure their lifetime.

Physicists from Harvard, Purdue, and the University of Wisconsin are setting up a smaller version of the salt-mine experiment in the Silver King mine near Park City, Utah. Another similar setup, but at nearly twice the depth inside a mine in Homestake, South Dakota, has been providing data since 1979. So far, its University-of-Pennsylvania operators have made no claims. A fourth U.S. experiment, run by researchers from the University of Minnesota and Argonne National Laboratory in an iron mine in northern Minnesota, uses a massive block of concrete (instead of water) as its source of protons.

In April 1981 an Indian-Japanese team working with an iron slab buried some 3,600 meters (12,000 feet) deep in the Kolar gold field south of Bombay reported evidence of two proton decays, but their data have been disputed. Other groups, in Russia's Baskan Valley and in the Mont Blanc tunnel, which links France and Italy, have also begun.

BURYING THE SOURCE

Any detector designed to spot proton decay involves compromises. The larger the source of protons chosen, the more difficult it becomes to bury it very deep in the ground. Therefore, experimental teams that opt for the greatest possible depth must use compact proton sources—slabs of concrete or iron. And because particles that proton decay might produce would not travel far in such materials, the detectors must be embedded in the slabs.

The Michigan-California-Brookhaven group chose to sacrifice some depth to obtain a maximum volume of protons. Their reservoir is an astonishing 10,000 tons of water treated, according to Michigan physicist Jim Stone, to make it "literally the purest water on earth." Water of that purity is remarkably transparent. Peering down a cylindrical test tank holding such water in an unused elevator shaft at the University of Michigan, I could see to the bottom more clearly than in any Caribbean waters.

That much water obviously requires a large and strong tub. The experimental team first had to make a hole large enough to hold the container and then find suitable materials to store the water without leakage.

CAVE OF FORTUNE

After a careful search for a suitable site, the team chose the Morton salt mine in Fairport, Ohio, partly because group co-leader Fred Reines had successfully performed experiments there before. But a whole new cavern would have to be dug out to accommodate the prodigious pool. There the team hit on a piece of luck.

The Dosco Company, makers of automatic mining machines, wanted to demonstrate a new machine to Morton. The companies agreed to test the device by using it to carve the needed 24 by 21 by 18 meter (80 by 70 by 60 foot) hole. Not only did the scientists have their hole dug much more cheaply than expected, they sold the salt obtained by the drilling to Morton for $60,000.

Next came the problem of choosing the materials to line the cavity and contain the water. The group first sank huge rock bolts into the cavern walls to prevent large chunks of salt from breaking loose. Then they surrounded the area with wire mesh to hold back smaller pieces. Then they settled on the criteria for the tank lining. It had to be flexible enough to withstand the pressure of water forcing it against the mesh floor and walls, sturdy enough not to spring any leaks, and inert enough not to pollute the water.

They chose a high-density polyethylene made by the Schlegel Corporation of Rochester, New York. "You can take a screwdriver and slash down with all your strength, and not scratch the material," Jim Stone told me as we walked along the springy floor of the already lined pit. Even with that proved strength, the researchers were cautious: they

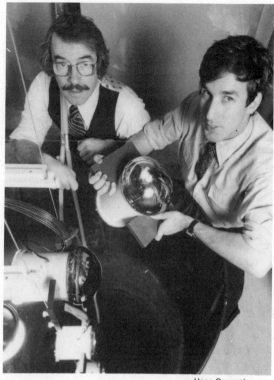
Hans Courant

University of Michigan physicists test a string of photomultiplier tubes in a six-story, water-filled pipe inside an elevator shaft.

installed two 2½-millimeter (0.1-inch) thick layers of the material.

It remained to choose a material for the top of the cavity—something that could support the weight of the equipment that would be attached to it yet be buoyant enough to float on the water. The team chose a reinforced rubber called Hypalon, made by Du Pont. Sixteen rafts of the material would form the cover. Shortly after my tour of inspection, the team planned to fill the pool, starting with the Hypalon rafts on the floor and letting them float as the water level rose.

Filling a cavern with 10,000 tons of water takes more time and effort than preparing the backyard swimming pool for summer. The group planned to run the purified water in through four horizontal sprinkler-type pipes around the floor of the cavern.

FASTER THAN LIGHT

However well prepared the pool may be, the detection of proton decay will depend on the perfect performance of the instruments installed in it. When protons in water decay, physicists believe, they produce electrically charged particles that travel through water faster than light does. (They don't travel faster than light in a vacuum, so they don't disobey Einstein's relativity theory.) The fast-moving particles will emit the equivalent of a sonic boom—a cone of bluish light called Cerenkov radiation. Detectors lining all six faces of the cavern will pick up these fleeting flashes of Cerenkov light. They will then amplify them and feed the data to computers in a control room in a cave adjacent to the pool.

The detectors are devices called photomultiplier tubes. When the experiment is ready to begin—before the end of 1982—2,048 of the monitors will be lowered into the tank. The team has tested the tubes extensively in what is called the "disco room"—a small, darkened laboratory on the Michigan campus. The lab contains a scaled-down version of the photomultiplier array that will line the walls of the water tank. The response of the tubes was tested by exposing them to bursts of diffuse light emitted by a small ball attached to the end of an optical fiber. Computers checked the performance of each individual tube.

Plans to place the 2,048 tubes in the underground water tank posed a minor engineering problem. The main difficulty was their buoyancy. Left to themselves, they would tend to float out of position. Larry Sulak solved that problem. The tubes are weighted with lead to give them neutral buoyancy. Strung in columns on inert nylon thread, they are relatively easy to maneuver.

READING THE TRACKS

Having overcome the technical challenges, the researchers will soon face the scientific riddle of differentiating proton decays from the many other subatomic events that leave similar fingerprints in the photomultiplier array. One major source of confusion is

Dr. Frederick Reines, a noted physicist at the University of California at Irvine, is a co-leader of the team conducting the monumental underground experiment in Ohio.

Physicist Kenneth Lande of the University of Pennsylvania adjusts a proton-decay detector 1.6 kilometers (1 mile) underground in a South Dakota experiment.

likely to stem from particles created when cosmic rays smash into atomic nuclei in the salt that surrounds the tank. Fortunately, those events should produce tracks only around the edges of the tank. Therefore, the team will ignore any "corner clippers" that show up within a few meters (yards) of the tank walls.

More difficult to diagnose will be collisions produced by neutrinos. Neutrinos are penetrating particles that can travel through the entire earth without interacting with anything, but that would occasionally also strike atoms in the pool. Team members feel confident that their computerized scanning techniques will be able to separate neutrino effects from proton decays, in part because they already know roughly the rate at which neutrinos should produce such events.

IMMENSE DIVIDENDS TO COME

The cost of this single experiment is as monumental as its size: $3,200,000 of U.S. Department of Energy funds. The researchers assert, however, that their device is not only a scientific bargain but one that is ahead of its time. "This is one experiment where America leads the world. That's why I joined the group," declared Tegid Wyn Jones, a Welshman from University College, London, who has come to Michigan to take part.

Certainly, the detector and similar devices around the world will offer immense scientific dividends if they work satisfactorily. If they measure the proton's lifetime, they will show that present theories about the nature of matter and the start of the universe are substantially correct. If the systems cannot spot any proton decays, they will cast grave doubts on those ideas. Either way, theorists are waiting eagerly while experimenters on three continents race to be first with the news □

 SELECTED READINGS

"Decay of the proton" by S. Weinberg. *Scientific American,* June 1981.

"Is the proton stable?" by M. Goldhaber and others. *Science,* November 21, 1981.

"They just don't make protons like they used to" by James Trefil. *Science 80,* November 1980.

"Underground experiments look for proton decay" by B. M. Schwarzschild. *Physics Today,* January 1980.

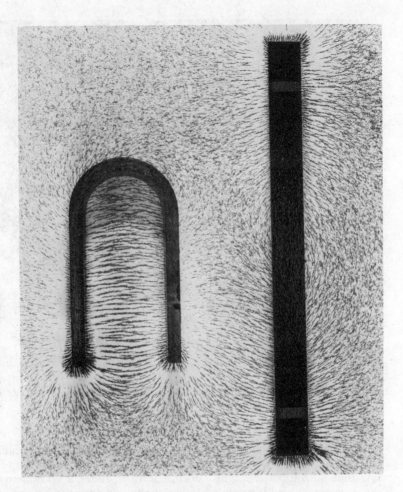

A horseshoe magnet, which is really a U-shaped bar magnet, and a typical bar magnet are arranged close together. Fine iron filings sprinkled near them have aligned with the magnetic force in each magnet's field. The greatest magnetism appears to be concentrated near the ends of both magnets in two regions, or poles.

MAGNETIC DOMAINS

by W. E. Wallace

MAGNETISM is as old as the hills, and older yet. It is one of the elemental forces of nature, and human beings have had at least a passing acquaintance with it for thousands of years. Many of the ancients were familiar with the strange attraction that lodestone has for iron (though they probably did not guess that lodestone is itself an oxide of iron). For centuries, that was as much as anyone knew about the mysterious phenomenon of magnetism—the push, tug, and shove that bits of a dark mineral gave to other bits of itself, and the way they all seemed to seize and fasten upon the polished blade of a knife.

In the early part of the 19th century, our notions of the subject took a great leap forward when the Danish physicist Hans Christian Oersted discovered a curious new kind of magnet. If he wrapped a wire around a piece of iron—a nail, for example—and passed a current through the wire, the nail would behave like a magnet. Turn off the current, and the new magnet shuts off too. Oersted showed that when any conductor (even a nonmagnetic conductor such as copper) carries a current, it is surrounded by a magnetic field that increases proportionally with the current and disappears as soon as the flow of electricity stops.

ALL FROM THE SAME SOURCE

Permanent magnets like lodestone and the temporary ones—electromagnets—that Oersted discovered are surrounded by a field that we conventionally draw with the familiar north and south poles and lines radiating between. These lines represent the ability of the magnet to interact with other magnets. Fundamentally, of course, both varieties of magnets—permanent and electromagnetic— derive their force from the same source. All magnetic fields are produced by the motion of negatively charged particles called electrons through space. The electrons may be free and streaming along a copper wire, or they may be tethered to an atom and orbiting around it, spinning as they go.

Such matters are interesting enough in their own right, but they are fascinating in their applications. We live in a society that is at once gadget-dependent and gadget-ignorant. Most people know there is a magnet in their refrigerator door, and perhaps they use another three or four magnets to tack memos to the front of the door itself. But few are aware that there are magnets in most of the electrical and electronic devices in their lives, from air conditioners to wristwatches to hair dryers. Automobiles not only include many magnets, they would not work without them.

AND NOW—THE SUPERMAGNET

The last few decades have seen yet another leap forward in the history of magnets, one which has enormous value for applications. A new kind of magnet has been synthesized that is hundreds of times more powerful than any ever made. The new development is called the supermagnet. Simply by its existence the supermagnet has made futuristic dreams into technologic possibilities. It seems likely that the advent of supermagnets will revolutionize the electronic motor, reducing the size of many of them by a factor of ten. This may have profound implications for energy conservation. Lightweight, high-efficiency motors using supermagnets may make the electric car a competitive and attractive item. Japan and West Germany are already operating high-speed experimental trains, suspended magnetically to reduce friction, that may soon attain routine speeds of more than 400 kilometers (250 miles) per hour.

THE INGREDIENTS

These supermagnets are compounds not found in nature. They are formed by chemi-

cally uniting the rare-earth element samarium (Sm) with cobalt (Co), or with an alloy of cobalt. The first and simplest supermagnet ever made was $SmCo_5$, synthesized in my laboratory in 1959.

The rare-earth elements are very active chemically, reacting with nearly 90 per cent of the elements in the periodic table. They readily react with oxygen to form oxides. They also react with most known metals to form a large class of inorganic compounds— the rare-earth intermetallic compounds, more than 1,000 of which are known. $SmCO_5$ is neither a mixture nor a solid solution of its elemental ingredients. It is a compound with its own characteristic structure and properties.

There is one quite dramatic difference between the intermetallic compounds, in-

This electron micrograph reveals the structure of the domains (meandering strips) in a garnet crystal. The domains are too narrow to be seen clearly with an optical microscope.

IBM Thomas Watson Research Center

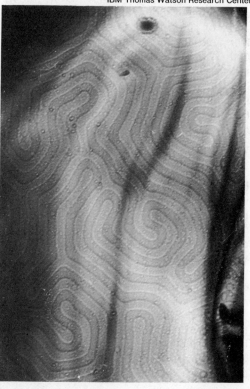

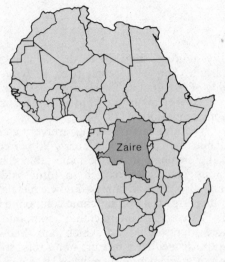

Troubles in Zaire, Africa, the world's chief source of cobalt, may affect supermagnet manufacturers.

cluding $SmCo_5$, and the more conventional inorganic compounds. In the latter, the ratio of the atoms making up the compound is precisely fixed. Take common table salt, an inorganic compound made up of sodium and chloride, for example. Everywhere one looks in a crystal of common table salt, one finds a single atom of sodium paired up with a single atom of chlorine. The ratio does not vary from unity by more than a few parts per 10,-000. This fixed ratio of constituent atoms is not true of the intermetallic compounds. In $SmCo_5$ for example, the ratio of cobalt to samarium varies all the way from 4.6 to 5.6, a (relatively) extravagant variation that has important consequences.

TINKERING POSSIBLE

Because the ratio varies, it can be tinkered with in the laboratory. We can add more cobalt (or certain other metals, such as nickel or iron) to replace some of the samarium. At first the cobalt fills spots randomly in the crystal lattice of $SmCo_5$. But as we add more, the cobalt begins to organize within the lattice and ultimately generates an entirely new compound, with a new geometric structure—Sm_2Co_{17}.

Other rare earths besides samarium may be tinkered with in this way, by adding cobalt or nickel or iron until the ratio is 2 to 17. This entire class of compounds, the 2 to 17 class, is extraordinarily stable. Such compounds were first reported in the scientific literature in 1977, and hit the market only in 1979. (They were developed independently by the Swiss and the Japanese—the Swiss having perhaps a slight priority in the discovery.) Sm_2Co_{17} is so potent that it should perhaps be referred to as a super-supermagnet: it is more than 30,000,000 times as powerful as a magnet made of iron.

MAGNETIC MOMENTS

A material that can be used to form a permanent magnet—such as iron and many of its compounds—usually does not have any net magnetic force, called magnetic moment, until it is specially treated by exposure to a powerful magnetic field. Until then, it behaves as if it were not magnetic at all. Lodestone, the naturally occurring magnet, is no exception to this rule: it has been exposed to the magnetic field of the earth itself.

In 1907, to explain how this might come about, the French magnetician Pierre Weiss proposed the domain theory. Magnetizable material, he suggested, consists of many small regions, called domains, within the metal. The atoms within a domain each behave like a tiny individual magnet, with a north and south pole. The atoms are all aligned in parallel, so that the domain itself is like a bar magnet (albeit very small). In their natural state, the domains themselves are not regimented—not lined up with each other—and so their forces cancel each other out and there is no overall magnetization.

Only when an assemblage of domains is exposed to a magnetic field will the individual domains align themselves (a bit like iron filings around a bar magnet) and become parallel. Essentially, the magnetic field converts the piece of metal into one single, very large domain. The material then becomes magnetic—and is said to have a magnetic moment.

Clearly, then, not every material has magnetic potential. First and foremost, its atoms must themselves be miniature bar magnets (not all atoms are). If an atom has an odd number of electrons, then it will have a north and south pole and a magnetic field. But if it has an even number, then the fields generated by its spinning and whirling electrons will cancel each other out and there will be no net magnetic moment. And then, even if the material's constituent atoms are themselves magnetic, there are many ways that its crystalline structure can irrevocably cancel out the charges of the atoms, locking them strongly in patterns that are not parallel, so that they will never align, even when placed within the most powerful magnetic fields.

MAGNETIC SIGNATURE

What is more, magnetizable materials do not all react identically when placed in a magnetic field. They each show a resistance in responding to changes in the field. This resistance, or lagging-behind, is called hysteresis (from the Greek for "later, behind"). We can use each material's characteristic pattern of reactions to changes in the magnetic field to catalog and define the material's magnetic properties.

To chart this pattern—the signature of a magnetizable substance—we place it under the influence of a powerful, pulsing electromagnet. First we gradually increase the strength of the field in one direction, and then just as smoothly diminish the field and reverse it until it has become as strong in the opposite direction. The substance's pattern of response (always lagging by varying degrees behind the changing magnetic force) is called its hysteresis loop.

A block if iron, for example, is merely a randomly arranged set of domains with no magnetic force of its own. But when placed in a magnetic field, the iron's magnetization rises rapidly and approaches saturation at the highest applied field. Then, as the force is reduced, the iron loses its magnetic moment as well. By the time the outer force has been reduced to zero, most of the domains in the block of iron have jumbled about randomly again, scattering away toward all points of the compass, and the block retains only a bare residue of magnetic force.

THE SPECIAL TALENT FOR RESISTANCE

When a supermagnet like $SmCo_5$ is subjected to a magnetic field, its behavior is quite different. It acts much like any other magnetizable substance as the force field is applied and is increased in strength: it eventually reaches a saturation point, where virtually all its atoms and domains are aligned. But when the outer field is reduced, the magnet lags way behind in its reaction to this change.

Indeed, the outer force field can be reduced to zero and still the supermagnet will remain strongly magnetized—for hours, weeks, months, years. Even after the field has been turned in the opposite direction, the supermagnet resists demagnetization. The opposing field must be powerful indeed before it will utterly undo the supermagnet's field (the strength of the field required to do this kind of atomic violence is called the "coercive force").

This resistance is the chief talent and virtue of the supermagnet. The supermagnet is not inherently—that is, atom for atom—stronger than iron; in fact, it has a magnetic moment lower than that of elemental iron. But, as we have seen, there is nothing permanent about a piece of iron: one can magnetize it, turn off the current, and three minutes later the block is a jumble again. The supermagnet, however, really is all but permanent. Iron has the greater potential, but because of its internal structure that potential can never be realized. An $SmCo_5$ magnet is very roughly 100 times as powerful as one of pure iron. About 50,000 times the coercive force is required to demagnetize it. Sm_2Co_{17}, as we have seen, is 30,000,000 times as strong.

CLAMPING MECHANISM

In 1975, the author and his colleagues traced this gift of resistance, with which supermagnets are so generously endowed, to its ultimate source. We now know that a "clamping mechanism" allows a supermagnet compound like $SmCo_5$ or Sm_2Co_{17} to hold on to its own atomic orientation, even under tremendous pressure to let go and swivel in the opposite direction—to do an about-face, as it were. The secret lies not in the shape of the domains but in the shape of the atoms themselves.

In a crystal, each ion, or charged atom, is suspended in formation and floats there surrounded by atoms of its own kind. Each atom is held in place by electrostatic interactions with its own fellows. Different ions exhibit different interaction patterns, just as the geometric patterns of crystal fields differ.

If the ions are perfectly spherical, they can roll about in position as much as they like. They have no up or down. But if they happen to be shaped like footballs, as samarium ions are, then their interactions tend to keep them aligned. Samarium ions prefer to float end to end, point to point, in parallel rows. And it is this quite strong preference of theirs for alignment—a preference, ironically enough, which has nothing whatever to do with their magnetic moment, but is caused by interactions within the crystal field—that makes $SmCo_5$ the stubborn magnet it is. The footballs simply do not want to tilt. It takes an extraordinarily strong magnetic field in the opposite direction to make them flip over.

The ions of elemental iron, on the other hand, are clamped so lightly that they can hardly be said to be clamped at all. They wander all over the lot, one pointing one way, the other another. Pure iron is clamped by a force of one hundredth of a unit, $SmCo_5$ by a force of half a million.

Five domains are shown in a microscopic region of iron. In (a) there is no externally applied magnetic field. Domains (indicated by arrows) are of equal size. In (b) an external field applied to the left causes the left-oriented domains to grow larger at the expense of the right-oriented ones. In (c) a stronger field to the left is applied, producing an even greater growth of the left-oriented domains.

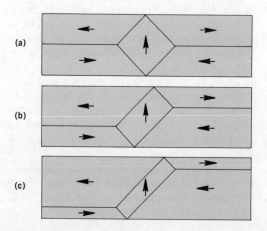

MAKING A SUPERMAGNET

Several steps are needed to make a supermagnet. First the samarium and cobalt must be combined—melted together and mixed under a protective atmosphere (usually argon) with which they cannot react. In lump form, the new compound has no magnetic moment at all. Next the compound is ground into very fine particles (on the order of 0.000010 meter). Ideally one would like to grind it into particles so fine that each is a single domain. The particles are then aligned in a magnetic field and pressed and compacted together at pressures in the range of 7,000 kilograms per square centimeter (100,000 pounds per square inch). The results, called "green compacts," are 60 per cent as dense as the theoretical maximum, and have a certain small magnetic moment.

The green compacts are heated without combustion at high temperatures (typically 1,125° Celsius (2,257° Fahrenheit for half an hour) and achieve a density within 90 to 95 per cent of the theoretical maximum. Finally, they are placed in a powerful magnetic field, and they emerge from it as supermagnets.

MANY APPLICATIONS

At least seven countries are making supermagnets: Japan, Switzerland, England, France, China, the United States and the Soviet Union. About $50,000,000 worth are made per year, and the volume is growing rapidly. Japan leads the field, its sales accounting for about 85 per cent of the world total. Indeed, the United States ships raw materials to Japan to be made into supermagnets, then buys them back and inserts them into U.S.-made items. Ironically, then, in this department the Japanese are dealing with the United States as a highly developed nation treats a less developed one.

The applications of the supermagnets are legion—in microwave and audio equipment; in timepieces; in biomedical technology, such as catheters, implantable pumps and valves; in frictionless bearings, motors and generators. Their first widespread application was in the tubes used to generate and focus microwaves. In such tubes, electrons are directed along a complex path by a per-

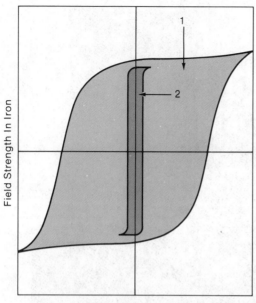

Applied Magnetic Field

Drawing above shows hard iron (1) is more difficult to magnetize and demagnetize than soft iron (2).

Field Strength In Iron

manent magnet. In the mid-1960's this magnet was a platinum-cobalt alloy that was about 77 per cent platinum and cost about $4400 per kilogram ($2,000 per pound). It was replaced by $SmCo_5$ at about one-fiftieth the cost, and with improved performance.

However, the largest application of the supermagnets still lies ahead. It will come in the fabrication of electric motors. Conventional motors are driven by two electromagnets, called the stator and the rotor. They are arranged so that the fixed one, the stator, causes the loose one, the rotor, to rotate at high speeds. Formerly, one could not consider replacing either of these with a permanent magnet, because the current flowing through one would generate a magnetic field powerful enough to demagnetize the other. But the supermagnets have much higher resistance to demagnetization, as we have seen. If we replace the electrically powered rotor with a supermagnet, this will immediately reduce the power the motor requires to operate.

Indeed, in small motors like the one that powers a window air cleaner, this change would dramatically increase efficiency—so dramatically that were all the small motors in the United States redesigned to take advantage of the capabilities of supermagnets, the energy savings nationwide would be enormous.

Large motors (75,000 watts, or about 100 horsepower or bigger) are much more efficient than smaller ones, even without supermagnets, but they would also benefit from the new technology. A conventional 75,000-watt (100-horsepower) motor weighs about 450 kilograms (1,000 pounds). Built with supermagnets it would weigh only 45 kilograms (100 pounds). The electric vehicle of the future may need a 75,000-watt (100-horsepower) motor, and, if it uses supermagnets, will have almost half a ton less weight to carry around.

BUT PROBLEMS

The world of supermagnets is developing rapidly—especially in Japan—but it is hindered by two shortages—of people and of supplies. The number of universities in the United States educating people in fields germane to supermagnets can be counted on the fingers of one hand. And industry is providing little help. Neither are the government laboratories.

Industry is reluctant to commit itself to this new technology, which would entail so many revolutionary changes, because access to the necessary materials has been seriously restricted—at least until very recently. Samarium is a rare-earth element. The "rare" in rare-earths is a misnomer, since most are quite common. Samarium, unfortunately, really is hard to find. And the world's chief source of cobalt is Zaire, a politically turbulent area upon which the world's major manufacturers are reluctant to rely for supplies.

Until now, motor manufacturers have hesitated to construct facilities for producing the new generation of electric motors, a step of vital importance to the energy future of the United States. However, China has recently revealed that it has large amounts of samarium and is willing to make them available. This news is already quickening industrial development, development that may prove decisive in moving the United States toward large-scale commercialization of the supermotor. And when that happens, the stubborn supermagnets may at last come into their own □

All artwork by Cameron Gerlach

Thinkers have struggled with the concept of nothingness for centuries, only to find that vacuums are not empty as they once believed.

NOTHING

by James S. Trefil

HAVE you ever tried to picture a vacuum? A real vacuum, with absolutely nothing in it? I have to admit that I can't. Whenever I try, I always wind up thinking of an empty space between a pair of material objects—two atoms, or maybe two stars. The human mind has difficulty in picturing a state of true nothingness. The concept of the vacuum has always generated debate among scientific thinkers.

Thinking about the vacuum today can be even more of a strain on the mind. It turns out to be nothing, just as we always thought, but a nothing with energy and structure. It may be even that our everyday universe with its solid matter is nothing more than a lower state of a more energetic universe that would appear to us as a vacuum.

Throughout most of history—well into the 19th century, in fact—the prevailing opinion was that there just had to be something to fill up all the empty space between material objects. In 1881, however, Albert Michelson and Edward Morley, two American physicists, presented experimental proof that there really is not any material pervading the universe and filling in all the voids. In so doing they established the existence of the vacuum once and for all.

But the problem refused to remain solved. The discovery of antimatter in the 1930's raised the possibility that what appears to be a vacuum might, if examined on a small enough scale, exhibit a sort of fleeting structure. Today, that structure figures strongly in one of the most exciting intellectual adventures ever undertaken by science—the attempt to trace the history of the universe back to the very beginning. Moreover, theoretical physicists have speculated that it might be possible to go beyond this beginning point and probe a still more fundamental question—why there is a universe at all.

After all, asking why there is something instead of nothing is simply another way of asking why the universe itself is not a complete vacuum. So although the study of "nothing" may appear to be a singularly unrewarding endeavor, "nothing" may in fact be the key to finding the answers to some very compelling philosophical questions.

VACUUM UNTHINKABLE FOR A LONG TIME

As with so many long-standing intellectual debates, the arguments about whether there was such a thing as a real vacuum started with the ancient Greeks. Aristotle felt that there could be no such thing because he believed that for anything to move, something had to push on it. Anything in a true vacuum, then, would be condemned to an eternal stability and, since we know that everything does move sooner or later, it follows that nothing can be surrounded by a vacuum.

So forceful did this line of reasoning seem, and so great was the prestige of Aristotle, that we find essentially the same argument being used by the French mathematician René Descartes in the 17th century. How, he asked, could the earth be made to move around the sun if something weren't

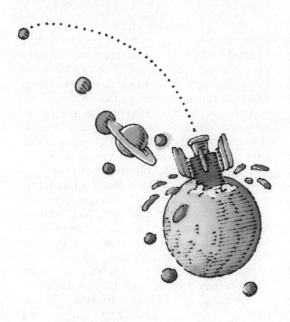

Interplanetary probes prove that it is no problem to travel through a vacuum, despite the doubts of ancient philosophers.

pushing it? Clearly, nature not only abhorred a vacuum, but found it completely unthinkable.

Today, of course, we know that this sort of argument isn't valid. We routinely send space probes to the far reaches of the solar system, and once these probes are launched, they have no further need for propulsion. The truth is that, once something starts moving, it will keep moving until something else makes it stop. Once you realize this fact, you see that the vacuum is really quite "thinkable."

In opposition to the Aristotelian viewpoint, there was in ancient Greece another group of philosophers called atomists, whose followers remained a slightly disreputable minority until well into modern times. They believed that matter was made of small indivisible units called atoms, and that the space between atoms was completely empty—a true vacuum. In retrospect we know that they were right all along, of course, but they never succeeded in convincing their contemporaries.

ETHER

Practical applications of the vacuum eventually forced everyone to admit that there could be such a thing as an absence of air, but Aristotle's legacy couldn't be killed that easily. Forced to admit that all of the air could be removed from a container, philosophers fell back on the concept of the ether. Ether was supposed to be a colorless, tasteless, undetectable fluid that fills all the empty spaces in the universe. At this point, I imagine, philosophers felt confident that they had set things up in such a way that scientists could never prove them wrong.

But even this compromise was not destined to last. Michelson (who in 1907 became the first U.S. scientist awarded the Nobel Prize in physics) reasoned that if the ether did indeed pervade the universe, then the motion of the earth should produce an "ether wind," much as driving a car in still air produces a "wind" for the occupants. If a beam of light is directed across this "ether wind," it will be deflected in the same way that a boat crossing a rapid river will be swept downstream. Using delicate optical techniques,

When a subatomic particle and its opposite meet, they annihilate each other, leaving only energy.

Michelson and Morley showed that there was no evidence whatsoever for an ether wind, and hence no evidence for an ether.

ABSENCE OF MATTER

So the idea that the texture of the universe is woven from bits of matter separated by regions of vacuum came to be the dominant view of scientists about a century ago. Perhaps the best way to visualize what we usually call a vacuum would be to imagine a small thimble. If the thimble were full of air, there would be many atoms in it—thousands of quadrillions of them. If you put the thimble inside a TV tube, the number of atoms would drop to a few billion. If, on the other hand, you went to a laboratory and put the thimble in the best vacuum that could be created artificially, it would hold only about 500 atoms.

In near-earth space or on the surface of the moon, this number would go down by a factor of ten. (We still can't produce as good a vacuum on earth as nature has provided a few kilometers up, which is one reason why the exploration of space can be expected to lead to new industrial advances.) Finally, if we took our thimble out to the empty spaces between stars, we would expect it to hold, on the average, only one atom. This represents the best vacuum in our galaxy.

These numbers show us that even the vast spaces between stars contain occasional stray bits of matter. But if we imagine this space filled with our thimbles, each thimble would have only one atom rattling around in it. The rest of the space in the thimble would be truly free of matter and consequently would represent the ultimate vacuum.

While the view that space contains either matter or vacuum is a comfortable one, the increased knowledge of the atomic world that has been gained during the 20th century has tended to lead toward a more complex view. In this view the space in the thimble, if examined in close enough detail, is seen to have an evanescent, almost ghostly type of material structure. The most important element in the modern view of the vacuum is the existence of antimatter. In 1932—just four years after P. A. M. Dirac predicted the existence of antimatter—a strange new particle was seen in the debris resulting from the collision of a cosmic ray with an atom in the atmosphere. This new particle had the same mass as the electron, but the opposite electrical charge. Carl Anderson, then a research fellow at the California Institute of Technology, performed the experiment, so he had the privilege of naming the new discovery. He called it the positron (for its positive charge). The particle he saw was the first piece of antimatter ever detected.

MATTER—ANTIMATTER PAIRS

The most striking property of bits of antimatter such as the positron concerns their behavior when they get near an ordinary particle, like the electron. The two particles come together and annihilate each other. They disappear as their mass is converted entirely into energy. The reverse process, in which a large amount of energy can be converted into mass and the particle-antiparticle pair created from nothing, is performed routinely in laboratories around the world.

In the years since Anderson's discovery, many different kinds of antiparticles have been seen. It appears that every time we find an ordinary particle in nature, we will be able to produce its antiparticle, if we try hard enough. In each case, the antiparticle and the particle have the same mass, but in all other respects they are the opposite of each other.

An analogy can help explain the properties of matter and antimatter. Suppose we were standing on a level field with a shovel. We could dig a hole in the ground and pile the removed dirt next to it. This would require some expenditure of energy on our part, of course, but when we finished we would have taken the level field and turned it into one that had two things in it—a pile of dirt and a hole.

If we equate the level field with the vacuum, the pile of dirt with an ordinary particle, and the hole with an antiparticle, then the digging process is analogous to the conversion of energy into matter—the creation of a particle-antiparticle pair.

If we now took the shovel and filled in the hole, the final product would be a level field again—a vacuum. If we did this, some energy would be released as the dirt dropped into the hole, resulting in a (very small) increase in the temperature of the dirt. Filling in the hole, then, would correspond to the process of annihilation in which the particle and antiparticle disappear and the only thing left is energy.

In our normal experience, we would not expect holes and piles of dirt to appear spontaneously in an open field. A physicist would say that this sort of thing can't happen because it violates the principle of conservation of energy. Someone has to expend energy to dig the hole, and unless that energy is supplied, nothing will happen on the field.

But suppose we looked at the field now, went about our business for an hour, and then came back and looked again. Could we be sure that during our absence someone had not come, dug a hole, and then filled it up again? All we actually observe is that the field is level at the beginning and end of the hour, and anything could have happened in between. If we pursue this thought, we realize that no matter how closely we watch the field, we cannot rule out the appearance and disappearance of a hole, provided that the process takes place in a sufficiently short time.

So long as we restrict our attention to large-scale things like piles of dirt, this seems a reasonable way to proceed. When we start to talk about microscopic things like electrons and positrons, however, we run into a basic problem. The only way we can detect

If holes were dug and re-filled in an otherwise featureless field so quickly that we couldn't see it happen, the situation would be analogous to particles appearing and disappearing in a vacuum.

the presence of a subatomic particle is to bounce another subatomic particle off it. Unlike the pile of dirt, which is not affected by the light from our camera, an electron or positron cannot be measured without affecting it in some way.

UNCERTAINTY PRINCIPLE

This fact—that the measurement of a subatomic system must change the system—gives rise to something known as the uncertainty principle. In practical terms, it means that if we want to know two things about a system—its energy and the time at which it has that energy, for example—the measurement of one variable will change the result for the other.

If we want to know precisely the total energy that a system has, then we have to make our measurement over a long period of time and we can't be very accurate about the time at which the system has that energy. Conversely, if we measure for a very short period, so that we know the time precisely, then we only know the energy within some rather wide limits.

For ordinary large-scale objects, this limitation on measurement isn't important because the limits imposed by the uncertainty principle are far below those of even the best instruments. But for small subatomic systems, they become very important, and they are extremely important in the modern conception of the vacuum. Consider the following point: if the time during which the subatomic system is observed is so short that the energy uncertainty is greater than the total energy required to make an electron-positron pair, then there is no way we can tell whether such a pair has appeared and then disappeared during the observation.

VACUUM LIKE A DROP OF WATER

This is a rather strange concept, but if we take it seriously for a moment we can see that it leads us to a totally new—and more complex—picture of what a vacuum really is. To the casual observer, the space between atoms is really just empty. But if we could examine it in minute detail, we would see that the seemingly cold lifeless vacuum is, in fact, teeming with activity. In a sense, this situa-tion is not too different from the experience we have in our first biology course, in which a simple drop of water is seen to be full of living things. The primary difference between these two situations is that, in the case of the vacuum, the matter-antimatter pairs must disappear in a brief time, while in the case of the water drop the microorganisms are always there, waiting to be revealed.

By this time, you may well be wondering what the point of this sort of speculation is. After all, if the particles in the vacuum disappear before they can be measured, what difference can it possibly make whether they are there or not? It turns out that there are consequences that actually can be seen in the laboratory.

Think of a simple hydrogen atom—one electron circling one proton—sitting alone in space. In the empty space all around it, electron-positron pairs are appearing and disappearing at irregular intervals, with the randomness of popcorn in a popper. If one of these pairs should appear near the atom, then the electron going around in its orbit would feel a short push or pull from the electrical forces exerted by the pair. Instead of going around in a serene, undisturbed path, the electron in the atom would be jostled. This jostling, in turn, would affect the light emitted by the hydrogen atom. It won't be a big effect, of course, but it will be there. Its effects were first seen in light emitted from hydrogen in the late 1940's.

This effect provides a concrete test of the notion of the vacuum that we have developed. If there were no process by which pairs were being created and destroyed in a continual, ever-changing pattern, there would be no effect on the electron path and no effect in the light emissions of hydrogen.

NO MERE LABORATORY CURIOSITY

If the story of the vacuum stopped at this point, it would be merely an interesting sidelight in our view of modern science. In the last few years, however, the vacuum has taken on a new significance. As physicists have learned more and more about elementary particles and the forces that operate between them, they have begun to trace the development of the universe backward to the

Like a ball rolling down a flight of stairs, the universe went through a series of "freezings" to lower and lower energy states.

very early moments of creation. According to our present ideas, the universe was created in an explosion called the Big Bang and has been expanding ever since.

At the very earliest times, all of the matter that is now spread throughout the galaxies was compressed into a small space. The densities and temperatures of that small space were beyond anything known in the present era. In this primordial fireball, species of particles existed with masses billions of times greater than that of the proton. At this early time interactions took place which have long since ceased to be important in our everyday world.

What physicists are trying to do right now is take the universe as we see it, take the faint evidence left from this early fireball, and deduce from them the laws which must have operated in the beginning.

BACK TO THE FIRST SECONDS

We want to go back not to the first minutes or even seconds of creation, but to the first 10^{-36} seconds after the Big Bang (that's a decimal point with 35 zeroes and then a 1). At that time the universe we would see would bear no resemblance at all to the one we know today. The temperature would be so high that all the matter around would behave in the same way, regardless of its electrical charge or mass, and all the forces between particles would be the same. A physicist would say that this situation represented a high degree of symmetry. As the expansion of the universe progressed, the fireball cooled off and distinctions between particles and forces began to become important. The symmetry began to disappear.

Perhaps the best analogy to this process would be the freezing of water. In the liquid state, water is highly symmetrical. If we were suspended in a bathysphere in the ocean, we would see the same thing—liquid water—no matter in which direction we looked. A physicist would say that the liquid water represented a state of high symmetry, because what we observe does not depend on the direction in which we look. If the water were to freeze, however, this situation would change. Ice crystals are hexagonal in shape, and hence frozen water no longer has the same degree of symmetry as liquid water—it does make a difference which way you look in ice.

SERIES OF FREEZINGS

In just the same way, we can think of the universe undergoing a series of "freezings" during which symmetries vanished. For example, at one stage in the early universe, the temperature was so high that all forces were indistinguishable from one another. This is a situation with a high degree of symmetry. The temperature fell as the universe expanded, however, and a series of "freezings" occurred, leaving us with our present universe and different types of forces—a situation with a low level of symmetry. And, all this happened well before the universe was a second old.

When water freezes, the energy of the ice is lower than that of the water which preceded it. We know this because we have to add energy in the form of heat to an ice cube to get it to melt back into the water. In just the same way, the total energy of the universe after each "freezing" is lower than it was before. In a sense, then, the early evolution of the universe is not too different from a ball rolling down a flight of stairs. In each case, we have a system proceeding to a state of lower energy, and in each case the progression is discontinuous instead of smooth.

AND EVEN BEFORE THAT?

But where does the vacuum fit into this scheme of things? We have seen that the vacuum is not simply the absence of matter—that the vacuum is, in fact, a system which contains matter. Of course, this matter is not

The dance of atoms is affected enough to be seen when particles appear out of space near them.

the permanent state we're used to, but consists of the kinds of transitory particle-antiparticle pairs we've described. Nevertheless, it is perfectly reasonable to talk about the energy and symmetry of the vacuum, just as it is reasonable to talk about these qualities for any of the stages through which the matter of the universe has progressed.

And this, in turn, leads to one of the most exciting ideas that I've encountered in a long time. One persistent question that always comes to mind when discussing the Big Bang concerns the nature of the universe *before* the initial explosion. Some scientists simply refuse to consider this question, pointing out that it is not, properly speaking, a question that can be answered with the techniques of science. Others postulate that the present expansion of the universe will someday reverse itself, and that the subsequent contraction will produce once again the infinitely dense state that will serve as the beginning of a new Big Bang.

To these scientists, the universe is a never-ending cycle of expansion and contraction, so the question of what was there before the universe is meaningless—there never was a "before." Both these positions are intellectually defensible, and I have often used them when asked difficult questions by my students. But I have always found them to be unsatisfying.

A HIGH-ENERGY VACUUM?

But now we have a new way of approaching this question. If we think about what must have existed before the beginning of our present universe, the best candidate is nothing—the vacuum itself. The question of why the universe exists, then, comes down to the question of why matter in its present form should have come into existence out of the primordial vacuum. Once we realize that the vacuum is not a total absence of matter, but just a state in which matter has a certain rather specialized form, the question loses its mystical overtones and becomes one that can be answered, at least in principle, in scientific terms.

We simply want to know whether the state that we call the vacuum has a higher energy than the state that began the Big

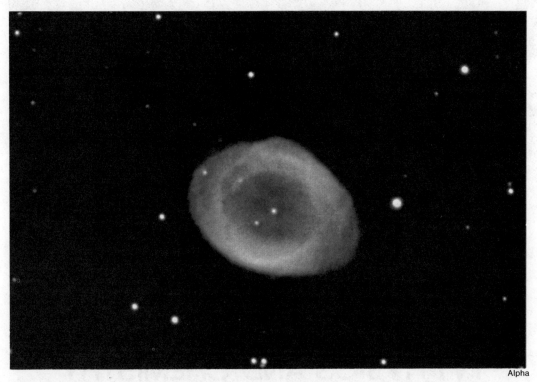

Today we know that most of the universe is not simply empty space but is, in fact, a system teeming with activity from transitory particle-antiparticle pairs.

Bang. If it did, then the appearance of stable matter out of the vacuum would simply be one more "freezing" of the type that occurred several more times as the universe expanded. The universe would be here because the energy of the universe with matter is lower than the energy of the universe without—and nature always proceeds to a state of lowest energy.

Now I have to emphasize that this scenario is a hope—a speculation—based on some tentative current trends in theoretical physics. There are many ways in which it could fail to be realized. The theories used to trace our way back through the Big Bang could turn out to be wrong, or the calculations we are doing might be giving us misleading answers. But whichever way things turn out, the fact is that for the first time in the history of science there seems to be a way to apply knowledge gained in our laboratories to questions relating to events billions of years ago.

Perhaps this point was made best by Sidney Drell, a well-known theoretical physicist and the deputy director of the Stanford Linear Accelerator Center in Menlo Park, California: "When the universe began, we were sitting on a mountaintop where everything appeared to be the same no matter which way we looked. We've been rolling down that mountain for billions of years, and now everything is unsymmetrical—we have the mountain on one side and open air on the other. What physics gives us is a telescope that lets us look back up the mountain and see what it was like at the top."

Or just possibly, we might add, what it's like a little beyond the top ☐

 SELECTED READINGS

"Missing mass mystery" by W. Tucker. *Science Digest,* September 1981.

"Structure of the early universe" by J. D. Barrow and J. Silk. *Scientific American,* April 1980.

Three 1981 Nobel laureates accepting their awards for their work in physics. From left to right: Nicolaas Bloembergen, Arthur Schawlow, and Kai Siegbahn.

THE 1981 NOBEL PRIZES IN PHYSICS AND CHEMISTRY

by Howard Siner

WHERE physics and chemistry meet is the realm of subatomic particles. This was the focus of five men who earned Nobel Prizes in 1981 for work that reduced the gap between the two scientific disciplines. Their research—important to everyday tasks such as measuring pollution and creating new drugs—looked deep into the physics of chemistry.

In physics, the Royal Swedish Academy split the $180,000 Nobel Prize. One half went to Americans Nicolaas Bloembergen and Arthur Schawlow for using lasers to analyze the chemical makeup of substances. Sweden's Kai Siegbahn received the other half for developing an innovative focusing technique using X rays and ultraviolet light in chemical analysis.

In chemistry, the $180,000 Nobel Prize was awarded to Japan's Kenichi Fukui and America's Roald Hoffmann. They used quantum mechanics, the basic tool of modern physics, to explain and predict chemical reactions.

THE PRIZE IN PHYSICS

A skill dating back to Sir Isaac Newton, who in 1666 examined sunlight directed through a prism into a rainbow of colors, is used by today's scientists to fingerprint our universe. This technique is called spectroscopy. Spectroscopy is the analysis of electromagnetic radiation matter can be made to emit in telltale colors, or wavelengths.

Spectroscopy was the technique used by all three Nobel laureates in their award-winning work. Arthur Schawlow of Stanford University and Nicolaas Bloembergen of Harvard University led the way in the application of lasers to spectroscopy. Lasers are devices for creating and transmitting a narrow intense beam of coherent light. The light differs from ordinary light in that it is made up of waves all the same wavelength and all "coherent"—that is, in phase, or in step, with one another. Pioneering work in the related field of electron spectroscopy, involving X rays and ultraviolet light, brought Nobel recognition to Kai Siegbahn of Sweden's Uppsala University.

The successors of Newton learned that any incandescent source will, like a star, produce clearly defined spectra of colors. The colors result from shifts of electrons in the source. The electrons shift from one orbit—or, to use the language of physics, energy levels—to another. (Electrons surround the nucleus of an atom in specific orbits, or energy levels.) The distribution of energy levels differs in all substances and varies—in ways that can be measured—due to conditions such as temperature and pressure. Spectra can also be produced by directing light or X rays at a sample in a laboratory, a process that has been intensely refined by modern scientists.

Lasers directed at a sample cause particles in the substance to become excited. Physicists can then learn from the scattering, absorption, and reradiation of light what atoms are present in the substance. They thus unravel the innermost secrets of the substance.

Schawlow, who helped in the late 1950's to propose the theory for building a laser, brought new precision to spectroscopy. For example, in his study of hydrogen, the simplest of all elements, he helped scientists to understand the energy that binds an electron to the proton in the nucleus. This "Rydberg constant" is a fundamental property of matter.

An originator of the maser—the laser's less sophisticated predecessor—Bloembergen extended the range of modern spectroscopy. He mixed three laser beams to generate new high-intensity ultraviolet and infrared light. This laser blend can analyze everything from the shift of molecules in living tissue to combustion inside automobile engines.

Siegbahn, developer of electron spectroscopy, is the son of the 1924 Nobel physics laureate Karl M.G. Siegbahn, who was honored for similar X-ray work. "It's a decided advantage if you start discussing physics every day at the breakfast table," he recalls.

© Pressens Bild/Photoreporters

Chemistry laureate Kenichi Fukui of Japan proudly displays his Nobel prize.

A new focusing technique developed by Siegbahn enabled physicists to use electron spectroscopy to infer the chemical structure of samples. He used a high-resolution spectrometer to clearly track electrons bombarded by X rays or ultraviolet light. This process can reveal much about the internal structure of a substance; it can, for instance, measure infinitesimal signs of corrosion in metals.

Arthur Schawlow was born in Mt. Vernon, New York, on May 25, 1921. He was educated at the University of Toronto (B.A. 1941; M.A. 1942; and Ph.D. 1949). Before moving to Stanford in 1961, he worked for ten years at Bell Telephone Laboratories in New Jersey. There he pioneered in lasers with his brother-in-law Charles Townes, winner of the 1964 Nobel Prize in Physics. *Microwave Spectroscopy* by Schawlow and Townes is a classic text.

Nicolaas Bloembergen was born in Dordrecht, the Netherlands, on March 11, 1920. He studied at Utrecht University (B.A. 1941; M.A. 1943) and at Leiden University (Ph.D. 1948). He joined the Harvard faculty in 1949 and later became a naturalized U.S. citizen. Asked if he expected Nobel recognition, Bloembergen said: "I did not count on it.

Laureate Roald Hoffmann gained honors for research involving quantum mechanics.

There are so many physicists, so many good works."

Kai Siegbahn was born in Lund, Sweden, on April 20, 1918. He is the son of Karl M.G. Siegbahn, who experimented in X-ray spectroscopy. The younger Siegbahn received his Ph.D. at Stockholm University in 1944. He became a professor at the Royal Institute of Technology in Stockholm in 1951 and joined Uppsala University in 1954. A member of the Royal Swedish Academy, he got an inkling of his Nobel Prize when he was asked not to help in the 1981 selection.

THE PRIZE IN CHEMISTRY

Why do some chemical reactions occur while others do not? Finding the answers in quantum mechanics—the basis of modern physics—was perhaps the most significant conceptual advance in chemistry in the past 30 years. Now scientists can speed the hunt for new drugs and chemicals by avoiding many random, hit-or-miss experiments.

Two chemists who rarely go into the lab—Kenichi Fukui of Japan's Kyoto University and Roald Hoffmann of Cornell University gained their Nobel honors for separate research involving quantum mechanics. Quantum mechanics is a mathematical view of the dual nature of matter—as waves and as particles. Their findings make it possible to predict the chemical reactions between atoms and molecules. Explained Hoffmann: "We use mathematics, physics, computers—and a great deal of thinking."

In work dating from the 1950's Fukui, virtually ignored until recently, established his theory of "frontier orbitals." It shows that the outermost clouds of electrons—those bound in the looser outermost orbits—play the key role in chemical reactions. (The nucleus, surprisingly, does not play the key role.) By the mid-1960's Hoffmann had reached a similar understanding independently. He found that nature's effort to preserve symmetry makes it likely that a chemical reaction will occur if the atoms or molecules can retain their orbital properties after joining.

Fukui's pioneering work, based on highly complicated mathematics, was extended by Hoffmann, who shared certain important research with the late Nobel laureate Robert B. Woodward (1965 Prize in Chemistry). The "Woodward-Hoffmann rule" helps to bridge the gap between quantum theory and practical chemistry. It provides guides that can be understood even by chemists who lack a strong knowledge of mathematics.

Kenichi Fukui was born October 4, 1918, in Nara, Japan. Trained as an engineer, he received undergraduate and graduate degrees at Kyoto University. He is now a professor of physical chemistry at that school. His Nobel acclaim contradicts a popular belief that Japan's excellence in practical technology hides a weakness in fundamental scientific research. Explaining his long wait for recognition, Fukui said, "The Japanese are very conservative when it comes to new theory. But once you get appreciated in the U.S. or Europe, then appreciation spreads back to Japan."

Roald Hoffmann was born on July 18, 1937, in Zloczow, Poland. After a childhood marred by the Nazi occupation, he immigrated to the United States at age 11. A naturalized U.S. citizen, he was educated at Columbia University (B.A. 1958) and at Harvard University (M.A. 1960; Ph.D. 1962). He is now chairman of the chemistry department at Cornell University, where he has taught since 1965 □

REVIEW OF THE YEAR

Mark Antman

Technicians in New Mexico assemble a high power electric-discharge cable to one of eight lasers being used to simulate fusion reactions.

TECHNOLOGY

Courtesy of Bio Logicals

The revolutionary "gene machine," developed by Bio Logicals of Canada, is a computerized synthesizer that strings together nucleotides to make short strands of DNA.

TECHNOLOGY
REVIEW OF THE YEAR

There were many important developments in technology during 1981. Among the most significant were the development of a "gene machine;" renewed interest in the steam engine and sail power as fuel-efficient means of transportation; and the development of a technique for long-range sign language for the deaf.

Genes Off the Assembly Line. The stuff of life, geneticists tell us, consists of complex chemical molecules called DNA. It is the DNA in the cells of all living things that directs the work of the cells. What a cell is and what it does is determined by information handed down to the cell from its parents. The process is called heredity, which is responsible for the structure and function of organisms small and large. By manipulating the structure of genes, or segments of DNA molecules, scientists have been able to prompt such simple organisms as bacteria and yeasts to produce scarce and life-saving human substances such as insulin and human growth hormone. However, building new genes has been a laborious and time-consuming task. A machine developed in 1981 promises to make this task simple, rapid, and automatic.

The device, popularly called the "gene machine," is able to string together sequences of the four chemical units that make up DNA molecules. The order in which these units, called nucleotides, appear in the DNA molecule dictates a particular function of a cell. To learn more about how DNA does this dictating, genetic engineers need to be able to study the effects of short strands of DNA on the functions of cells. It is such short strands that the "gene machine" is capable of manufacturing. Produced by Bio Logicals, Toronto, Canada, the machine is a computerized chemical synthesizer. An operator instructs the machine as to the sequence of nucleotides that are to be strung together. All the chemicals required for the construction job are housed in a kind of storage column and reservoir bottles. With the push of a button, valves begin to open and close in an order determined by the machine's computer. Every 45 minutes, a nucleotide snaps into place on the growing DNA strand. A spokesman for Bio Logicals reports that the "gene machine" has constructed DNA segments consisting of at least 20 nucleotides. The same result could not have been achieved in less than a number of months using standard hands-on laboratory techniques. Moreover, years of training are not required to turn out the vital DNA segments. A technician can be taught to do the job in 30 minutes. Developers of these machines, and there are now a number of these, point out that their machines are theoretically capable of producing complete genes, which may consist of thousands of nucleotides. Such genes would not only further the study of genetics but might also be used to treat serious genetic diseases of human beings.

Renewed interest in fuel-efficient kinds of transportation has prompted certain U.S. agencies to study the feasibility of using sail-assisted motor ships and steam engines.

Norman Fortier/Wind Ship Dev. Corp.

Steam and Sail—Power for the Future? If two United States agencies have their way, the hiss of the steam engine and the snap of wind-whipped sails may be part of the sounds of U.S. transportation once again. Oddly, this return to the "old ways" of moving people and goods is really an imaginative new way of dealing with a critical current problem; the high and ever increasing cost of fuel oil. Proponents of the back to steam and sail movements concede that steam-and-wind power are not the most efficient means of propelling vehicles around the globe. However, they insist that with improved techniques, such modes of transportation can be made cost-effective.

The search for a coal-burning steam locomotive capable of competing favorably with the oil-burning diesel-electric variety has been sponsored by the U.S. Department of Energy (DOE) and administered in a presently on-going three-year study by the Jet Propulsion Laboratory, noted primarily for transporting objects to the far reaches of the solar system. The JPL study, called the Future Propulsion Systems Project, has already helped stimulate the production of a steam locomotive that can hold its own with the diesels. The locomotive, dubbed ACE 3000 by its designers, American Coal Enterprises, Inc., of Akron, Ohio, looks very much like its predecessors, which served the nation for 150 years before tooting their last in 1959. But on closer inspection, the resemblance fades. The ACE 3000 operates in a new two-stage burning process. First, the coal is heated to a red glow. The hot coal produces gases. These gases are then burned, yielding heat that turns water into steam. The efficiency of such an engine is more than twice that of U.S. steam locomotives of the 1950's, and about 75 per cent that of current diesel locomotives. However, the comparatively low cost of coal versus that of oil makes the ACE 3000 almost three times less expensive to run than diesels. Although the ACE 3000 costs more to build than a diesel, $1,250,000 against $791,000, the difference is made up by a lower maintenance and running cost over the lifetime of the engine. Finally, the two-stage burning process of the ACE 3000 greatly reduces the production of air pollutants associated with traditional coal-burning locomotives.

Kodak

Kodak

In 1982, the Eastman Kodak Company introduced a new line of extremely compact cameras (upper photo) that use a film disk (above) instead of standard roll film.

Crossing the sea by sail requires no fuel at all, produces no pollution, but makes for unacceptably long voyages. However, a sail-assisted motor ship that takes advantage of modern weather and wind monitoring techniques might well be able to compete with traditional motor-only vessels. This is a conclusion reached by a U.S. Maritime Administration-sponsored study carried out by the Wind Ship Development Corp. of Norwell, Massachusetts. The study suggests that sail-assisted motor ships traveling over certain specified trans-Atlantic routes would consume 15 to 25 per cent less fuel than their motor-driven counterparts. The motor-sailers would be equipped with metal wing sails similar in design to airplane wings. To reduce the need for large and costly crews, normally required to man a sailing vessel, the sails would be automated and operated remotely. The Wind Ship Development Corp. has built a prototype sailing rig that is being tested on a motor-driven cargo ship of the Ceres Hellenic Ship Enterprises, Inc. of Greece. The Japanese, who rely totally on foreign sources of oil, are already operating an oil tanker equipped with sails.

Hearing by Seeing. Sign language has long been used by deaf people to communicate words and phrases. However, the system has, of course, been restricted to line-of-sight communication. The individuals had to be able to see one another's hand and finger movements at relatively short range. They certainly could not communicate over long distances. Due to the research of Vivien Tartter of Rutgers University and Ken Knowlton of Bell labs, that restriction may soon be a thing of the past. Psycholinguist Tartter and computer-graphics expert Knowlton have devised a system that uses an ordinary telephone, a small TV-like screen, and a pair of specially equipped black gloves that will allow deaf people to communicate from office to office, town to town, or city to city.

The black gloves are equipped with patches of reflective tape at each finger tip, knuckle, and at the wrist. The glove is worn by a deaf person who uses the standard signals of the American Sign Language to form letters and words. A small electronic camera picks up the flashes of the reflective tape, which are transmitted by telephone to the "listener's" display screen. By using the same technique and equipment, the listener responds.

Carl Proujan

Vivien Tartter and Ken Knowlton display the specially-equipped gloves they devised as part of a system that allows deaf people to communicate over long distances.

Courtesy of Vivien Tartter

This hollow glass tube has already been treated with many layers of chemicals that relate to the refraction of light. After the tube is heated, the fiber pulls out like taffy.

LIGHT WAVES OF THE FUTURE

by Mathew Tekulsky

FIBER optic technology, now sweeping the United States at the speed of light, promises to radically alter our lives. Imagine a beam of light that is pulsating 44,700,000 times per second. Now take that beam of light and shine it through a glass fiber 0.005 millimeter (0.0002 inch) thick, the thickness of a human hair. At the receiving end, decode the pulses into data or a human voice or a television picture. That, essentially, is what a revolutionary new technology called fiber-optic, or light-wave, communication is all about.

DIAL ANYTHING . . .

This new technology could change the way we live. In the future, you may be able to call a store on your home communications center and order a suit or dress right off the screen. You will have instant access to any page of any book in the Library of Congress. If you want to watch *Gone With the Wind*, just press a button and it will appear. If you want to learn how to cook shrimp curry, turn the dial and the Julia Child of the future will show you how to do it, right in your own kitchen. No longer will you have to commute to work: you can do all your work at home, with all the information you need at your fingertips. If you're a college student or if you'd like to get a better job, you can go to school in your own living room.

If you need a washing machine, you can find out which stores carry the particular model you want, how much they charge, whether it's on sale, have it demonstrated, contact a consumer service, and find out what they think of the product, place your order, pay for it, and have it delivered. If you want to buy a used car, you can find out where all the used cars of a certain make and year are within an 80-kilometer (50-mile) radius of your home and how much they cost.

. . . OR ANYONE

If you want to play chess with someone nearby or a great distance away, you simply call him or her up and the board appears on the screen. If you want to play bridge with three other people in different parts of town or in different cities, contact them and the table will appear on the screen before you. If a child comes home after school and still doesn't understand fractions, he can dial the lesson at home and have his very own teacher go over it again. Medical problems will be diagnosed via your home terminal, and mobile units will provide the same service in emergency situations away from home. International business will conduct instant transactions and provide goods and services to consumers more quickly and cheaply.

By getting to know one another over home terminals, people around the globe may suddenly discover that their communities are drawn closer together, that new friendships are formed between individuals and nations, and that an age of human understanding is beginning.

NEW INFORMATION SOCIETY

All this may sound amazing, even far-fetched, but perhaps the most astounding thing about it is that the technology for constructing such an electronic information network exists today. In fact, a system called HI-OVIS (Highly Interactive Optical Visual Information System) is already being used on an experimental basis in Japan. There, people in the town of Higashi Ikoma can, with their home video terminals, obtain train and plane schedules, take home-study courses, and shop by television. A group of housewives linked together by the system have even produced a community cookbook.

According to most of those at the forefront of fiber-optic technology, the HI-OVIS scenario is already beginning to evolve in the United States, and it should become a reality by the year 2000. Dr. Charles K. Kao, chief scientist of International Telephone and Telegraph's (ITT) Electro-Optical Products Division and the pioneer who first conceived of fiber-optic communication back in 1964, calls it, "The new information society. We really don't know what it will look like, but we know that it will be different from what we are doing now. It will revolutionize our way of life."

Dr. Lee L. Davenport, of General Telephone & Electronics, says it is "the information revolution, and it's changing the way in which we record and transmit and store information. You're seeing terminals showing up everywhere, at the airline counter, in hospitals, in libraries, and the reason they're being used is that it's instant communication. The day will come when there is a terminal in everybody's house and an optical fiber going to it."

Fiber-optic, or light-wave, technology promises to have widespread applications and may dramatically alter our lives.

© Howard Sochurek/Woodfin Camp

A fiber circuit is seen in this device, called a snooperscope, which uses infrared radiation for viewing objects that are somehow made obscure (as by darkness).

© Howard Sochurek/Woodfin Camp

PIONEERING SYSTEMS ALREADY IN USE

Optical fibers are already being used to carry telephone conversations in the United States. In 1977, General Telephone Company of California installed the world's first optical link providing regular telephone service, connecting Long Beach, California, with nearby Artesia. Illinois Bell Telephone has inaugurated an optical system in Chicago that carries video as well as voice communication. In November 1979, a GTE lightwave system transmitted a network television broadcast—a football game from Tampa Bay in Florida. Meanwhile, the Bell System has been introducing light-wave systems at a rate of one every two months, and it used optical fibers to transmit television signals of the 1980 Winter Olympics. Worldwide, optical communication systems now total over 100, and, according to Paul W. Shumate, Jr., of Light-wave Transmitter Subsystems at Bell Labs, "Fibers are going into the telecommunications network at a staggering rate."

MERGING OF TWO TECHNOLOGIES

But what, exactly, is fiber optics, and how does it work?

Fiber-optic, or light-wave, communication is essentially the merging of two separate technologies. First came the laser. Originally, the laser was over 90 centimeters (3 feet) long and a few centimeters in diameter. Today it's about the size of a speck of pepper. (Light-emitting diodes, or LEDs, such as those used in pocket calculators, are also used as light sources, but they're not nearly as strong as lasers.) Since the information-carrying capacity of a light beam is a very thin, pure, and powerful light source, scientists realized immediately that they had an extraordinary communications device at their disposal—if only they had something over which to transmit the light. Roughly 10 years later, at Corning Glass Works, the low-loss optical fiber was achieved. This fiber is highly transparent glass, thin as fishing line, and drawn out in kilometers-long lengths. It is so clear that if you made the ocean out of it, you could go out to the middle and look down and see all the way to the bottom.

GLASS MAGIC

The method for making an optical fiber is quite remarkable. Dr. Albert D. Bender of ITT calls it "magic." First you take a hollow glass tube, about a meter in length, and put it on a lathe. Then you pass various chemicals, in gas form, through the hollow section, where they are deposited as thin layers of glass by a torch that moves back and forth very slowly under the tube. After a hundred or so layers are deposited, each of a different chemical composition related to the refraction of light, the still hollow tube is heated so that it collapses into a solid rod, called a preform, about 19 millimeters (0.75 inch) thick. The preform is then fed into a special tower-shaped machine (a draw tower), where the bottom tip is heated and the fiber is pulled out like taffy. From the original meter-long tube, 4–5 kilometers (2.5–3 miles) of fiber can be produced. Amazingly, the exact chemical structure that was created in the preform is maintained.

The original tube, meanwhile, forms a reflecting layer that serves to keep the light inside the fiber. The reflecting layer is called the cladding. It operates on the same principle that makes light rays bend when they enter water from the air. Thus, light rays from the laser that strike the cladding around the fiber at certain angles will be reflected back into the core of the fiber.

Furthermore, each of the interior layers operates in the same fashion, so that the rays of light are effectively controlled, in order to emerge at the opposite end at the same time. In this way, each pulse of light becomes a distinct unit in time and can be identified easily by the receiver. The result is that many more pulses can be transmitted and thus more information can be sent over the fiber.

VOICE BITS

How these rays of light actually transmit information is another fascinating process. Telephone companies routinely put 672 simultaneous phone conversations over a single pair of fibers, one transmitting voices from one end and the other carrying voices from the opposite end. This is accomplished by a technique called pulse-code modulation. First, your voice is electronically sampled 8,000 times per second. Each sample has a certain wave height, which is converted into a binary sequence of zeros and ones—on and off commands to the laser or LED. At the receiving end, the light pulses are detected and converted back into an electrical signal, which reconstructs your voice.

In order to get 672 conversations onto the same pair of fibers, a process called time-division multiplexing is used. This arranges each conversation sequentially as it travels down the fiber. "What we do," explains Davenport, "is take your voice and chop it into little bits, and we have spaces in between those little bits that are wide enough so that we can fit other people's voices in the spaces that we leave out of yours." While the laser has to turn on and off 44,700,000 times per second to accommodate 672 voices, Davenport says that 300,000,000 pulses per second have been sent down a fiber in the laboratory.

ENORMOUS CAPACITY

Fiber-optic communication systems currently use only one wavelength, in the infrared region. But, says Dr. Tingye Li, head of the Transmission and Circuits Research Department at Bell Labs, "We can use two lasers going at different wavelengths, and we could combine the output from these two lasers onto one single fiber. In fact, you might be able to put something like ten to one hundred wavelengths onto one fiber." Since future cable systems will go at 274,000,000 pulses per second, which will give something like 4,000 telephone conversations, you could multiply the 4,000 by the 100 and get 400,000 conversations on one fiber! "God help you if it breaks," Li adds.

What all this means is that the information-carrying capacity of optical fibers is so enormous that you could hook up a comprehensive electronic-information system to it. For if an optical fiber can transmit the contents of an entire encyclopedia in a single second (which it does now by sending each letter as a sequence of off-on pulses), then

Looking like a dazzling display in the night sky, these "stars" are really patterns that were simulated by fiber optics for astronauts to study.
© Howard Sochurek/Woodfin Camp

why not use this power to develop a full range of information services? It should be noted, however, that although fiber optics is an excellent transmission medium for carrying an almost infinite amount of information, it's just one part of the total information system of the future. The other parts are home-terminal equipment to process information, a network of computers to control the flow of information and serve as a data bank, and a vast array of vendors supplying information and maintenance services to the sophisticated system.

EFFECTS ON SOCIETY

But what will the effect of such a system be on society? Will it bring people closer together, or will it create a mass of individuals who never leave their homes—who, in a sense, do everything vicariously? Fiber-optics experts contend that electronics will not replace social contact but will supplement it. Kao reports people hooked up to the HI-OVIS in Japan develop friendships that otherwise wouldn't have developed.

"After getting rid of their shyness, which initially was tremendous, they began to con-

The fiber bundle in foreground can transmit and receive as many messages as the telephone cable behind it can.

© Howard Sochurek/Woodfin Camp

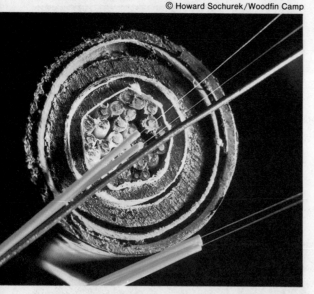

tribute to community life as individuals much more than if they hadn't had that system. And when an information bank with a very powerful center exists, we will have a much better choice of what we want to do, instead of going through the drudgery of doing the unnecessary things."

Kao has suggested that we are moving from a material-based society into an information-based society. If this is so, could we then be on the verge of the next great evolutionary step in mankind, away from a physical outlook on the world and into more of a mental or spiritual realm? And could this new outlook, coupled with the electronic-communication revolution, lead us into a new age of world cooperation and even world peace?

According to Davenport, "It is not impossible that this concept could bring a greater measure of world peace and understanding, but it surely is a difficult concept for nationalistic countries to accept. We have been living in a world of physical possessions. Now we're saying we can turn to an intellectualized world in the future with this kind of an information society. You could always go to the library and get books. You could always learn things. But it was not made easy for you to do; in the future it will be easy to do."

Kao puts it this way: "We have learned how to use our hands and how to extend our physical efforts with tools such as the hammer and the car, and we wanted to project our senses, so we invented the telephone for our voice and the television for our sight. Now we are trying essentially to project our brain out a little more. Fiber optics is one of the principal tools that we need to enable us to do that" □

SELECTED READINGS

"Fiber optics finally sees the light of day" by Gene Bylinsky. *Fortune,* March 24, 1980.

"Fiber otics starts a revolution in our telephone systems as threads of light replace copper wires" by J. Free. *Popular Science,* May 1980.

"Lighting up the switchboard" by D. E. Thomsen. *Science News,* May 30, 1981.

"Harnessing light by a thread" by A. A. Boraiko. *National Geographic,* October 1979.

Courtesy of Channel One

This huge dish-shaped parabolic antenna serves a single family. It is tucked against a small hill that blocks microwave interference from a local telephone company.

BACKYARD SATELLITE TV

by Robin Lanier

"THERE'S nothing good to watch tonight."

Sound familiar? Well, maybe not for much longer. Soon you may be able to choose from a vast selection of programs, not dependent on the major networks or local stations.

How? With a backyard terminal tuning into radio and television programs directly from space.

Today, thanks to the development of the communications satellite, a large section of space 35,000 kilometers (22,000 miles) above the earth is literally filling up with radio and television programs. And thousands of people in the United States are using backyard

terminals, called earth stations, to tune in the programs they want from this array in space.

The programs are being sent up to the satellites—which are orbiting broadcast relay stations—in order to get the material to local broadcast stations across the United States. More and more radio and television stations are getting the earth stations that let them tune in the satellite-carried programs. Each local station management chooses the programs wanted, and usually pays the producer of the programs a fee, or "barters" air time for advertising. The station rebroadcasts the program locally so that the audience can get it on regular radio and television receivers.

The satellite method of distributing programs across the United States is transforming the broadcast industry. It is cheaper than the old method of transmitting programs, has much higher fidelity, or adherence to the original program signals, and gives producers many more channels for sending out programs. Many new radio and television networks are springing up to take advantage of these new factors, and the old networks—NBC, ABC, CBS, Mutual, and others—are rapidly converting to satellite distribution.

Buyers of backyard earth stations rotate their antennas toward whichever satellite carries the programs they wish to see.

Courtesy of Channel One

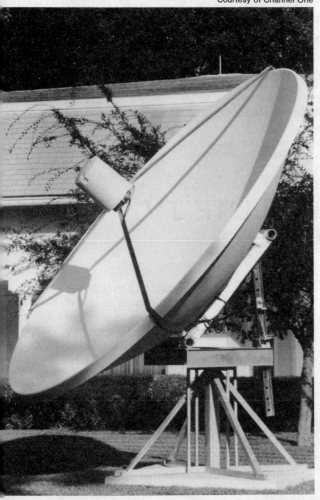

SMORGASBORD OF PROGRAMS

The backyard earth station shortcuts the satellite route by letting the home viewer get the programs directly, without the help of a local radio or television station. Since the signals coming down from the satellites are spread over a large area—usually the entire United States—any receiver in the area, of proper design, can bring in any of the programs.

Backyard reception has a big advantage over getting the programs through the local broadcast station. In the latter case, the home owner gets only what the local station chooses to rebroadcast. The backyarder can get any programs sent up, within broad limits set by the sensitivity of the receiver and its exact location in the United States.

That has opened up to the "backyarder" a variety and number of programs far beyond anything available in broadcasting before. And the satellite smorgasbord is going to extend its spread of goodies in the coming years. Industry predictions are that there will be 20 to 30 regular radio and television networks by 1984, producing almost everything in entertainment: classical concerts in stereo, interviews with night-club singers, advice on health and money, and comedies, as well as lessons in science and dozens of other things, some old, some new. The material will come not only from the large networks but also from occasional producers who can easily hire time on a satellite system from one of the outfits that has satellite channels for rent.

Not let's back up a bit for some fundamentals to show better how this all came about, what a backyard terminal is, and how to get and use one.

WHY USE SATELLITES?

It hardly seems a sensible way of getting a program from, say, Chicago to Miami, to send it on a 70,000-kilometer (44,000-mile) round trip into space and back. But the trip has a vital purpose: getting the signals around the curvature of the earth.

If we beam the signals from an antenna in Chicago in the direction of Miami, the signals will simply go off into space and not follow the earth's curvature to Miami. Most carrier frequencies used in radio and even more in television tend to travel in straight lines. But if the signals are directed toward the earth, in a broad beam from high above the earth, they will reach a very large area, nearly a whole hemisphere. That was the brilliant idea first advanced by the talented science writer Arthur Clarke (author of the movie "2001," the novel *Childhood's End,* and much else) in the 1950's.

It took the development of satellite launching and orbitry by the National Aeronautics and Space Administration (NASA) and the extraordinary advances in electronics in the space program and in radio astronomy to make the communications satellites real. Each satellite must carry very light and compact electronics sensitive enough to respond to the signals that have travelled up from earth and powerful enough to get them all the way back down to earth again. The satellite must be powered by solar cells, which turn sunlight into electric power. No battery to store electricity would last the five to ten years a satellite must work unfailingly in order to pay its way.

Rocket techniques must put the satellites into precise orbits—here we come to the significance of the 35,000-kilometer (22,000-mile) spacing between the communications satellites and the earth. At that distance a satellite going around the earth "in exact step" with the earth's rotation will be held in orbit by a balance between centrifugal force pulling it out and gravitational force pulling it toward the earth. The satellite will then stay in the same place as far as an observer on the earth is concerned. Such an orbit is called a geosynchronous orbit. If communications satellites were put closer in towards earth they would have to move faster to keep from

By remote control, an airport receives all the satellites from its control tower. This closeup shows the typical installation on any polar-type mount antenna.

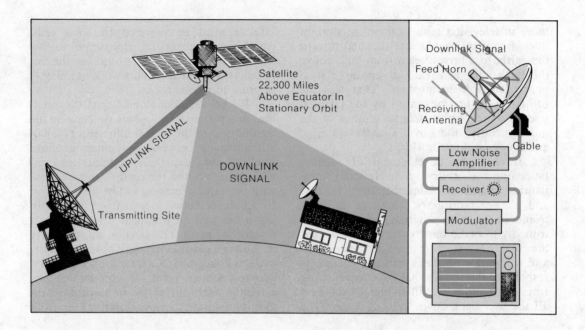

Satellite
22,300 Miles
Above Equator In
Stationary Orbit

UPLINK SIGNAL

DOWNLINK
SIGNAL

Transmitting Site

Downlink Signal
Feed Horn
Receiving
Antenna
Cable
Low Noise
Amplifier
Receiver
Modulator

being pulled, by gravitational force, to earth. If farther out, they would have to move slower than the earth's rotation to avoid flying off into space.

UPLINK

A program's trip by satellite starts at the uplink, where the program is put onto a carrier. The carrier is one of a band of frequencies clustered around 6 gigaHertz, or 6,000,-000,000 cycles per second. This microwave frequency is chosen because, among other things, it can be focused into a narrow beam by dish antennas of practical size and because it penetrates quite well through moisture and dust in the atmosphere. Uplink antennas are usually about 9 meters (30 feet) across, which gives a good balance between cost and efficiency.

The large dish-shaped antennas, familiar in all photographs of satellite gear, are really parabolic reflecting mirrors, acting like the parabolic mirrors in back of powerful searchlights. The antenna sends the signal out in a narrow beam—narrow because the signal must be sent to a particular satellite. The beam from the uplink must go in the right direction within about 1/10th degree. Focusing the beam into a narrow path also keeps the energy in the signal high so it will

come through the long trip in space strong enough to be useful.

SATELLITE TRANSPONDERS

Each satellite (of those now in use) carries 12 transponders, or 12 complete, separate electronic paths from incoming signal to outgoing signal. Each transponder is tuned to one of the 12 standard bands used, near 6 gigaHertz. Tuning the uplink signal to the right band, activates the desired transponder.

Each transponder has two modes—one for a horizontally-polarized signal—that is, one for which the carrier vibrates in a horizontal direction—and one for a vertical signal. Thus each satellite now in use has a total of 24 program-carrying circuits. Each one is capable of carrying one television program.

For radio signals, each transponder can be subdivided into hundreds of pathways. Thus, the voice and music capacity of the satellite is enormous. There is intense research now going on to pack even more carrying capacity into a satellite. The more material a single satellite can carry, the less expensive the system is for everyone.

AND TO THE BACKYARD ANTENNA

Each transponder converts the signal to one of 12 standard frequencies clustered around 4 gigaHertz for the trip back to earth. Then the antenna sends it out in a broad beam that covers a large area. The receiver on the earth starts with a dish-shaped parabolic antenna that captures a large segment of the energy being beamed down, and focuses it into the receiving equipment. Again, the larger the antenna, the more efficient; most backyard systems use antennas from 3 to 3.6 meters (10 to 12 feet) across for a good balance between cost and performance.

Fastened right behind the antenna is the "low-noise amplifier" (LNA), one of the key devices in satellite communication. This unit boosts the signal strength while adding only tiny amounts of noise, very much less than ordinary radio and television gear produces. The boost in strength is necessary because the signal is very weak after its 35,000-kilometer (22,000-mile) trip from space.

From the LNA the signal travels in a coaxial cable to the "receiver" installed in the user's house next to the television or radio set. The receiver tunes the system to one of the standard transponder frequencies the program is on.

POINTING THE ANTENNA

To bring the program in, however, the user must first point his or her backyard antenna toward the right satellite. With the purchase of antenna gear, there usually comes some form of indexing that tells how to set the antenna for each satellite. The antenna itself is on a rotatable mount, many on axes that are set up parallel to the axis of the earth. The antenna can be rotated by hand, or by remote control gear set up inside the house, very much like the familiar control gear for rotatable television antennas.

Where are the satellites? Those serving the United States are spaced along an equatorial line generally southwest of the continental United States. Buyers of backyard systems get from the manufacturer an up-to-date index of satellite positions.

HOW MUCH DOES IT ALL COST?

The cost of a backyard system ranges from about $3,500 for a basic array consisting of antenna, LNA, 30 meters (100 feet) of coaxial cable, and a receiver, to about $10,-000 for fancier systems. High prices are not limiting sales, however; industry estimates put the number in use in 1981 at between 6,000 and 10,000.

The backyarder even has an active trade association watching out for him or her. It is called SPACE, for "Society for Private and Commercial Earth Stations." SPACE will send a list of manufacturers of earth stations and has a newsletter reporting on technical, legal, and regulatory development affecting users.

And programming—how does a back-yarder find out what programs are on which satellite? As already pointed out, by 1984 or so, virtually every network radio and television program will be on satellite. The back-yarder will easily get a list of network satellite assignments from the networks or from SPACE. Eventually a listing will probably be run in the newspapers.

These domestic satellites, which serve the United States, are in geosynchronous orbits.

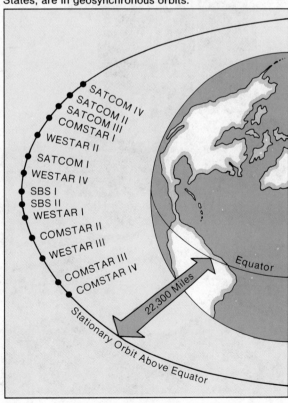

Meanwhile, at least two publications now give satellite listings. *Sat Guide Magazine,* published by Com Tech Publishing in Hailey, Idaho, lists all satellite assignments periodically. *Satellite Channel Chart,* from WestSat Communications in Pleasanton, California, gives an updated listing six times a year.

IS IT LEGAL?

While backyard terminals are expanding furiously, an important question remains unanswered—namely, is it legal for

An uplink antenna in Detroit, Michigan, transmits coverage of election activities at a Republication convention to an orbiting satellite.

© Gianfranco Gorgoni/Contact-Woodfin Camp

the user to bring in copyrighted material without authorization of the copyright owner?

According to the copyright law it is unlawful for anyone to retransmit for public use any copyrighted radio or television material without authorization. The law, however, exempts from "public use" the use of the material at home, within a family and its normal circle of friends. This would seem to put the backyarder in the clear as long as he or she does not set up a mini-theater and charge for admission to view or listen to a program.

Some still think that the backyarder is acting outside the law. Apparently a court must rule on the intent of the law. A solution offered by SPACE and some groups of backyarders is to pay a reasonable fee to program producers. This idea has, however, been rejected by several program producers.

MORE TO COME?

The current backyard earth station activity must be distinguished from another satellite-to-home proposal, one now simply in the talking stage. It is called "direct broadcast service," or DBS. It would use satellites of much higher downlink power so that very simple receivers, with small antennas, would bring in the signal. The whole system would be addressed to getting programs directly into the home.

DBS is tentatively assigned frequencies in the 11-12 gigaHertz band, to avoid interference with regular satellite transmission on 4-6 gigaHertz. A number of groups are agitating for DBS, mainly petitioning the U.S. Federal Communications Commission to let the service start, at least on an experimental basis—it is illegal at present. The broadcast industry is strongly opposed to the idea: DBS eliminates the local broadcast station from national program distribution □

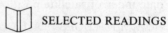

SELECTED READINGS

"Direct satellite TV" by James Fawcette. *High Technology,* January–February 1982.
"Build this satellite TV antenna" by H. D. McCullough. *Radio-Electronics,* August 1981 (Part 2-September 1981).

ELECTRONIC MAIL

by Larry Kahaner

ALTHOUGH still far from being widely used, electronic mail is handling a growing share of everyday business correspondence. The term "electronic mail," even though it differs sharply from what is usually thought of as mail, covers an assortment of message delivery techniques tethered by a common thread: electronic systems used as communication media.

COMPUTER-BASED

Computer-based electronic mail is by far the fastest growing of the techniques and the one receiving the most publicity. It uses computers and video terminals to send and receive messages—often as an additional feature of an existing computer system. In fact, computer-based mail adapts easily to the typical office because many workers already have terminals on their desks. The electronic-mail feature is nothing more than a computer program that sets up a message blank on a terminal screen. Users fill in the blank, using the terminal's keyboard, and the computer routes the message on its way.

These computer-based systems and services are available from a variety of sources. Many manufacturers offer software packages that enable their customers to add electronic mail to their existing computer networks. The trouble with these packages is that they usually operate only on their suppliers' computer equipment. However, electronic-mail packages are also available from software vendors, and some of these packages operate independently of computer make.

PUBLIC NETWORKS

Companies that wish to avoid the expense and trouble of installing a private electronic-mail network can turn to the electronic-mail services offered by public computer networks.

U.S. Postal Service

The Electronic Computer-Originated Mail (E-COM) Service allows volume mailers to transmit messages electronically to "serving post offices."

Typical of these public network offerings is GTE Telenet's Telemail service. Telemail is available in 200 U.S. cities and is used by about 120 companies and organizations—a number that GTE claims is growing by 15 per cent every month. Telenet's main computer in Vienna, Virginia, handles all messages, even those between terminals in the same office. Most of the service's 7,000 individual users send messages between offices within the same building, although about 20 per cent of the correspondence travels through the Telenet network to other companies. It accommodates most brands of computer terminals.

GTE Telenet's Telemail service uses prompting messages to guide its many customers through every step of the procedures for message exchanges.

Courtesy of GTE

EASY-TO-USE

Electronic-mail systems all strive for one thing: ease of use. In fact, Telemail officials claim that anyone can master the basics of their system in less than 30 minutes. Prompting messages guide users step-by-step through message exchanges. For example, when a user turns on a terminal to send a message, prompts ask for the user's company name, ID numbers, and password. Once this "sign-on" procedure is completed, the computer offers various services—again through a series of prompts—such as scanning the mailbox, choosing which messages to read, forwarding messages to others, deleting messages, composing new messages, and mailing them. Whenever a user responds incorrectly to a prompt, a message explains the error.

Electronic-mail systems resemble their paper counterparts in many ways. Telemail users, for instance, can classify their messages for special delivery. Messages classified URGENT are placed first in a recipient's mailbox; PRIVATE messages are rendered invisible to everyone but the intended recipient; senders are notified when REGISTERED messages are accepted; and TIMED DELIVERY messages are sent at a predetermined time even in the sender's absence.

ELIMINATES TELEPHONE TAG

Most customers use Telemail as an electronic-memo service. GTE says the average message length for electronic-mail systems is about half a page. However, the system is also used for more specialized applications, such as communications between salespersons and their home offices. GTE will design custom message forms. In a sales application, for example, the system can be programmed to display an electronic version of an order form instead of the usual memo form. A salesperson then fills in the blanks and transmits the form to the warehouse, and perhaps a copy to the supervisor. Users can even use a portable terminal to send in orders while on the road.

Perhaps the greatest advantage of electronic mail comes when messages have to cross time zones. "You send them when you're ready and read them when you're ready," says Tom Taylor, Telenet's vice president for network applications. "You don't have to look at the clock to decide when to contact someone who isn't operating in the same time zone. This technique also eliminates "telephone tag," the syndrome in which callers keep missing each other.

Vendors claim to have encountered very little resistance among their customers. In fact, once they're exposed to electronic mail, most users never want to go back to the old way of doing things. "It's a bit like a narcotic," says Julius Marcus, group vice president of commercial operations at DEC, Maynard, Massachusetts. "Once you start using it, you can't stop." DEC uses electronic mail extensively in its own operations and has recently begun to market a $12,000 software package for its minicomputer systems.

Rather than resisting, users are demanding more features, such as better facilities for creating and editing messages. "People who have worked on word processors are used to moving words and sentences around easily. Electronic-mail systems just don't have that flexibility yet," says Connie Gibbons, training specialist for the U.S. House of Representatives Computer Information System.

VOICE-MAIL SYSTEMS

Voice store-and-forward systems are the most recent development. These systems operate something like automatic telephone answering systems, but they offer much more sophisticated services. For example, "call store-and-forward" systems, often referred to as voice-mail systems, not only record telephone calls and play them back on command, but can also forward calls—either immediately or at a later time—to their intended recipients.

These services use a central computer to convert all incoming messages to digital form and then record them on a magnetic disk. Each message is filed under the intended recipient's telephone number. The recipient can retrieve messages by calling the central computer and entering an identification code using the telephone's touchtone keypad. The computer searches the disk, finds the messages, converts them back into voice, and transmits them over the phone. In some systems, the computer automatically sends a voice message to the recipient at a set time.

Vendors of call store-and-forward systems say they also eliminate telephone tag. "It's estimated that business calls fail to reach their intended recipients 70 percent of the time," notes John Sawyer, product line director for Digital Voice Exchange (DVX)—a call store-and-forward system recently introduced by Wang Laboratories, Inc., Lowell, Massachusetts. Sawyer points out that systems such as DVX can replace not only traditional phone calls but memos and other written messages as well.

Courtesy of Wang

Wang's Digital Voice Exchange, a call store-and-forward system, eliminates telephone tag.

A synthesized voice in Wang's system asks for a user ID, password, and destination telephone numbers. The caller chooses immediate delivery or delivery at any time within 30 days. He or she then creates a "voicegram" up to 90 seconds long that can be reviewed, rerecorded, or canceled. If the message is sent, the DVX system delivers it directly to the recipient's phone or holds it until the specified delivery time. Wang expects DVX to handle as many as 200 users over 4 telephone lines, or 800 users on 16 lines. The cost is $125,000 per system.

Wang is not alone in the market. ECS Telecommunications Inc., Richardson, Texas, has been marketing a $500,000 system since 1980. ECS's customer roster includes such industry giants as Westinghouse, 3M, American Express, Shell Oil of Canada, and Hoffman-La-Roche. IBM recently joined the voice-mail fray with a software package called Audio Distribution System (ADS), that turns its IBM Series/1 minicomputer into a call store-and-forward system for as many as 1000 users. Complete systems including software and hardware will cost between $115,000 and $225,000.

As might be expected, the voice-mail market is attracting telephone companies. AT&T began voice mail as part of its Custom Calling 2 service around the middle of 1982. Radiofone, a New Jersey-based paging company, plans to offer voice mail with a twist: recipients will be notified of calls through their pocket pagers. In the future, recipients may be able to request that they be

U.S. Postal Service

The U.S. Postal Service's International Electronic Post (INTELPOST) service combines electronics and paper for a hybrid system that uses a digital facsimile network.

paged at a certain time of day, when they have received a certain number of calls, or when the computer receives messages classified "urgent" or "rush."

FAX REBORN

The advent of electronic mail is breathing fresh life into facsimile (fax): a technology used to transmit and receive messages and graphics over telephone lines. Although fax first arrived on the office scene in the 1930's, it fell out of favor because of slow scanning and transmitting times. Until recently, it took more than 6 minutes to scan and transmit a page using a standard fax machine. As telephone costs rose, 6 minutes worth of daytime rates became prohibitive. In addition, many users balked at the received document's poor quality, and thus became disenchanted with the system.

Recent technological advances, however, are forcing businesses to take another look at fax—which still accounts for more messages than any other electronic-mail medium. New machines based on digital technology are smaller, cheaper, and faster than

their predecessors. Some models can scan and send a page in less than one minute. And image quality, once the fax's bane, appears much improved. "Digital devices are the up and coming technology," says H. Paris Burstyn, editor of a report on electronic mail published by the Yankee Group, a Boston-based market research firm.

According to Burstyn, fax sends more than 400,000,000 pages a year—more than any other form of electronic mail. And that number will increase as machines become more sophisticated. "As they gain more functions, facsimile machines will gain more applications," says Burstyn. He suggests that some new functions will include computer-to-fax and fax-to-computer transmissions. "We're just beginning to see computer-to-fax," he says.

The Japanese are the major users and suppliers of these fax machines, because their written language does not lend itself to ordinary computer communications. In the United States, graphics account for only about 10 per cent of transmissions. However, good graphics reproduction would be a strong incentive for businesses to choose fax. "The graphics are getting better all the time," notes Burstyn. As an example, he points to a new machine developed by Nippon Electric Company (NEC) that reproduces graphics with 400-line-per-inch density—more than twice that of previous machines. "It's output looks like a Xerox copy," he says.

INTELPOST

Hybrid electronic-mail systems, combining the speed of electrons and the universal acceptability of paper, show the strongest promise. The U.S. Postal Service operates one such system for international correspondence and plans another for domestic traffic.

Inaugurated in September 1980, the U.S.'s International Electronic Post (INTELPOST) service initially linked the United States and Canada and has since been expanded overseas. It uses a digital facsimile network as its communications me-dium. At specially designated post offices in Washington, D.C. and New York, fax machines scan paper documents, convert them to digital pulses, and transmit them by microwave relay to Toronto, Canada. From there, an earth station sends the signal to the Intelsat IV-A satellite. The satellite then relays it to an earth station at the overseas post office. (FCC regulations prevent the Postal Service from transmitting messages directly to Intelsat IV-A.) Once there, impulses are converted back into black and white facsimiles of the original documents and either placed into the first class mailstream for delivery, or picked up at the receiving post office.

These high-speed machines scan an 8½-by 11-inch page in less than 12 seconds; one page costs $5. Perhaps because of the cost, most INTELPOST traffic comes from businesses, especially brokerage houses, commodity traders, and banks.

A sales executive on a business trip carries a portable terminal that she uses to transmit orders rapidly to her home office.

Courtesy of GTE

The Intelsat IV-A satellite, seen here atop its apogee kick motor weeks before its launch, relays IN-TELPOST's international communications.

England, Canada, and Germany have already established limited INTELPOST networks throughout their countries allowing domestic fax mail to flow in addition to accepting INTELPOST messages originating in other countries. Although Japan isn't connected to INTELPOST, it is experimenting with similar high-speed networks connecting major cities.

E-COM

The U.S. Postal Service hopes one day to tap the business market with its domestic electronic-mail system, known as Electronic Computer-Originated Mail (E-COM). At present, it has a more modest market—bulk mailers who currently rely on first class mail.

With E-COM, mailers transmit correspondence in digital form via telephone lines to a "serving post office" (SPO) in one of 25 major cities. The SPO automatically prints the letters on paper, folds them, inserts them in envelopes, and mails them first-class to their destinations.

Since 200 messages must be sent per transmission, E-COM is not suitable for the average consumer. It's perfect, however, for businesses that mail out bills, direct-mail so-licitations, or other large volume mailings. The system will support all popular computer communications interfaces, enabling mailers to establish a link between their computer systems and an E-COM computer at an SPO, either directly or via a public computer network. This feature will be especially popular with bulk mailers who use computers to generate form letters.

E-COM has drawn the wrath of common carriers who don't relish another competitor—especially not the Postal Service—in an already tough and crowded market. They argue that the U.S. Postal Service might subsidize E-COM with revenue from other classes of mail, therefore engaging in unfair competition. In addition, they say that handling electronic mail makes the Postal Service a common carrier, something it is forbidden to do under the law. If the fight continues, it could threaten E-COM's future.

Opponents also charge that the service is impractical because first-class mail is used to deliver messages from the SPO to their ultimate destinations. They argue that using first-class mail from the sender's home territory in the first place might take the same time. Only if SPO's are connected electronically, they say, would E-COM be worthwhile.

To all these objections, the Postal Service has a simple reply: it must go electronic to fulfill its mission—delivering the mail in the most economical and speedy manner. "Since its earliest times, the Postal Service has applied new technology to the task of moving the mail," Postmaster General William Bolger told a meeting of the Computer and Communications Industry Association in Washington in March, 1981. "Now that there are systems that make it possible for us to transport mail electronically, we must use them too because they're fast and economical" □

📖 SELECTED READINGS

"Electronic mail" by J. Free. *Popular Science,* September 1980.

"Voice mail arrives in the office." *Business Week,* June 9, 1980.

"Gonzo computer mail" by D. Meredith. *Technology Review,* February 1979.

Zenith Radio Corp.

Two dancers discuss their own performances while watching a video cassette recording that was made the day before.

VIDEO CASSETTE RECORDERS

by Robin Lanier

THE home video cassette recorder (VCR) has become the wonder of the consumer electronics industry over the last several years. It—and the rival, but less popular, videodisc system—have revolutionized home entertainment since the mid-1970's. Both provide sight-and-sound programs for use in the home.

In the video cassette recorder system, the program is on magnetic tape in a cassette about the size of a small book. The cassette is slipped into a special recorder, which is connected to the user's television receiver. The television functions as the display system, with the program appearing on the television screen. (In the videodisc system the program

is recorded on a disc that, like a phonograph, is spun on a turntable, and the turntable, which is part of a videodisc player, is connected to a television set.)

The video cassette recorder brings to the home another never-before-possible feature—namely, the ability to record video programs. This ability to make home recordings is one great advantage the video cassette has over the videodisc. All videodiscs must be commercially recorded.

With a video cassette recorder you can record any program you want from television and then view the program at any time. In addition, if you want you can invest in a video camera and can record any "live" scene. The VCR-camera-TV set system becomes a home-movie system. It has the virtue that the "movies" can be seen just a few moments after they are shot.

The video cassette recorder user thus has three sources of programming, which he or she can use in any mixture: the commercially "prerecorded" cassette; the television program recorded off the air; and the "home movie," made with the addition of a video

A father records his son's soccer game with a light-weight, color video camera and an advanced, portable, Betamax video recorder.

camera. Since the mid-1970's the program fare on the market in the form of prerecorded cassettes has reached to some thousands of items, a majority of them movies from the large studios, including most of the box-office blockbusters of the last several years.

The first successful consumer video cassette recorder was the Sony Betamax, which came on the U.S. market in late 1975. The initial sales push emphasized the "time shift" operation, with an automatic timer that would turn on the television set and the video cassette recorder at any preset time to "catch" a television program on the air when the user was away from home. The user could then see the program when he or she got back and whenever thereafter he or she wanted. Time-shift is still one of the major selling points for video cassette recorders, and all popular models include automatic timers of one kind or another.

Sales of Betamax grew extremely well almost from the start. This sent the worldwide consumer electronics industry into a video cassette recorder development spree. Today about 20 firms, including all the electronic giants, are selling about 60 models of video cassette recorders. Most are, however, made in Japan, including several with the brand names of U.S. companies. By 1982 worldwide sales of video cassette recorders passed the $1,000,000,000 mark. The video cassette recorder even topped color television in export value for Japan, the first electronic product to come near to doing so.

CASSETTES

All video cassette recorders use the same form of cassette: a flattish box about 6 inches by 4 inches by ¾ inch. Each cassette has two reels, one at each end. Magnetic tape, ½ inch wide, is wound around the reels. When the cassette is pushed into the recorder and the "start" button depressed, the machine automatically picks up a loop of the tape. It then moves the tape over magnetic heads inside the player, the tape going from one reel to the other.

Although all cassettes have the same form, there are two different "formats," or arrangements of the signal, on the tape. One is the "Beta," originated by Sony in the Betamax. The other is the "VHS," originated by Matsushita (Panasonic). Recordings made on a Beta machine cannot be played on a VHS machine—and vice versa. Consequently virtually all the commercially recorded programs are made in both formats. Although the two systems differ in a number of respects, including the mechanics of the tape pickup and the details of the tape path through the machine, there is no large overall quality difference. The precision with which a machine is made influences quality more than the difference between Beta and VHS format does.

RECORDING ON TAPE

Tape recording basically involves putting a pattern on magnetic tape. The pattern corresponds to the electric signals of the program being recorded. Signals from the program affect the magnetic field of a recording head. The tape passes over this magnetic head and is magnetized. It is magnetized in a pattern corresponding to the strength of the magnetic field—and thus to the program signals. In playback, the magnetic pattern on the tape is changed back into signals that are converted into a sight-and-sound program.

Both VHS and Beta use a "helical scan" system. The tape moves horizontally at a slight angle in a helix. It winds around a drum that is about three inches in diameter. The magnetic heads that record the program are fixed on the circumference of the drum. The tape moves slowly, about one-half to one inch per second. This slow speed is necessary so that the quantity of tape in one cassette will last from one up to five, and even six, hours. The drum also moves. It rotates at a speed much faster than the tape. The circumference of the drum therefore moves the magnetic heads repeatedly across the section of tape that is around the drum.

The combination of these two motions puts a series of magnetic tracks on the tape. These tracks are very thin, parallel, and very close together. They make a slight angle with the axis of the tape. The result is a recorded track that is many times as long as the tape itself. Each of the slightly slanting "lines" on the tape is played separately, one after the

other. Only in this way could the immense amount of information in a video program be packed onto magnetic tape moving so slowly.

The converse is that the "writing speed," the speed at which the magnetic heads traverse the tape, is nearly one hundred times the speed of the tape through the machine. This high writing speed is essential to get onto the tape the extremely high frequencies, up to about one megaHertz, or 1,000,000 cycles per second, that must be recorded.

PLAYBACK

During playback the tape must go around the drum in the same position relative to the heads that it had when the recording was made. The positioning must be very accurate—within an extremely small dimension of one micron, or 1/25,000 inch. The drum itself must have no irregularity—again down to the same tolerance of about one micron. The magnetic head, in other words, must line up with one of the slanting tracks on the tape—and just the right one.

To produce magnetic signals small enough so that up to 1,000,000 or more will fit onto a second's worth of tape, the gap in the recording head has to be a fraction of a micron across. This implies very advanced electronic circuits to feed the signals to the head.

In video cassette recording, a program is put on a tape by passing it over a magnetic recording head. This magnetizes the tape in a pattern corresponding to the program signals.

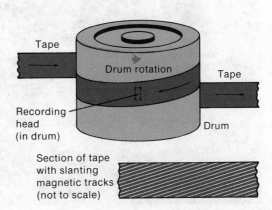

Tape

Drum rotation

Tape

Recording head (in drum)

Drum

Section of tape with slanting magnetic tracks (not to scale)

FOR HOME USE

All the basic electronic knowhow was first worked out for professional videotape machines. Starting in the late 1950's video recording on tape quickly became an essential part of television broadcasting. A large percentage of television programs are now put first on tape and then put on the air from the tape or from an edited version of the tape.

Professional videotape machines weigh several hundred pounds and cost more than $5,000. They use a large quantity of tape to record a half-hour program. The basic problem then was how to get the enormous amount of information in a video program onto a small quantity of tape. The tape had to fit in a home machine of small size and reasonable cost. A number of advances in electronics and mechanical precision in the mid-1970's made the consumer version of the video cassette recorder thinkable.

The amount of information is measured in *bits* (short for binary digit). A bit is the basic technical building block of all information. Any program can be broken down into the number of bits making it up. With any given recording technique a given area of tape will hold a certain maximum number of bits. This is the storage density of the tape and the technique. Other things being equal, the amount of information goes up directly with the area of tape being used.

Professional machines using one-inch tape use about 120 square feet of tape to record a one-half hour program. Betamax and other similar home video cassette recorders put a one-half hour program on about five square feet of tape. Because of this difference, home video tapes cannot match the quality of professional video tapes. Nor do they pretend to do so. The quantity of tape practical in a home design simply doesn't have the storage density to hold all the information in a fully detailed program. Home video cassette recorder makers have, however, succeeded in producing a picture that is fully acceptable for home playback.

A close-up of RCA's video cassette recorder shows some of its operation features. Many models on the market today offer special features to attract prospective buyers.

Courtesy of TDK Electronics Corp.

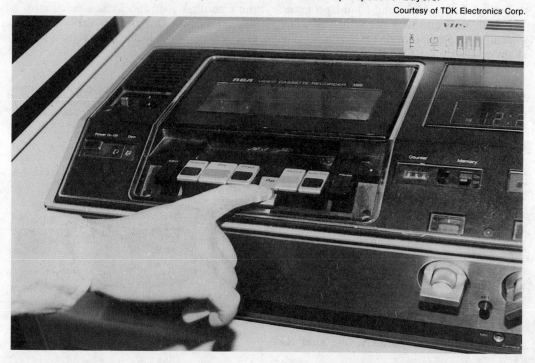

It may be interesting to note here that the videodisc has inherently many times the storage density of magnetic tape. It is potentially able to provide better reproduction than even present professional tape systems.

SPECIAL FEATURES

Home video cassette recorder makers, with picture quality that the consumer quickly accepted, have gone on to give the consumer a raft of operation features, an array of "bells and whistles" that now form the main substance of the vast promotion for video cassette recorders. Long playing time on one cassette was one of the first features. The original Betamax ran for one hour on one cassette. Rival machines with two-hour playing time started a race that has ended with machines on the market that run up to five or six hours.

There is a price for long playing time on a single cassette, however. The extra time is achieved either by using thinner tape so that the cassette can hold more or by running the tape more slowly. Both are likely to degrade quality, the slow speed especially. It is a case of putting even more programming onto a given quantity of tape and the amount of detail in the picture has to be reduced in order to fit it all in. The very slow speeds are also more productive of faults in the picture: jumps, tears, and similar things.

With some video cassette recorder models the user can shift from the slow to the fast speed; in other brands, there is a slow-speed and a fast-speed model. The buyer with strong feelings about picture quality must stick with high speed operation.

Automatic timers have become very elaborate. Some can be programmed for a number of days in advance to turn the recorder on a number of different times. Many models are also available with built-in television tuners. You can then record an off-air program without tying up your television.

Most machines now also allow the user to "freeze" a frame—that is, to hold any picture still on the screen. Fast forward and reverse speeds can also be had as can remote controls, and automatic rewind at the end of the tape. You can get slow motion and "instant replay" on the VHS machines. You

Ira Berger

This young boy is watching a playback of his favorite television program that he taped with a home video cassette recorder.

cannot get this feature on Beta-type machines.

AND TO COME?

It is hard to imagine any further large evolution in the home video cassette recorder. High-definition television is just beginning to come out of the laboratories; it would be even harder to cram into the video cassette format. Since the 1960's there has, however, been enormous ferment in the telecommunications field with many unexpected developments. Continued advances may well bring more home entertainment news □

Courtesy of Sony Corporation of America

A teenager recorded some of her favorite songs on a blank cassette to play at her party.

BLANK AUDIO TAPES

by Stephen Booth

JUDGING by the increasing popularity of home and portable stereo-tape equipment, there will probably be no slaking America's thirst for blank-tape cassettes. A trip to any hi-fi or record store reveals a perplexing array of cassette brands akin to the proliferation of imported beers. It's enough to set your head spinning if you're using tape equipment for the first time. Buying and testing aside, the brand names and manufacturers' claims can leave you with a hangover.

Blank tape comes in a variety of styles, each producing a specific result. There's metal-particle tape, chromium dioxide, ferrichrome, and high- and normal-bias ferric oxide. Confusing matters further, some manufacturers offer more than one selection within each type.

BARGAIN BRANDS NO DEAL

There are blank cassettes on the market that will leave you with a headache, not only because their sonic quality resembles the howling of cats, but also because of their effect on your recording equipment. These are the so-called bargain tapes that you'll find three-to-a-bag for $1.19 in the kind of place that sells souvenirs, comic books, arthritis cures, and rabbit's-foot charms. You'll need the latter if you make a practice of recording with inferior cassettes.

Typically, the bargain tape is thin and poorly coated, and the cassette shell cheaply made. They can jam in your machine and shed oxide deposits on the recording and playback heads. This type of cassette is a holdout from the days before the cassette became a high-fidelity recording medium. In those days, the cassette's very small size and slow recording speed ($1\frac{7}{8}$ inches per second compared to $7\frac{1}{2}$ for open reel) made it suitable mainly for recording speech.

BIAS AND EQUALIZATION

The next time you stand before a cassette rack at any store, you may be baffled by two terms you'll see on every tape: bias and equalization. Bias current and playback equalization are really fairly simple concepts. Bias is required only during the recording process. It's an electrical current applied to the tape (via the record head). The current prepares the tape's magnetic particles for arrangement in the pattern of whatever is to be recorded. The amount of bias applied depends on the type of tape particle. All you need to do is flip the switch on your equipment to the correct setting.

Equalization must be set properly for the best sound when you play back the tape. Why equalization? Simply put, all musical frequencies receive equal emphasis during recording. The lowest bass and highest treble sounds tend to diminish when played with the middle registers. Left unassisted—that is, with equalization—certain parts of the musical spectrum would lack proper tonal quality (if not become entirely lost) upon playback.

Equalization boosts these frequencies to abnormal levels during recording—overemphasizing them in order to get them onto the tape. But when played back at the same EQ (equalization) setting, the frequencies return to their normal balance.

EQ SETTINGS

A final word on EQ switches. Suppose your home tape deck has the Type III/ferrichrome/FeCr setting, but your car-stereo system or the Walkman-type stereo portable you just purchased doesn't. Don't despair. Since the FeCr, or Type III, tape shares seventy-microsecond playback equalization with Types II and IV, it can be played at those settings. If your playback equipment has no EQ settings (typical among older portables and car-stereo systems, which assumed use of the most common Type I tape), you can still play your Type II, III or IV tape. But the tapes will sound a bit shrill because the Type I equalization of 120 microseconds boosts up the treble tones. A solution: lower your treble tone control according to taste.

TYPES OF TAPE

Before discussing the importance of tape quality and shell precision to high-fidelity recording, let's examine the types of tape available and how they correspond to your cassette hardware. Basically, there are four types or "formulations."

Type I Normal Bias/Ferric Oxide. The Type I cassette is the lager of blank tape inasmuch as it's the single category with the largest number of entries. This is because the Type I setting is available on all cassette equipment—unlike Types II, III and IV, which require special settings. The Type I cassette uses ferric-oxide tape—the first kind of tape available and the most common. It requires normal bias upon recording and 120-microsecond equalization upon playback.

Type II High or Chrome Bias. High-bias tapes are made of either chromium-dioxide tape or chrome equivalents—the latter being ferric-oxide particles enhanced by the

TDK Electronics Corporation, one of many tape manufacturers, markets a wide variety of audio recording products to meet the needs of even the most demanding enthusiast.

Courtesy of TDK Electronics Corp.

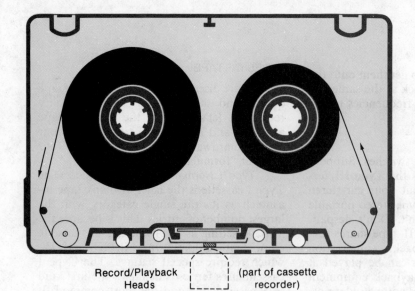

An internal view of a cassette reveals a reel-to-reel tape transport system in miniature. The tape must align precisely with the record and playback heads of the recorder.

Record/Playback Heads   (part of cassette recorder)

stronger magnetic properties of cobalt. Each offers better high-frequency (treble) recording and lower background noise (tape hiss) than Type I tapes. Because they require a higher bias current for recording and seventy-microsecond equalization for playback, these tapes should be used only with recorders that offer the Type II/chrome/CrO_2/high-bias setting.

Type III Ferrichrome Bias. Ferrichrome tape, sometimes represented by the Type III or FeCr setting on cassette equipment, is composed of a bottom layer of ferric-oxide particles glazed with a top coat, or veneer, of chromium dioxide or chrome-equivalent particles. Like Type II tapes, ferrichrome uses seventy-microsecond playback equalization. It is best recorded with a bias current of its own—stronger than Type I but weaker than Type II. If your equipment lacks a Type III switch, however, you can still achieve good results by recording at the Type I position.

Type IV Metal Bias. If metal tape were a beer, it would be like stout: expensive and an acquired taste, requiring a strong constitution. Unlike the others, Type IV tape uses pure metal-alloy particles—not oxide or rust. It offers less tape noise and greater high-frequency head room—that is, the ability to record treble tones at a greater volume without saturating the tape (and thereby distorting the sound).

Metal tape, though, is harder to record and erase. It requires a stronger bias current

than any of the others. For best results, you should only record on equipment that has a Type IV metal switch. However, because metal tape uses seventy-microsecond playback equalization, you can play already-recorded tapes on any equipment that handles Types II or III.

TAPES FOR ALL TASTES

The type of tape you choose should depend on application, budget, and informed taste. The brand you choose is a matter of preference and can be determined only by experimenting and comparative listening. In some cases, the hardware manufacturer will indicate the types and brands of tape used to develop the performance specifications of your tape equipment. This information can help you make an educated choice.

Type IV metal tape offers a clear-cut choice. Its high cost—about twelve dollars for a ninety-minute cassette—is commensurate to its high-fidelity capabilities. Tape manufacturers recommend its use for live recording or for dubbing (transposing sound already recorded to a new tape) expensive audiophile records. It is most efficiently used for recording music with a wide dynamic range (deep bass to high treble) and "hot" transients—such as when a rumbling kettle-drum roll is punctuated by sharp rim shots or a bash on the cymbals.

Type II tapes and the hybrid ferrichrome variety are universal in use and occupy the midfield price range between Types

I and IV. Because of their treble sensitivity and quiet background (lack of pronounced hiss), Type II tapes are best used for critical listening, especially for music that alternates soft passages with delicate high trebles.

Tape suppliers who offer a Type III cassette tout its use for car-stereo players. The ferric undercoat, they say, offers good bass reproduction, while the chrome or chrome-equivalent veneer provides sharper highs. This is important because of the automobile's hostile acoustics—upholstery that muffles treble tones, and road and engine noise that combine to drown out the bass. Although the Type III's ferric content exhibits more hiss than Types II or IV, ambient car noise can mask this.

Because of the multiplicity of tape grades available, cassettes of the Type I category present the most bewildering choice to the would-be home recordist. Most manufacturers offer two and some supply three grades within Type I—everything from inexpensive dictation-quality tapes to modestly priced general-purpose music tapes to premium ferric-oxide tapes, whose price and performance approach that of Type II formulations.

BENEFITS WITH CHOICE

Why the multiple choice? In the case of dictation tapes, there's no sense charging a premium to customers who don't require hi-fi sound. The general-purpose Type I music tapes are now in the mid-price range of Type I cassettes, thanks to the later appearance of premium ferric-oxide formulations, which are usually the most expensive. Premium ferric-oxide tapes use "enhanced" particles, which were developed around 1970 in the wake of Type II formulas in order to offer customers with older cassette equipment (lacking the Type II setting) performance comparable to Type II cassettes. Although most home equipment that is sold today has settings for all four types, the premium Type I tapes still play a valuable role by facilitating high-fidelity recording on stereo portables—the Walkman, for example—that offer only one setting.

Simple arithmetic shows that Type I tapes offer the lowest recording cost per minute compared to the others. A twelve-dollar

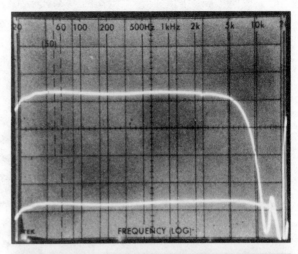

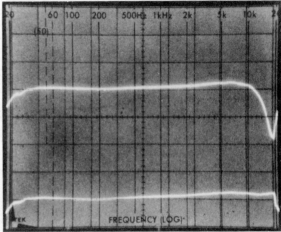

Courtesy of POPULAR MECHANICS

Top: oscilloscope oxide-tape traces show how those tapes distort highs at high outputs. Below: metal-tape response shows that distortion of highs is minimal at a high output.

C-90 metal tape is suitable for archival recordings—for example, dubbing your eighteen-dollar audiophile discs to preserve them against damage. But if you want to record half a dozen cassettes for a party—where the high noise level will mask musical subtleties and tape hiss—a general-purpose Type I tape will do the trick.

The benefits of using cassettes are that they free the user from having to handle phonograph records in situations like parties and eliminate the hazard of discs being carelessly treated. When you stop to consider the fragility and increasing cost of LP's (phonograph

Blank audio tapes are clearly marked with bias and equalization specifications. This high-bias, Type II tape requires seventy-microsecond equalization for playback.

Courtesy of Sony Corporation of America

records), especially the audiophile variety, recording a dub for frequent listening makes economic sense. Retaining the LP as a master assures you a nearly pristine recording of a cherished title should the record company drop it from its catalog. With a little practice, you'll be able to turn out satisfying dubs on your home cassette hardware. Instructions and helpful hints are almost always included in the manual that accompanies your equipment.

A BONANZA OF BRANDS

Experimenting with different types and brands of blank tape is part of the fun of owning tape-recording equipment. To prevent the experience from becoming a nightmare, a few words on cassette tape and shells may prove helpful.

On your first trip to the cassette rack at a local record or hi-fi store, you'll notice that the blank-tape business rivals the razorblade industry for the number and complexity of patented metallic compounds and "super" formulations. Don't be fooled. Fancy names like "Super Avilyn" or "Chromdioxid" or "Beridox" or "Epitaxial" signify nothing more than the manufacturer's jealously guarded chemical formula for that type of tape.

Nearly two dozen reputable manufacturers vie with one another to produce particles with improved magnetic properties and uniform size. The better they do their job, the more likely you are to hear the sound of music and not the sound of tape.

SHELL PRECISION

The cassette, or tape shell, is the other half of your tape hardware. If you were to take it apart, you'd find a miniature reel-to-reel tape-transport system. Such miniaturization entails tolerances that are as fine as 0.0001 of an inch. Shell manufacturing must be exact because encoded on the 0.15-inch tape are four recording tracks—two for each side.

In a game of hairsplitting fractions, only precise alignment of the tape to your hardware's record heads and play heads will reproduce the entire recorded signal with proper stereo phasing and separation. Not only must the cassette's transport mechanism guide the tape in a perfectly straight path across the heads, but the tiny felt-like pressure pad must hold the tape in even contact with the heads as it travels by. Friction-free shell components and warp-resistant shell materials help keep the tape on the straight and narrow.

BUY WISELY

Your best bet to avoid taping horrors is to stick to nationally advertised cassette brands and buy from established, reputable retailers (who often sell at a discount anyway). You should check to see that the cassette carries a lifetime warranty, which serious manufacturers display prominently on their cassette packages. If you economize too much on your purchase, you'll get what you pay for. As I recall, Ernest Hemingway once wrote, "The bill always comes" □

Charlie Nye/Gamma-Liaison

A marine biologist examines a dying sperm whale that stranded itself. Scientists believe that whales may strand due to sickness, congenital problems, or confusion in direction.

WILDLIFE

© Georg Gerster/PR

In late 1981, enforcement of wildlife protection laws improved when President Reagan mandated increased penalties for violations of the Lacey Act, a fundamental wildlife law.

WILDLIFE
REVIEW OF THE YEAR

There was both good and bad news for wildlife during 1981. Good news included an increase in populations of some endangered species and additional protection for some threatened species. The bad news was the continued loss of natural habitat and consequent endangerment of other species. Perhaps overshadowing all was concern that economic and political decisions made during 1981 do not bode well for wildlife.

Government Policy. Perhaps the most ominous development of 1981 was the apparent political swing against wildlife values at the federal level. Professional wildlife staffs were decimated; refuges were opened for mineral development; and funds for wildlife programs were reduced, especially funds for federal-state wildlife research programs which are at the heart of efforts to safeguard wildlife habitat and thus wildlife itself. Conservationists expressed particular concern after U.S. Secretary of the Interior James Watt indicated that he would open refuges and wilderness areas to mineral development. Then, in February 1982, Watt surprised conservationists by calling for legislation that would forbid mining and drilling on federal wilderness lands until the year 2000. While encouraged by this change of attitude, conservationists were cautious in their optimism, waiting to see what future developments bring.

On the plus side, Watt did come out strongly for continued land acquisition to preserve wetland habitat. The urgency here, he said, is that wetlands may not be available if they are not purchased for preservation now. They are by nature fragile and in addition are usually located in prime areas for residential, commercial, industrial, and agricultural development. For instance, the wildlife-rich swamps and marshes of the Mississippi Delta are being drained or flooded at the rate of more than 100 square kilometers (40 square miles) per year. This nursery for shrimp and fish, home for muskrats, alligators, wild turkeys, black bears, bobcats, foxes, mink, white-tailed deer, and wintering grounds for waterfowl has been drained and timbered for decades. Its rich resources produce one fourth of the U.S. total fish catch and it is the leading fur-producing area in the United States. In cooperation with Watt's wetland initiative, Louisiana Governor David Treen announced a plan in November 1981 that would provide habitat protection easements on nearly 1,500 square kilometers (365,000 acres) of prime wildlife habitat in the Atchafalaya Basin. The easements would prohibit most development, though oil and gas drilling would be permitted. The 2,800-square kilometer (690,000-acre) basin is the largest wetland area remaining in the once-vast Mississippi River wetland ecosystem.

On another front, enforcement of wildlife protection laws improved. In November 1981 President Reagan signed a bill that increased penalties for violating the Lacey Act, the oldest and most basic wildlife protection law in the United States. Passed in 1900, the measure makes it a federal offense to transport across state lines any wildlife that is taken, possessed, bought, or sold in violation of the laws of states or other countries. In an effort to curtail the massive illicit trade in wildlife, law-enforcement agencies broadened their use of undercover operations. On one summer day, federal and state conservation officers arrested scores of people, culminating an 18-month investigation into suspected illegal commerce in snakes, turtles, lizards, and birds. The stakes for criminals are high: a Texas graybanded kingsnake retails for $200; a brightly colored hyacinth macaw for as much as $8,000.

A multimillion-dollar recovery plan is underway to save the extremely rare California condor. Biologists are trying to breed some of the remaining birds in captivity.

© Carl B. Koford/PR

Success Stories. The year 1981 also saw several success stories for wildlife. For example, the alligator population in Louisiana has grown up to the limits of its habitat. The U.S. Department of the Interior has therefore removed that state's alligators from the "threatened" category under the Endangered Species Act. Some alligators may now be hunted, though there are still strict regulations controlling trade in alligator hide. ■ Conservationists scored another victory in the summer of 1981 when the International Whaling Commission (IWC) voted for a virtual ban on the hunting of sperm whales. The IWC has gradually reduced quotas for whales caught worldwide from 46,000 in 1975 to fewer than 15,000 in 1981. ■ Eagles also seem to be winning. The National Wildlife Federation's third annual midwinter bald eagle survey in the lower 48 states in January 1981 counted 13,709 eagles, an increase of 5 per cent over the previous year's tally. And finally two species gave conservationists some pleasant surprises. Some black-footed ferrets—a species feared extinct—were found in Wyoming. And a bowerbird—the yellow-fronted gardener bowerbird (*Amblyornis flavifrons*)—long thought extinct was discovered in New Guinea. (See also "The Bowerbird," on page 183.)

Endangered Species. Extinctions of wild animals and plants that used to be caused primarily by drastic climatic changes are now caused mainly by human activities that alter the living space of the species to such a degree that they cannot survive. Our industrial society has so changed the face of the United States that scores of species now depend on humans to take steps to preserve them. The U.S. Endangered Species list now includes 35 mammals, 69 birds, 25 reptiles, 8 amphibians, 45 fish, 8 snails, 23 clams, 1 crustacean, 13 insects, and 61 plants. The addition of more species to the list has now been deemphasized in favor of spending more money on rescuing some of the listed species. Even so, 19 birds are so threatened that they may be added to the list. Some like the Amak song sparrow from the Aleutian Islands off Alaska may already be extinct; some, like the flightless Guan rail, are unique examples of birdlife. ■ The Tecopa pupfish has been taken off the Endangered Species list because it is now believed to be extinct. The U.S. Fish & Wildlife Service made the announcement in November 1981 after extensive searches revealed no survivors. Fish & Wildlife Service Director Robert Jantzen pointed out that the fish might have already been extinct when it was put on the list in 1970. He added that recovery programs should not be abandoned. They have unquestionably benefitted many endangered species, notably the alligator, peregrine falcon, whooping crane, and the brown pelican.

Recovery plans are not cheap, however, and the costs of saving a species loom larger and larger. A 4-year, $25,000,000 program has been launched to preserve the habitat of the California condor and to breed in captivity some of the few remaining birds, now estimated to number only 25. A less spectacular bird, but one threatened even more seriously, is the dusky seaside sparrow, now disappearing from the salt marshes of Florida's east coast. Only 5 individuals remain, and all are believed to be males. Conservation groups argue over whether the captive males should be crossbred with females of similar species to preserve a semblance of the seemingly doomed species. Though the last known sighting of females was in 1975, the Fish & Wildlife Service has refused to allow the dilution of the species without more conclusive evidence that no females remain. ■ Another debate raged over how much protection lower life forms should receive. Obviously it is much more difficult to garner public support for saving crustaceans, clams, snails, and plants than for species tinged with historic romanticism such as the grizzly bear and the whooping crane.

Bob Strohm

UPI

Conservationists were delighted to find some black-footed ferrets living in Wyoming. Feared extinct, these animals are believed to be the most severely endangered species in the U.S.

The dusky seaside sparrow, another species threatened with extinction, has all but disappeared from its Florida east coast habitat. Scientists believe only five males remain.

© Bill Wilson/PR

Peter D. Capen

The stinging tentacles of a South Pacific sea anemone serves as both shelter and protection for this colorful little clownfish.

SEA ANEMONES

by Peter D. Capen

ANYONE exploring along a rocky seashore invariably pauses to gaze in fascination into the shallow pools formed by the ebbing tide. Amidst the seaweed, the scurrying crabs, the limpets, chitons, and periwinkles, the beachcomber's eye quickly comes to rest on the gently waving tentacles of the flowerlike anemones.

Named for the windflowers of the mountains and woodlands, sea anemones are some of the most striking and interesting creatures to be found in the ocean. They are found all over the world, inhabiting both warm and cold seas. They dwell in shallow tidepools and at great depths. One species was even discovered living in the bottom of the Philippine Trench, over 9,000 meters (almost 30,000 feet) down into the abyss. But most of the 800 or so known types of sea anemones seem to prefer shallower waters; thus, they are particularly abundant along coastlines and on coral reefs.

MANY SIZES AND COLORS

A diverse group, anemones come in a wide variety of sizes and colors. They range from tiny individuals scarcely larger than one's fingernail to the giant, tropical specimens of the South Pacific and Indian Ocean that can reach more than 1 meter (3 feet) in diameter. The graceful plumose anemone, *Metridium senile,* found throughout much of the Northern Hemisphere, can also grow quite large. Its size, however, is due less to its girth than to its height. Its sleek, muscular column, fringed with a crown of numerous, tiny tentacles, can rise more than 20 centimeters (8 inches) tall.

Perhaps more than any other single characteristic, color is what usually first attracts attention to the anemones. Sea anemones come in nearly every hue or combination of hues imaginable. Their coloration can at times be captivatingly subtle; at other times, shockingly vivid. In the cool waters off the Pacific coast of North America, the small, brilliant red club-tentacled anemone *Corynactis californica* carpets undersea boulders and canyon walls. Why *Corynactis,* as well as many other anemones, display such bright colors is not clear. Some biologists feel they are simply the result of random hereditary variations, or natural biological processes within specific individuals. Other think the colors can be a form of protection from the harsh rays of the sun. In several other species colors clearly relate to the food they eat or to organisms within their tissues. The large, American Pacific coast anemone *Anthopleura xanthogrammica,* for instance, owes its rich green hue to the single-celled algae *Zoochlorella* that live in its body.

FEW ENEMIES

Sea anemones belong to a large, diverse, wholly aquatic family of animals called either coelenterates, or cnidarians. The name Coelenterata, meaning "hollow gut," was given to the group because each member is characterized by having a digestive cavity that connects with the outside through a single opening, the mouth, which is surrounded by tentacles.

The name Cnidaria refers to the fact that all the members of the group are armed with microscopic stinging capsules termed cnidae, or nematocysts. Only sea anemones and their relatives possess these remarkable structures. Used for both self-defense and to capture food, the nematocysts are densely arrayed on the tentacles and less densely in many other parts of the coelenterate's body.

When a would-be attacker, or potential victim is brushed by the tentacle, the stinging capsule fires off. Threads wound up inside the nematocyst, some of which are armed with spines reminiscent of a medieval mace, shoot out and either penetrate, wrap around, or stick to the offending object. The capsule may be filled with toxin, which is then injected through the thread into the blundering predator or hapless prey. With such effective armament, it is little wonder that these animals have few enemies. One puzzling exception, however, is the case of some sea slugs who dine with impunity on various sea anemones and hydroids.

EFFICIENT SIMPLE BODIES

Sea anemones have a relatively simple body structure, which, nonetheless, is extremely efficient. Their stout muscular column forms into a smooth pedal disc at its lower end. The anemone can either slide about on this slimy disc, or can cling so tenaciously to the rocks with it that it is nearly impossible to pry the animal loose without tearing it. At its upper end the column ex-

Atop its thick, smooth column, the plumose anemone has a crown of tiny tentacles that filter plankton from the water.

Peter D. Capen

Two color variations of *Tealia piscivora* cling to underwater rocks off the Pacific Coast. These delicate anemones can reproduce sexually in different ways.

Peter D. Capen

pands into a broad oral disc, which is surrounded by one or more circlets of hollow tentacles armed with nematocysts and adhesive glands. In some species the tentacles completely cover the oral disc, rather than being arranged around it.

The anemone's mouth leads into a flattened, instead of cylindrically shaped, muscular gullet that extends down into a gastrovascular cavity. Within this gullet are two types of flagella. The larger of these two types are located in grooves in the gullet. Beating in a downwards motion, these flagella draw in a continuous current of water, which provides life-sustaining oxygen to all of the internal parts of the animal.

The smaller flagella line the gullet proper and they generally beat in an upwards motion. This motion sweeps a current of water out of the anemone and takes with it carbon dioxide and other wastes. When food is caught, however, the smaller flagella will reverse their beat. This aids in bringing the captured prey down into the individual's digestive cavity. There, powerful enzymes quickly digest the meal, while anything that is undigestible is simply spewed out.

Of all the anemones, the tube anemone is easily one of the most tantalizing to watch feed. It has two distinct sets of tentacles, one of which is quite short, while the other is long and slender. Raking the water with its long set in broad, graceful arcs, it snares small victims. It then passes them off to the shorter set clustered around the mouth, which, in turn, pushes the tasty morsels on into the hungry animal's gullet.

A few types of anemones will congregate in dense aggregations, or clones, but most forms live solitary lives. They individually attach themselves by their strong muscular bases to the rocky substrate and wharf pilings, or, as in the case of the tube anemones, burrow into the sand and soft mud of the bottom. In some instances, sea anemones also find homes with other animals.

Although rather sedentary creatures, anemones do move about their undersea world. But their movement is generally so slow that it is virtually impossible for the casual observer to detect. Gliding on its flat base by means of imperceptible muscular waves, an individual sea anemone might cover as much as 5 or 8 centimeters (2 or 3 inches) an hour. Notable exceptions to this are an unusual deep water form that extends its body into a barrel shape and literally rolls across the sea floor and another that floats across the surface of the ocean by means of a chitinous float secreted by its pedal end.

A dense clone of the spectacular red club-tentacled anemone thrives in the cool waters off the California coast. The tentacles' bulbous ends have coral-like nematocysts.

Peter D. Capen

Some anemones will also exhibit dramatic escape responses when threatened. One North Pacific species propels itself away from a would-be assailant by detaching its base and rapidly flexing its column to the left and right. Others swim away from danger by a coordinated paddling of their tentacles. Yet, if left undisturbed, most anemones will continue to occupy their same general locations. And if the proper combination of natural conditions is maintained, they can live very long lives—perhaps even 90 years.

REPRODUCTION

Sea anemones may reproduce by either sexual or asexual means. In sexual reproduction the males and females of a particular species eject their eggs and sperm directly into the surrounding water through their mouths. So many eggs and sperm are released that they can actually turn the water around the anemones cloudy. After fertilization takes place, the eggs develop into tiny, ciliated larvae, called planulae. The planulae swim around for a little while, usually two or three days, and then attach themselves to rocks or any other available objects and continue their development into adulthood.

In some species the egg fertilization takes place inside of the female, rather than simply left to chance out in the open. Sperm shed by the male are drawn directly into the female's body along with the continuous incoming current of water. The larvae develop inside the cavity of the parent. As they get older they migrate out of the female's mouth and begin lives on their own. In one Pacific coast species, the young anemones attach themselves to the base of their parent after leaving its mouth and remain there until they grow sufficiently large to fend for themselves.

In asexual reproduction, the anemone commonly divides into two separate individuals or provides the basis for the regeneration of a wholly new individual from a portion of its body. As they glide over the rocky surface, some species leave behind bits of themselves—bits that are capable of reorganizing into tiny, complete anemones.

MANY SPECIAL FRIENDS

Sea anemones have many plant and animal relationships. These associations are sometimes an advantage to the anemone; at other times they are quite the contrary. An anemone-plant relationship that has been studied in great detail exists between the large green anemone *Anthopleura xanthogrammica* and the single-celled algae *Zoochlorella*. This association is advantageous

Peter D. Capen

The tentacles of a red anemone are completely hidden when the creature is contracted.

to both the tiny marine plants and to their animal host. The *Zoochlorella* make use of the metabolic wastes given off by the anemone. *Anthopleura* benefits by having its metabolic wastes removed, by having access to a plentiful supply of oxygen given off by the plant (through photosynthesis), and, if hunting is poor, by having a ready supply of food.

There are numerous instances where sea anemones live together with other undersea creatures. They have been known to cling to jellyfish, attach to sponges, and live with sea pens. In the quiet waters of Truk Lagoon many wire corals on the sides of the sunken World War II wrecks boast a whole complement of a beautiful, small yellow anemone with delicate, long white tentacles. Several anemone species also regularly live with hermit crabs. These relationships are often so close that when a particular hermit crab out-

grows its shell and finds another, it will normally transfer its guest to the new home.

Of all the anemone relationships, none is more familiar than that between the vividly banded clownfishes and the giant Indo-Pacific anemones, primarily of the genera *Heteractis* and *Stichodactyla*. Visit any large public aquarium and you are bound to see a display of the gaudy little fishes darting in and out or contentedly sleeping nestled among the waving tentacles of these formidable anemones. The clownfish will fearlessly rub, nibble, and dart back and forth among the lethal tentacles. When threatened, the little fish will all but dive into the center of its protector. In fact, the fish has little chance of survival in the wild without the security of its host. Nor are the benefits all one way. Clownfishes have been observed in aquaria bringing food to their benefactors. And only recently it was discovered that butterflyfishes will prey upon anemones without resident clownfishes, but not on those with the clownfishes.

How the weak little clownfishes avoid being stung and devoured by their hungry host is an intriguing case of subterfuge. Researchers have found that the clownfish coat themselves in the mucus of their host, thereby effectively disguising their presence. Removed from its anemone, the clownfish soon begins losing its mucus layer. Replaced again, the fish appears to realize its vulnerability and does not immediately dash headlong into the anemone's tentacles. Rather, it gingerly makes repeated contact with them, gradually increasing the contact as it once again builds up its protective coating.

A SIMPLE PLEASURE

The ubiquitous flower animals of the sea occupy a special niche among the ocean's denizens. Their adaptability to a wide variety of physical conditions and habitats, together with the many puzzles that surround them, have long made these striking, primitive yet complex, creatures unceasing objects of curiosity and scientific research. But no less than their value to science is the simple pleasure of discovery they bring to the beachcomber, who chances upon one of their kind in a shallow pool at the edge of the sea □

THE BIRD BEHIND THE SYMBOL

by Peter Steinhart

© Charles G. Summers Jr.

TWO hundred years ago, the U.S. Congress adopted the bald eagle as the United States' national symbol, touching off a long controversy. Ever since, Americans have argued over the nature of both the symbol and the bird. We have accused the creature of being nothing more than "a good-looking vulture." We have praised it for its power and beauty. We have displayed it for commercial advantage. We have abused it to the point where it became threatened with extinction in some areas. And though the symbol and the nation are now synonymous, the future of the eagle itself remains in question.

It is as if Americans sometimes see two different birds. To Jim Grier, for example, the eagle represents the essence of wildness and grace. A North Dakota State University zoologist who has banded more than 1,000 of the birds, Grier recalls climbing to the top of a tall aspen in northern Ontario to band some eaglets. High overhead at the time, apparently unaware of the scientist's presence, an adult eagle was returning to the nest. Just as Grier reached the eyrie, the bird lowered its wings and parachuted straight down. It sideslipped on the wind, dropping as quietly as a dandelion seed 150 meters (500 feet) to the nest, where it locked eyes with the astonished researcher.

Fritz Kahl had a different view of the eagle. A former Texas sheep rancher, he remembers seeing concentrations of the birds during the wintertime around his pastures. "They lay in wait," he recalls. "Then, once they see clear, down they come. They will harass an antelope fawn or a lamb on the run. They are predators of the worst kind." The creatures Kahl had seen were golden eagles, but at the time it didn't matter. To him, all eagles were villains.

ENDANGERED

There are some 50 different species of eagles throughout the world, but the bald eagle is the only one unique to North America. It feeds primarily on fish and other live prey. Only when such prey is scarce does the creature turn to scavenging. Unlike its cousin, the golden eagle, however, the bald seldom attacks lambs or other livestock. Since it does not develop the distinguishing white head and tail until it is four or five years old, the bald eagle is often confused with the golden.

Ornithologists believe that bald eagles were once found throughout all the continental United States. But as settlers pushed back the frontier and destroyed wilderness habitat, the birds' numbers steadily declined. That decline reached epidemic proportions during the 20th century, when pesticides heavily contaminated the eagles' food supplies. Today, the nation's symbol is classified as "endangered" in 43 of the Lower 48 states, and "threatened" in all of the others. Only in Alaska and Canada is the creature faring well.

IMPOSING BIRD

The bald eagle is an imposing bird. It may stand 90 centimeters (3 feet) from head to tail, and have a wingspan of 2.3 meters (7.5 feet). Its eyes are huge and pale, and its warlike appearance is sometimes matched by its behavior. Bald eagles have been seen intimidating ospreys out of freshly caught fish, catching the jettisoned prey in midair, and soaring away.

"I've seen eagles circling around together, higher and higher," says Helen Cummings, a naturalist who has watched the creatures nesting at a Wisconsin lake for more than 50 years. "They get so high that you almost lose sight of them. It takes your breath away and makes you think of freedom." This lofty flight has, in the past, suggested to some people that eagles belong in

Bald eagles often mate with just one partner for life, returning annually to the same nesting site.
© Leonard Lee Rue III

the realm of gods. The Greeks said that their god, Zeus, could transform himself into an eagle. In ancient Rome, when an emperor died and his remains were kindled, a live eagle was released to bear his soul to heaven.

ANCIENT SYMBOL

As long as humans have drawn upon animals to express abstract qualities, they have used eagles as symbols. Asyrian, Persian, and Roman armies marched under banners depicting the birds. Charlemagne, Napoleon, Peter the Great, and Bismarck all included the eagle in their national emblems. The Aztecs of Mexico pictured their sun god, *Tonatiuh*, as an eagle, snatching up the heroic dead and bearing them to the Mansions of the Sun. The Bible is also filled with praise for eagles. Job thought them wonderful because they could look into the "terrible majesty" of God. Isaiah spoke of the birds' fortitude when he prophesied: "The Lord shall renew their strength. They shall mount up with wings as eagles."

Nations often adopt animals as symbols: England has its lion, India its peacock. On the afternoon of July 4, 1776, just after the signing of the Declaration of Independence, the Continental Congress appointed a committee made up of Thomas Jefferson, John Adams, and Benjamin Franklin to select a design for an official national seal.

EARLY IDEAS FOR THE U.S.

The three patriots had different ideas, and none of them included eagles. Adams suggested a picture of Hercules with the maiden Virtue pointing to distant mountains and urging him to climb them, while the figure of a sloth lounged temptingly nearby. Franklin preferred an image of Moses dividing the waters of the Red Sea, as the Pharaoh's chariots perished in the background, accompanied by the words: "Rebellion to Tyrants is Obedience to God."

Jefferson, meanwhile, proposed a picture of the children of Israel wandering through the wilderness. The three men finally agreed on a drawing of the woman Liberty holding a shield to represent the states, with the figure Justice to the left. Both were displayed over the motto, "*E Pluribus*

An adult eagle feeds its youngsters in a tall tree high above Kachemak Bay in Alaska.
The huge nest is enhanced with more branches every year.

Jeff Foott

Unum" (one out of many), a phrase taken from a popular British gentleman's magazine.

FINAL DESIGN

Congress, however, wasn't inspired by the design. Nor did it adopt a different proposal by a second committee six years later. In 1782, a third committee was appointed. It consulted with William Barton, a Philadelphian who was skilled in drawing and heraldry. Barton produced a design that depicted a golden eagle holding a sword in its right talon and an American flag in its left. Below the eagle was the maiden Virtue, holding a dove in one hand and a shield adorned with stars and stripes in the other. A soldier stood nearby.

Because the golden eagle also flew over European nations, the Secretary of Congress, Charles Thompson, specified that the bird in the seal should be an American bald eagle. He also simplified the images to make the bird the central figure. His revised design placed a bundle of arrows, symbolizing war power, in the eagle's right talon, and an olive branch for peace in the left. Over the creature's head, a ring of 13 stars was arranged in

a sunburst emerging through a circle of clouds. A banner in the eagle's beak displayed the words, *"E Pluribus Unum."* On June 20, 1782, the design was approved by Congress.

CONTROVERSIAL CHOICE

At the time, the new nation was still at war with England, and the fierce-looking bird seemed to be an appropriate emblem. But the eagle was at once a controversial choice. Franklin scowled at it. "For my part," he declared, "I wish the eagle had not been chosen as the representative of this country. He is a bird of bad moral character; he does not get his living honestly. You may have seen him perched in some dead tree where, too lazy to fish for himself, he watches the labor of the fishing hawk and, when that diligent bird has at length taken a fish and is bearing it to his nest for his young ones, the bald eagle pursues him and takes the fish. With all this injustice, he is never in good case."

Some people have questioned whether the eagle would have been chosen to adorn the seal if the nation had not been at war. A year after the Treaty of Paris ended the conflict with Britain, Franklin argued that the turkey would have been a more appropriate symbol. "A much more respectable bird and a true native of America," he pointed out. Franklin conceded that the turkey was "a little vain and silly." He maintained, though, that the turkey was a "bird of courage" that "would not hesitate to attack a grenadier of the British guards who should presume to invade his farmyard with a red coat on."

John James Audubon also had his doubts about the eagle. "The great strength, daring, and cool courage of this eagle, plus his unequaled power of flight, render him highly conspicuous among his brethren," the famed naturalist wrote. "Had he a generous disposition toward others, he might be looked up to as a model of nobility." But, he noted, the eagle had a "ferocious, overbearing, and tyrannical temper."

BUT IT TOOK HOLD

Despite such opinions, the nation took to the eagle. Twelve states included it as part of their official emblems. Over the past 200 years, hundreds of companies, clubs, and organizations have adopted the eagle in their logos. The creature also has been used in the designs of everything from stamps and coins to furniture and door knockers.

Americans have especially embraced the eagle at times of conflict. During the Civil War, for instance, a Wisconsin farmer traded a bushel of corn to an Indian for a captive eagle. He then sold the bird to some men who were forming a company of local volunteers. The soldiers made a special perch for the creature, draped red, white, and blue ribbons around it, christened it "Old Abe" after the President, and swore it into the Union Army. They also carried the bird into combat, where, reportedly, Old Abe clung to his perch and screamed menacingly while displaying his seven-foot wingspan.

At Corinth, a Confederate bullet severed his tether and Old Abe flew screaming over the battlefield, losing several feathers in the cross fire before returning to his stand. General Grant once doffed his hat in a salute to the bird while passing the Wisconsin company in review. On another occasion, Old Abe got loose and held up an entire army's march for an hour while the troops waited for him to return. Recognizing the box-office potential, P. T. Barnum offered $20,000 for the bird, but his money was turned down. Eventually, Old Abe was retired to a special room in the Wisconsin Capitol, where he lived as a celebrity for 16 years.

MANY SHOT

Bald eagles have not always been placed in such revered positions, however. As the young nation spread across the continent, rumors about the birds also flourished. The early South Carolina naturalist, John Lawson, complained that eagles stole pigs from barnyards. Ornithologist Alexander Wilson reported an attempt by one of the birds to carry off an infant while the mother weeded

An immature eagle is fitted with a radio-tracking device so scientists can keep tabs on where the bird goes, and ultimately learn more about the bald eagle's migration patterns and habitat needs.

Michael Gordon/Alaska Photo

Praised by many people for its sheer, majestic beauty, viewed by others as a villain, the bald eagle will always be a breathtaking sight as it soars on powerful wings.

her garden nearby. Farmers responded to such outlandish tales by shooting eagles and other birds of prey.

By 1904, writer John Burroughs declared, "I see fewer eagles along the Hudson River than I did 15 years ago. Throughout the land, the great birds have been shot for fun or to produce a stuffed trophy, or in a self-righteous war on vermin." So great was the toll, said Burroughs, that "only a small proportion of Americans today have ever seen the emblem of their country soaring above them, wild and free."

Finally, on June 8, 1940, the U.S. Congress took note of the eagle's precarious situation. It declared that the species is "no longer a mere bird of biological interest but a symbol of the American ideals of freedom," that the bird is "now threatened with extinction," and that henceforth it would be illegal to shoot one or take its eggs.

DDT AND OTHER TROUBLES

Meanwhile, other forces were taking their toll on the birds. Because much of their traditional nesting habitat was being converted to agriculture and other development,

the eagle's breeding potential began to decline. To complicate matters, the eagles do not breed until they are at least four years old, and then they may produce only two or three eggs each season. Unfortunately, the increasing use of chemical pesticides, beginning in the late 1940's, added another dilemma. More and more toxic substances such as DDT filtered into the country's waterways. Bald eagles began digesting the chemicals through contaminated fish. DDT caused the birds to lay weak-shelled eggs, and fewer and fewer eaglets hatched.

In 1957, researcher Charles Broley, who had banded eagles in Florida since the 1930's, reported that he could find only two nests along the coast where, a decade earlier, he had seen 80 of them. At Pennsylvania's Hawk Mountain, other researchers noted that only about 20 per cent of the eagles passing above them during migrations in the 1950's were immature, compared to more than twice that number a decade earlier.

Belatedly, scientists and politicians turned their attentions to protecting the national symbol. In 1962, to help prevent the shooting of brown-headed immature bald eagles, the federal Eagle Protection Act was amended to include a prohibition on the taking of golden eagles, as well. In 1972, after scientific study confirmed the adverse effects of DDT on bird reproduction, Congress banned the domestic sales of the pesticide.

EFFORTS TO PROTECT

In the mid-1970's the U.S. Fish and Wildlife Service set up five recovery teams, whose efforts are directed to the restoration of key bald eagle populations. The U.S. Forest Service implemented a new policy to delay timber harvests around nesting eagles, and to maintain buffer zones around known nesting trees. In addition, captive-bred eagles have been reintroduced in recent years in New York, Georgia, Tennessee, Kentucky, Missouri, Maine, Ohio, and California.

Since 1974, the National Wildlife Federation has established four bald eagle sanctuaries in prime wintering areas around the country. The Federation's Raptor Information Center in Virginia now serves as a clearinghouse for information on eagles. It has also published a major bibliography on the creatures. For the past three years, the center has conducted an annual midwinter survey of the birds—the first such survey ever undertaken. "With these surveys," says Center Director William Clark, "we can provide state and federal agencies with the most current and comprehensive information on wintering bald-eagle distribution."

In January 1981, census takers counted 13,709 eagles, about 70 per cent of which are migrants from Canada and Alaska. The center estimated the year-round resident eagle population in the Lower 48 states to be about 4,500. These figures represent a five per cent increase over the previous year.

Such population increases do make scientists cautiously optimistic. However, they are not yet certain if the domestic ban on DDT has slowed the decline of eagles. Chuck Sindelar, a researcher who has banded the birds in Wisconsin for many years, notes that many eagle eggs tested after failing to hatch show high DDT levels. But, he points out, since the chemical persists in the environment for many years, it may be too soon to expect much change.

Unfortunately, illegal shooting still daunts the birds in some areas. "It's the number one cause of death as far as banded eagles are concerned," says Sindelar. "And that's just figuring from the bands that are turned in." Organized eagle kills carried out by stockmen are a thing of the past. Today, according to Butch Olendorff, Endangered Species Coordinator for the U.S. Bureau of Land Management in California, most of the shooters are "indiscriminate plinkers who just go out and gun down anything that sits on a power pole." For the past few years, the National Wildlife Federation has offered $500 rewards to help corral eagle shooters. Thus far, 13 such rewards have led to convictions.

THE FUTURE

Will such efforts help save our national symbol? William Clark feels that the bird is reproducing better, "especially in the Chesapeake Bay and Great Lakes regions." Meanwhile, habitat loss continues to be the most dangerous, long-term threat to the eagles. "That's why it's important to have the data our midwinter surveys provide," he observes. "Finally, we're getting a feel for what habitat is essential to the birds."

Two decades ago, John F. Kennedy made a resounding plea for all Americans to come to the aid of the birds. "The founding fathers made an appropriate choice when they selected the bald eagle as the emblem of our nation," he said. "The fierce beauty and proud independence of this great bird aptly symbolize the strength and freedom of America." But, he cautioned, "as latter-day citizens we shall have failed a trust if we permit the eagle to disappear." It is a notion well worth remembering on the 200th anniversary of our national symbol □

SELECTED READINGS

"Council of eagles" by Matthew Donohoe. *Oceans*, Sept/Oct 1981.

"King of the heap" by Frank L. Jackson. *National Wildlife*, June/July 1981.

"Wild eagle chase" by Frank Graham Jr. *Audubon*, May 1981.

"Bald eagle: new hopes, new fears" by Frank Graham Jr. *Audubon*, January 1981.

Soaring through the darkness, an Indian false vampire bat searches for prey such as small bats and birds, insects, frogs, and geckos.

THE GHOSTLY WINGS OF NIGHT

by Fred Hapgood

THERE is a sinister demon in the folklore of southern Mexico whose name is transliterated "H'ikal." H'ikal is drawn to those whose natures have become anomalous, ambivalent, or blurred, those who are neither one thing nor its opposite. When such persons (soft men, hard women, dreamers or drunkards, rebellious children, corrupt officials) enter a crossing or a threshold, some zone that itself has an inbetween character, H'ikal will appear to them.

As the legends have it, at first they will be falsely confident, for they will see the demon in some other form, as something commonplace or innocuous, like a dog. They do not discover the truth until the demon attacks them. Then they will either die or defeat the demon by returning to their pure and true natues.

What H'ikal's own true nature is poses a difficult anthropological question, especially given its reputation as a master of deception

and illusion. Working from certain patterns in the tales, such as recurring descriptions of H'ikal as small, dark-skinned and having wings on its feet, American scholars have traced the figure of H'ikal back to a ferocious Mayan god depicted in pre-Columbian hieroglyphics. These pictographs associate that deity with blood, eroticism, sacrifice, and death. And they reveal one other point: H'ikal, or at least its inspiration, was a bat.

These Mexican legends are only one instance of an ancient struggle—one that appears over and over in the myths of many cultures—to make some sort of useful sense out of a creature that has hair and teats like a mammal but flies like a bird and yet is unlike most birds in that it flies almost exclusively at night. Aesop, for example, concluded that during a great war between the birds and the beasts, the bats capitalized on their dual nature to shift sides according to the changing fortunes of that war. When peace came, all

R. Mitchell/Tom Stack & Associates

An enormous colony of Mexican free-tailed bats blackens the sky as the creatures swoop out of their home in Bracken Cave, Texas.

the creatures joined forces against the bats and, to punish them for their opportunism, banished them to the night. Few peoples go as far as the Mexicans, who invest the very concept of anomaly with a batlike nature, but most do seem to feel that special explanations of some sort are needed to account for the pronounced sense of otherness and distance felt by humans when they contemplate the bat.

ANIMALS WITH A STRANGE SENSE

The first scientific attempt to investigate the nature of bats, as opposed merely to noting classification details, was made by Lazzaro Spallanzani, one of the great scientists of the 18th century.

In 1793, when Spallanzani was 64 and had been for many years one of the most famous scientists of the age, he discovered that bats can avoid obstacles in flight when their eyes are covered. After a series of experiments, he concluded that none of the other known senses was serving in place of eyesight and that "in the absence of sight there is substituted some new organ or sense which we do not have and of which consequently we can never have any idea." His findings were published. Then, during the winter of

1793–94, he learned that a Geneva surgeon named Louis Jurine had determined that if the ears of a bat were tightly sealed, the bat became helpless, whether it was blinded or not.

At first, Spallanzani was very skeptical of Jurine's work, but he soon confirmed Jurine's results himself. It was true: bats "saw" with their ears. He never published his findings, but for five more years, until he died, he performed one series of experiments after another, each of which confirmed and amplified on this basic fact. Why he never published we do not know. But one can be certain that a scientist as politically acute as Spallanzani understood the difference between postulating "some new organ or sense" and suggesting that bats see with their ears. The former is merely a mystery; the second, an anomaly. Mysteries risk, at most, demystification; anomalies risk ridicule. The scientist may well have decided that he had better things to do with his professional credibility than gamble it on advancing such a volatile proposition. For the next 140 years professional zoology was content with the idea that bats flying in the dark somehow became aware of their surroundings through a highly developed sense of touch.

ACOUSTIC SPOTLIGHTS

Spallanzani might have made a quite different decision about publishing but for the accident that he made his discovery when he was at the height of his career. A young man would have had less to lose. It thus seems no coincidence that modern bat studies began in the lab space of two undergraduates.

In 1938 a Harvard student and bat enthusiast named Donald Griffin heard that a physics professor had built a receiver that detected the high-frequency calls of insects. Remembering that a British acoustics expert had suggested in 1920 that bats might rely on the echoes of high-frequency sound for navigation, Griffin borrowed the receiver and began to experiment with some caged bats.

Over the next two years, together with another Harvard student named Robert Galambos, he proved that bats navigate by generating high-frequency sounds and then extracting the information they need from the echoes of those sounds. They light their way through the dark with an acoustic spotlight, as it were—using what amounts to natural sonar equipment. "This is now so rudimentary that it is difficult to realize how unexpected [this discovery was]," Griffin later wrote.

The experiments were powerfully persuasive, however, and acceptance of the results was not long in coming. Griffin and Galambos then faced a quite different, and equally disturbing, intellectual and emotional climate. "After these basic facts had been accepted," Griffin wrote, "there was an incredible lack of interest in further studies. A typical reaction was, 'Why do you want to spend any more time on this sort of thing?' This attitude was so pervasive I found it difficult to maintain my own motivation."

The students' teachers were probably just being protective, trying to prevent two highly promising young scientists from throwing away their careers. Science is a social enterprise. A scientist succeeds so far as other scientists can use his work to further their own. This ability of bats that Griffin and Galambos had discovered was just too different, too weird. Nothing that anybody else was studying was remotely like it. Who would referee their papers? Who would publish them? Why, the subject matter didn't even have a name. Griffin himself had to come up with a label for it: echolocation. It is one thing for an undergraduate to hit on

The strange-looking nose of this white-lined bat plays a part in the emission of ultrasonic sounds.

S. C. Bisserot/Bruce Coleman

With its lengthy tongue and muzzle, a long-nosed bat probes deeply into flowers to lap up sweet nectar.

Photo Trends

© Keith Gunnar/Bruce Coleman

The stomachs of these common vampire bats are like long, elastic tubes which can take in large quantities of blood. The razor-toothed mammals often swell up as they eat.

some offbeat fact. It is professional suicide for him to declare himself a professional community of one.

Nonetheless, Griffin persevered. First at Cornell University and later back at Harvard, together with Martin Eisentraut of West Germany and William Wimsatt of Cornell, he began building a profession. He trained students, established issues, coined and defined terms, worked out technical procedures, and laid out a structure of field observations and laboratory data. The process was slow, but eventually some sort of critical mass was reached. And now batology has come of age. What it has found, in brief, is that the Mexican mythmakers were right—bats are different, though some of the ways in which they succeed at being different look strangely familiar.

FROM A FLYING SQUIRREL

How and when the divergence between bats and other mammals began is still another mystery. The oldest fossil bat so far found has, despite its age of 50,000,000 years, a very contemporary look to it. The professional consensus is that not too much earlier than that, an insect-eating mammal similar

to a flying squirrel discovered that the night air was rich in food and free from competitors and predators. It moved into that niche, developing its wings and its sonar as it did so—and evolving into a bat in the process. Bats now come in about 1,000 species and subspecies and may well be one of the most diverse mammalian orders. (Rodents have more species but arguably are more uniform.)

For example, in regard to feeding habits, one can find bats that eat fruit, the nectar, and pollen of flowers, insects, many small vertebrates, including fish, frogs, rodents, birds, and other bats, and the blood of large animals. A few bat species are not strictly nocturnal, and a few more, particularly the fruit eaters, do not echolocate. Still, it is far more true than false to say that what sets bats apart, what makes them different, is that they hunt at night, from and in the air, and use sounds to help them locate potential prey.

ECHOLOCATION

As Spallanzani and Griffin might testify, this is not an ordinary accomplishment. It is one thing to listen to the echoes of a shout in a mountain valley and another to be able to tell how far away—say, to within two or three centimeters (one inch) or less—something is by its echo, or in which direction it is moving, or how fast, or what kind of body shape and surface it has. Despite decades of interest in "seeing by ear" (inspired by the example of bats), only a few blind people have learned how to use echolocation to guide themselves around huge obstacles. None have ever gotten adept enough to catch a basketball.

Bats have to handle far more complex tasks than that. In many cases they hunt insects as small as mosquitoes and fruit flies. Because ultrasound weakens rapidly in air, they seldom sense the presence of their prey from more than a meter (yard) away. Since bats fly at speeds of 15 to 30 kilometers (10 to 20 miles) per hour, all detection and interception problems involving two creatures maneuvering in three dimensions have to be solved in an instant, or the bat will have overflown its food. Finally—and this is what would seem to make the bat's way of life completely impossible—echolocation involves reading echoes returned from a target. This means that a potential victim can pick up the sounds of an echolocating predator in half the time it takes the predator to detect the prey. How could any kind of predator exist while giving its prey that kind of head start?

HIGHLY SUCCESSFUL

As formidable as these problems are, bats have evolved to deal with them. Bats are the most populous mammalian order—it has been estimated that one out of every 10 mammals is a bat. Since evolutionary theory closely links adaptive skill to reproductive success, these creatures are arguably the most skilled of all mammals at coping with their world. For example, the little brown bat, an insectivore very common in temperate zones, has been observed catching insects at rates of about 500 an hour, or one every seven seconds. Usually they "field" their prey (that is, find it through echoes that radiate back from a relatively wide area), locating its wing or tail membranes, but sometimes a bat will just snatch an insect right out of the air with its mouth, a feat of detection and agility that would be hard to credit had it not been photographed. The total time elapsed from detection to capture runs between one-third and one-half of a second. Within that time, the bat has not only detected the prey but calculated an interception trajectory and streaked along its course.

HIGHLY SKILLED

One of the more active lines of bat research has involved probing this high level of skill to measure just how proficient bats are. For instance, it has been determined that bats can detect and avoid superthin wires hung in their flight path—wires as thin as 0.2 millimeter (0.01 inch) and sometimes as thin as 0.05 millimeter (0.002 inch). Another set of experiments has tested the skill of bats at perceiving size, shape, and surface texture. A common experiment of this sort is to include a worm in a group of small metal or plastic objects of different shapes and sizes and then toss the whole cluster in front of a cruising bat. A lot of individual differences among bats emerge, but at least some bats will pick out and catch only the worm, toss after toss.

Clinging to a plant in New Guinea, this tiny fruit bat seeks food. Its long, slender tongue has brushlike projections that pick up pollen and nectar.

S. C. Bisserot/Bruce Coleman

As its broad, leathery wings beat slowly, the greater horseshoe bat flutters like a butter-fly. Sometimes the bat will fly quite close to the ground if it locates potential prey.

© N. Smythe/PR

Mouse-eared bats form large maternal colonies where they give birth during the spring and summer. Each mother usually bears just one offspring.

LOUD INTRICATE VOCABULARY

Another line of research has been concerned with the nature of bats' sonar calls. One of the first surprises turned up by this work was how loud bat calls are. The energy carried by the sonar pulse of the little brown bat, when measured close to the bat's mouth, is 20 times greater than the sound energy produced by a pneumatic drill measured at a distance of a few meters (yards).

Again, there is a lot of individual and species variation. Some tropical bats issue much quieter sounds than these. In other species, sound levels as many as 60 times

louder than a pneumatic drill have been recorded. Were these sounds not emitted at frequencies too high for us to hear, the night sky would bring with it an indescribable racket, sounding as though hundreds of high-speed motorboats were crisscrossing over our heads all night long.

The bat's sound pulse itself is less a burst of noise than an intricate acoustic device that interrogates the environment on many levels. For example, the pulses of the little brown bat might last from 0.002 or 0.003 second to 0.0003 second, depending on the situation. These are such short periods that it would seem as though a bat would have time to do nothing but push the physiological equivalents of its on and off buttons. In fact, both the focus and the frequency of each individual pulse go through smooth, continuous transformations.

Over its miniscule duration, each pulse drops in frequency about an octave and shifts from a narrow straight-ahead focus to a wider projective field. These shifts give the bat a rich mix of information from the returning echoes. Depending on how far away the target is—the farther away, the more time must be allowed between pulses for the echo to return—a bat might issue fewer than 10 pulses per second or more than 200.

There are a great many ways in which a sonar pulse can be put together. One of the early expectations of bat researchers was that different species would have their own characteristic sounds, on the model of bird calls. To some extent this has proved true, but as more species have been more thoroughly studied, researchers have been surprised by how broad the range of acoustic specializations commanded by most bats actually is. It is as if robins had been observed crowing like roosters and whistling like whippoorwills. If these pulses are the basic units out of which bats fashion the questions with which they interrogate the environment, then most bats have a very large vocabulary. They are the college graduates of the natural world.

THEY ASK QUESTIONS

Perhaps the most impressive single characteristic of bats to be uncovered by all the research has been a sense of their extraordinary mental powers, particularly their ability to learn and to adapt their sonar probes to new circumstances. There is one line of experiments that seems to show the contrary, but its evidence is equivocal. Once a bat has been trained to fly a maze, it ceases to attend to its physical structure. That is, if new obstacles are introduced, the bat will hit them, and if old ones are removed, it will not use the new passageways.

In the most dramatic experiments of this sort, bats are first trained to fly through a three-dimensional maze constructed of strung wires. Then the wires are removed and replaced by photoelectric beams and receptor cells. When the bats are reintroduced into the "maze," no beams are broken. They continue to fly in the old patterns, twisting and spiraling through a maze of wires that now exists only in their minds. While it is true that one can imagine more efficient ways of flying, it is also true that a creature has to be very bright before it can be that dumb. How many humans have the gift of remembering the structure of volumes with such precision?

The world bats live in is one in which no information comes to them for free. Our world abounds with the energies by which we see. Light streams from a multitude of sources and can pass with little loss of strength through great distances of air. By contrast, aside from sounds made by other bats and some insects, a bat sees nothing that is not illuminated by its own powers.

We now know that a bat possesses a set of precise acoustic tools that will probe just those aspects of nature in which it is interested. We also now know that bats have a heightened ability to learn about the world and remember it, an ability that allows the bat to ask the right questions at the right times and make immediate decisions based on the answers it receives.

PORPOISES OF THE AIR

Clearly, bats are very different creatures, and yet given the new information we have about them, certain parallels, certain analogies, begin to appear. There are other mammals that echolocate, that are famous for their ability to learn and remember patterns of movement in three dimensions, and that "fly" through intricate, volumelike mazes. Like bats, these mammals are highly social (though not *as* social; except for humans, bats are perhaps the most gregari-

Researchers in the Adirondacks band a group of bats. The scientists are studying the way bats use echolocation to get around obstacles.

Peter Arnold

S. C. Bisserot/Bruce Coleman

A cluster of greater horseshoe bats spend the winter months hibernating in a warm cave, with their wings wrapped around their bodies like tiny cloaks.

ous mammals of all). We call them porpoises; they are among the most dearly beloved of all nature's creatures.

It is hard to imagine two creatures whose roles in our culture could be more distinct. Bats are symbols of the night, of the psychic weight of night, of our fears of wandering lost and blind while alien creatures to whom we are nothing watch every blundering step. Porpoises are the noble savages of the late 20th century, representing the sweet and playful intelligence of spirits uncrushed by industrial civilization. There are few distinctions so wide and deeply etched. Yet here is this growing pile of evidence suggesting that, after all, bats are but the porpoises of the air, and porpoises the bats of the sea. H'ikal, the bat-god of anomaly, would be amused □

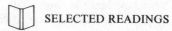 **SELECTED READINGS**

Bats: The Night Fliers by Anabel Dean. Lerner Publications, 1974.
The World of Bats by Charles E. Mohr. Lippincott, 1976.

BATS

Classification: Bats make up the mammalian order Chiroptera; this is the only mammalian order defined by true flight. Chiroptera consists of 19 families, 174 genera, and more than 1,000 species and subspecies. It is estimated that one out of every ten mammals is a bat. There are two suborders: Megachiroptera, containing bats that orient themselves visually; and Microchiroptera, containing bats that depend on echolocation.

Habitat: Bats are found worldwide but are especially prevalent in the tropics. In western Africa, there are about 100 species, compared with 30 in the United States.

Feeding: Most bats feed on flying insects. Some are carnivorous, while others obtain nourishment from flower pollen and nectar. Fisherman bats have developed large feet and claws for gaffing fish swimming near the surface. The true vampire bat, found in Central and South America, is the only vertebrate to feed exclusively on the blood of warm-blooded animals. It is estimated that a vampire will lap up more than 12 liters (3 gallons) of blood in a year.

Reproduction: Most bats give birth to one offspring, which may weigh from one-sixth to one-third as much as the mother. The infant bats have well-developed hind legs, which they use to cling to the mother while she is in flight.

Morphology: Bats have a basic mammalian skeleton, with front limbs modified for flight. The forearm and fingers of the bat are greatly elongated and connected by a delicate elastic membrane. When not extended for flight, the wing membrane shrinks into wrinkled folds, enabling the bat to move about freely on the ground.

RACCOONS

by Timothy Foote

NOT long ago on the island of Martha's Vineyard, a party of raccoons, in order to ensure a steady supply of rich leavings from the summer folk, managed to hijack a garbage truck. Their method of operation was apparently acquired from television by a raccoon that watched a TV set through the windows of a glassed-in sun porch. The heist involved stealing the truck's ignition key and the creation of a raccoon commando team, which used block and tackle to drive the stolen vehicle and to hoist garbage cans up high enough to empty them into it.

FACT AND FANCY

Do you believe that story? If so, chances are you've been victimized by raccoons already, and nothing they do will surprise you. For the above Vineyard goings-on are pure fantasy. At least I thought they were when I put them in a children's book in 1980.

At the time I actually wondered if readers might have trouble believing the story, in the way you have to believe in a story if it is to work for you. As it turned out, no need to worry. Everybody I meet, these days, has a raccoon tale to pass along. If even half of them were true, stealing an ignition key and hijacking a garbage truck would be nothing.

Watching television? A man in California tells of a big male raccoon that used to sit in the crotch of a tree outside the sun porch and watch "Dallas." All went well until his wife bought a new couch and switched the porch furniture around, so the television set wound up facing away from the raccoon's perch. That night a terrible scratching and chittering began. So they turned the television back toward the window again, and the coon contentedly settled down to watch.

Then there is the story about the raccoon that liked Beethoven. I've run into it on four occasions so far. Each time the human witness is somewhat different, but the character of the raccoon does not alter so much as a whisker. The scene is always a summer

Charles Palek/Tom Stack & Associates

A young raccoon in western South Dakota peeks out of its den in a hollow tree. The animal will also take refuge in almost any cozy crevice it can find, including the chimneys of many people's houses.

cabin in which a man regularly plays classical music at night. The raccoon comes out of the woods, handily lifts the latch to open the screen door, then climbs up near the speakers and listens. But only when the music is Beethoven's Ninth Symphony. That over, he gravely climbs down, walks to the door, and lets himself out the way he came in, returning for more Beethoven the following night.

A corollary account, also familiar, notes that when farmers leave a portable radio playing rock 'n' roll in the cornfields at night to ward off raccoons, the marauders simply turn the knob to get a more soothing sound, and continue eating the juicy ears of corn.

Leonard Lee Rue III/Tom Stack & Associates

Groping in the mud along the shallow bank of a stream, a raccoon uses its nimble fingers to feel for crayfish and other tasty tidbits hidden below the surface of the water.

Faced with such stories, an amateur raccoonteur thinks to separate fact from fancy by checking things out in scientific accounts of raccoon life. Consider, for instance, Dorcas MacClintock's splendid book, *A Natural History of Raccoons.* A trained naturalist who has raised a good many raccoons by hand, the author seems to have pulled together all existing information on the subject. The book is well written, beautifully illustrated, and fairly bristling with facts.

ALWAYS ON THE MOVE

Northern raccoons, we learn, weight up to 14 kilograms (30 pounds), although a celebrated whopper captured in Wisconsin weighed 28 kilograms (62 pounds) and measured 1.4 meters (4 feet, 7 inches) from nose to tail. The raccoon has a potential life span of about twelve years, but in the wild the average animal survives until only about age five. They spend a good deal of time on the move, "day bedding" in all sorts of shelters and foraging over as much as 2,400 hectares (6,000 acres) in the wilderness, or as little as 5 hectares (12 acres) when patrolling the rich suburbs.

In fall raccoons eat a lot, storing up fat for the cold weather, sometimes as much as 25 per cent of the animal's weight, including a 2.5-centimeter (1-inch) thick layer on the rump. They winter in hollow trees. The average entrance hole, MacClintock duly reports, is 8 meters (26 feet) above ground, and the nest within is sometimes 3.3 meters (11 feet) down inside the trunk. Even fully fattened, however, raccoons are not total hibernators. When the temperature outside rises to $-2°$ Celsius (28° Fahrenheit), they will stir out in search of food.

Mother raccoons have from two to seven cubs. Fathers do not help take care of them. The males are not monogamous, either, but they do provide a certain protection from other raccoons by patrolling a specific turf while females are raising their young. Like wolves, raccoons have elaborate social procedures for avoiding deadly fights. MacClintock notes that when a single raccoon approaches a strange group it is often exceedingly nervous. Sometimes it literally backs toward the others in order to avoid confrontation—or save face.

The French call raccoons *ratons laveurs,* meaning "rats that wash." The Germans prefer *Waschbär,* meaning "bears that wash." But raccoons are neither rats nor bears. Rather, the raccoon, *Procyon lotor,* makes up a separate family, Procyonidae. It descended from arboreal dogs of 3,000,000 years ago.

It is impossible not to have total confidence in *A Natural History of Raccoons.* The author, clearly, is no mere raccoonteur, likely to stretch a tale to heighten drama. So a properly skeptical reader is startled (and impressed) to come across an account of a woman who found a raccoon family nesting in her chimney. She telephoned for advice. "Just light a fire in the fireplace," came the reply. "We tried that," she said. "But they came down the chimney, shut the damper, and smoked us out!"

In short, when it comes to demythifying the exploits of raccoons, science isn't always as much help as might be expected.

GROPE AND GRAB

Despite its dexterity, *Procyon lotor* does not actually have an opposable thumb. But its paws look and act like human hands, with a thumb and four digits, the two long fingers in the center, the short ones on either side. Raccoon hands even sweat—and grow more sensitive when wet, which may be one of the reasons they seem to wash their food. It has been proved, however, that raccoons that dabble food in water are not trying to clean it. They sometimes gobble down earthworms and crabs, specially loaded up with dirt, without bothering to "wash" them at all. Yet they carefully douse and dabble and pat perfectly clean food in water before eating. Why? Raccoons douse food in captivity for the sheer tactile pleasure of it, and to keep practicing the grope-and-grab motions they normally have to use in the wild when searching shallows for crayfish and tadpoles.

Like crows and magpies (and humans), raccoons are collectors of small bright objects. In fact, raccoons are amazingly well equipped for thievery. In a study reported in *American Journal of Psychology,* it took one raccoon 17 minutes to solve a latch-type puzzle for the first time. Four minutes on the second try. And only two seconds on every succeeding try after the fifth. A year later, one of the latch openers was given the puzzle again—and solved it in two seconds.

Raccoons can grip like Beowulf with their powerful forepaws. The frequently cited lore on the subject tells of a 90-kilogram (200 pound) Yale University researcher who grabbed a raccoon by the tail as it was climbing a tree. The raccoon supported the entire weight of the pursuer without falling, a scene that must have looked almost as startling as those ads for Krazy Glue in which fullbacks were revealed hanging from goal-post bars by the tops of their glued helmets.

EAT? ANYTHING!

Findings of research teams and the everyday observations of householders overlap most on the matter of what raccoons eat and the way they have of getting it. Raccoons, in fact, will eat almost anything: earthworms, grapes, berries, nuts, baby birds, every sort of egg, baby rabbits, snakes, lizards, frogs, beets, corn, crickets, caterpillars, crayfish, every kind of crab, snails, clams and mussels, grasshoppers, tadpoles, minnows, and toads.

Around civilization, raccoons also develop a fatal weakness for junk food—barbecued potato chips and watermelon pickles, for example. They are also so fond of peanut butter that it is often used to trap them. A. B. C. Whipple, a raccoonteur who for

With its soft, dexterous hands wrapped around a cluster of wild grapes, a hungry raccoon settles down in a thicket to feast on the juicy fruit.

Karl H. Maslowski/PR

When danger threatens, a raccoon commonly scampers up a tall tree to safety. If cornered, the creature can put up a fierce fight.

years has been locked in combat with the coons around Greenwich, Connecticut, notes that they have the habit of distributing what's left of his garbage along the driveway in order to arrange it into courses. One morning he found a "spread of shrimp shells followed by clean-picked chicken bones followed by cheese and crackers followed by a cigar butt." I allowed for some poetic license there. Perhaps because they have read the surgeon general's warnings, raccoons don't actually smoke the cigars after dinner. They merely roll the deadly weed between their paws.

CROWDING IN ON HUMANS

Because they are such fierce fighters, raccoons have few natural enemies in the wild—bobcats, lynx, and cougars, all of them rare and getting rarer. Most dogs shrink from tangling with a raccoon. Cars, alas, don't. MacClintock cites a sample Michigan statis-

tic: 445 raccoons crushed along one 182-kilometer (114-mile) stretch of highway in 1971. An estimated 2,000,000 coons a year are shot or trapped for their pelts.

Even so, the current consensus says that the raccoon population of North America has stayed the same for the last 300 years. Raccoons are thriving, and at a time when many of their wild kin are becoming endangered species.

That is what makes their doings so interesting, and perhaps instructive. Other animals are being crowded out by people. Raccoons are crowding in, joining the rush to urban centers. They are even taking up residence in parks and vacant lots in cities where, although danger is great, foraging possibilities are greater. The key to raccoon survival is uncanny cleverness and an omnivorous diet. Just how closely the raccoon population can follow garbage is illustrated by MacClintock in a note about the Huntington Lake area in the Sierra Nevada of California. No raccoons lived there until "skiing became popular and cabins were occupied in winter, assuring a year-round food supply."

RACE TO THE SUBURBS

One result is that today people near cities have a better chance to know, and learn from, raccoons than do country dwellers. My own case is an example. I grew up in the woods on a trout stream in New York and didn't go to school regularly until I was eleven. So I spent days, years, in the woods. But in all that time, although I saw foxes, deer, beavers, muskrats, weasels, even a mink or two, I saw raccoons only once. That was on the Beaverkill River when, proceeding toward a big pool just at dusk, with the noise of my waders drowned in the rush of the rapids below, I found a mother raccoon nudging three cubs ahead of her out along the trunk of a big yellow birch that leaned over the river.

They were making a terrific racket because, I soon saw, this was a swimming lesson. The mother was trying to push the cubs off the tree and into the pool. The first two went in easily enough, hit the water with a small plop, came up snuffling, and struck out for shore as the gentle current carried them in a slow curve downstream. The last cub put up a battle, yelling and snarling and dodging under the branches whenever his mother pushed him. Finally, he too fell, complaining bitterly, into the river.

Now I live in a suburb, along the Hudson, but with houses crowding in on three sides. There are plenty of raccoons. A whole treeful of them spent last summer in a sycamore right in front of my next door neighbor's house. On Martha's Vineyard, which in summer is crammed with people, raccoons not only hijack garbage trucks, they lift door latches to get inside and wrestle garbage cans down off porches. They also sit on their hind legs and swallow spaghetti, one string at a time, like small boys slurping to annoy their mothers.

GONE PROGRESSIVE

Naturalists have not yet fully caught up with New Age Raccoondom. They tend to study the animals either in the wild, once their natural habitat, or in their most unnatural habitat, captivity. That is a bit like assuming the average American is still a Puritan, or a jailbird. For raccoon society has moved on, gone progressive, and may soon be living off humans entirely. One can imagine teams of them, this very minute, experimenting with cast-off can openers—the better to get at our stores of dog and cat food.

Art sometimes foreshadows nature. A few years ago Robert Lowell wrote a poem comparing doctors to raccoons wearing stethoscopes. And sure enough, a company that makes doormats now markets a mat with a picture of a masked raccoon, stethoscope in ears, intently listening to the tumblers of a lock on a garbage can. Beside him, an accomplice, also masked, waits with the "soup," ready to blow the lock sky high if his partner's skill fails to open it.

Some work has been done on raccoons in the suburbs. A pair of biologists at the University of Cincinnati, James Schinner and Darrell Cauley, did a 27-month study of the Cincinnati suburb of Clifton. After 3,452 "trap nights" they concluded that the suburbs are "ideally suited to maximal raccoon activity—garbage being one of the main sources of food." A. B. C. Whipple speaks for all suburbanites when he comments: "I could have told them that." Another study in Detroit calculated that the raccoon population of a typical suburb was as high as one raccoon for every .6 hectares (1.4 acres), a density not far below that of suburbanites themselves.

But if the ringtail myth is to be satisfactorily separated from raccoon reality, further studies are in order. Take the seemingly simple matter of corn, for instance. Everybody knows that raccoons love corn. Nobody seems to know how to keep them from getting it. Nightly vigils with gun and dog—exhausting and bloody—are ultimately inadequate. A portable radio tuned in to Kiss is apparently fruitless. The raccoons head for the sweet corn like Monopoly players passing "Go." MacClintock reports that the best way of saving some corn for yourself is to sow a fast-maturing, small-eared variety and plant it early. That way, it seems, you stand a chance of getting the corn before raccoon hordes think any is available. It's hard to believe that such a dodge could work for long.

A mother coon carries one of her cubs to a new hiding place when a bobcat comes prowling around her home.

Leonard Lee Rue III/Bruce Coleman

YANKEE INGENUITY

Things may get to a point where we need a national Raccoon Hotline, so vandalized citizens can share their woe, and hard-earned wisdom, in the wake of raccoon raiding. One caller to a radio talk show insists she has not had trouble with stolen garbage since she began to set out piles of dry dog food on pie plates for the raccoons each night. A second caller noted that, having done just that regularly for a while, and then having forgotten to do it one night, the family was awakened by a barrage of empty pie plates being angrily thrown at the side of the cabin.

Mel Maddocks, who writes a column for the *Christian Science Monitor,* believes that people embroider on the skill of raccoons to save face. If the raccoons are that smart, you don't have to feel so dumb for being repeatedly outwitted by them. One suspects that Maddocks has yet to feel the full brunt of ringtail rapacity. It seems more probable that people tell of raccoon exploits because raccoons represent a kind of Yankee ingenuity, those brash, problem-solving skills that Americans have always prided themselves on, but find so sorely lacking of late.

When Benjamin Franklin argued that in the bald eagle the fledgling nation had picked the wrong national emblem, he had a point. The bald eagle, Franklin noted, was both "lousy" and not overly bright—it has since become all but extinct. Franklin's preference was the wild turkey, a down-to-earth and most nourishing bird. But turkeys are scarce too, at least in the wild. My vote is for *Procyon lotor* □

 SELECTED READINGS

All About Raccoons by Paul R. Paradise. TFH Publications, 1976.

A Natural History of Raccoons by Dorcas MacClintock. Scribner, 1980.

World of Raccoons by Wyatt Blassingame. Dodd, 1977.

This feisty masked bandit topples over a garbage can to rummage for food. In urban areas, raccoons are thriving on a steady supply of trash scraps.

© Leonard Lee Rue III/PR

© Anne Heimann

Beyond a traffic light near Tottenville, Staten Island, these dwellings for purple martins reputedly house the only active colony of the birds within New York's city limits.

MARTIN HOUSES

by Erik J. Bitterbaum and Charles R. Brown

JOHN James Audubon once remarked that he could always judge the quality of a roadside inn by the condition of the purple martin house erected on the inn's signboard. Good bird accommodations usually meant good people accommodations.

Audubon's observation illustrates the longstanding interest that people have had in the large, purplish swallows known as martins. The first nest boxes in the United States were gourds hung by Indians to attract martins. In the 1800's, slaves in the South continued the practice of hanging out gourds. The belief that martins will chase many species of hawks provided a practical motive for such early martin houses: I offer you a nesting place; you protect my poultry. We feel, however, that the martin's desire to chase birds of prey has been greatly exaggerated. They do, however, consume large amounts of insects.

Today, in neighborhoods across the eastern United States, martin houses of all makes and models can be found. Birdhouse manufacturers, in promoting their product, proclaim that the purple martin is America's favorite backyard bird. This claim may be more hype than reality, but the purple martin is probably the only North American bird to have its own newspaper. In the *Nature Society News,* published by a birdhouse-manufacturing firm in Griggsville, Illinois, martin fanciers report on their experiences with these birds.

The purple martin (*Progne subis*) is one of five species of the New World genus *Progne.* The other four species are found almost exclusively in the American tropics.

Male purple martins, when about one and a half years old, attain a deep, glossy purple plumage over the entire body. They are the only dark-bellied swallows of North

This magnificent complex was constructed in the mid-1960's in Griggsville, Illinois, the self-proclaimed "Purple Martin Capital of the World."

America. Females, while having purple backs and crowns, are gray on the throat, breast, and belly. A first-year male resembles a female, except for a generally darker back and a lined patch of purple on its throat, breast, and belly.

EARLY SPRING ARRIVALS

Purple martins have a wide but patchy range throughout eastern North America. They also breed along the California coast, in the southwestern desert of the United States, and reportedly, in northern Mexico. They are largely absent from the Rocky Mountains except for small, local montane populations. Because martin houses are not prevalent in the West, the birds there depend largely on abandoned woodpecker holes.

Purple martins migrate through Central America and the Caribbean to the Amazon River basin of Brazil, where they winter. Their annual arrival in the United States begins in late January in Florida and Louisiana and continues through May farther north. Early arrival time may be related to finding a nesting cavity, a problem encountered by hole nesters that do not excavate their own cavities.

Early arrival probably resulted from competition for nesting sites. Before humans provided martins with birdhouses—when the only nesting sites available were unused tree cavities—competition for sites was probably intense. If early arriving birds got the best or the only cavities, and as a result raised the most young, then arriving early could be an advantage. A counterbalance to an increasingly early arrival in breeding areas is the probability that early birds will face periods of cold weather and starvation, and thus extremely early arrival could be a disadvantage.

ORIGINALLY SOLITARY NESTERS

When purple martins nested largely in abandoned woodpecker holes (as the small western populations still do), they were probably mainly solitary nesters. This is supported by two kinds of evidence. First, before people and birdhouses came along, colonies of martins would have been possible only where woodpeckers had excavated a number of holes close together. However, most woodpeckers in the eastern United States that excavate cavities large enough for purple martins to use are solitary-nesting woodpeckers. It is improbable that they bore and then abandon enough holes in any single tree to allow colonies of martins to form. Acorn woodpeckers (*Melanerpes formicivorous*) in the West are colonial and do dig many holes close together, but their extreme aggressiveness around their nesting sites prevents martin colonies from forming there.

Second, purple martins are not able to recognize their own young. This is strong evidence that they originally were solitary nesters. Biologists believe that whenever there is a chance that young of different parents may get mixed up, such as in dense colonies of birds, selection is intense for chick recognition so that an individual parent does not assist the young of competing adults. As a result, chick recognition has evolved in most colonially breeding animals. Not being able to recognize their nestlings is a trait purple martins share with the related and solitary-nesting rough-winged swallow (*Stelgidopteryx ruficollis*).

WHY COLONIAL NOW?

What could have caused purple martins, at least in the eastern United States, to abandon their largely solitary life style and become a colonial backyard bird? This was probably brought about by the original clearing of much of the eastern forest which eliminated many natural nesting sites and by the erection of birdhouses, both of which began in the early 1800's. This massive environmental disturbance essentially changed the nature of the purple martin's available nesting sites in the southern and eastern United States.

Multiroom birdhouses are especially conducive to coloniality because they contain many nesting sites close together. Single-room birdhouses are rarely built for martins, and when erected are quickly appropriated by other species. As a result, in many martin populations, solitary nesting seldom seems to occur.

BAD NEIGHBORS

Humans have provided these birds with many housing opportunities, and this has probably caused an overall increase in martin numbers. Yet all is not rosy for martins that nest colonially in birdhouses. For instance, interference between neighboring purple martin pairs is common, owing to the parents' inability to recognize their young.

Juvenile martins, when within one to four days of fledging, often come out on the birdhouse porches. Since in many martin houses all rooms on a tier are connected by the same porch, the young may mix extensively and move between nearby compartments. Older nestlings cause much disturbance among the birds nesting on a tier, and when they try to enter nests containing eggs, they are often knocked off the porches by the occupants of these nests.

These older nestlings sometimes successfully intrude into neighboring nests and usurp most of the food brought by parents of

© Leonard Lee Rue III/PR

The deep, glossy plumage of a male purple martin gleams in the midday sun. The dark-bellied swallow is perched right in front of its penthouse room.

the younger nestlings. On one occasion, one of us observed a nearly grown nestling from one nest enter an adjacent room in which the young had just hatched. The pair in that room promptly abandoned their newly hatched young, which later died, and fed the intruder, which rapidly gained weight and remained in the nest for four days until it fledged. Young birds from adjacent-nesting pairs are most frequently involved in these disruptions, but all pairs that use rooms opening on a common porch are affected.

Returning to her nest in a dried, hollowed gourd, a female purple martin brings food to her tiny offspring. The food will stifle their hungry cries.

Fred J. Alsop, III/Bruce Coleman

© Dana Downie

Still standing after a half century, this weathered birdhouse hasn't attracted many residents in the past few years. It was built by Howard Worthington in Iowa.

© Leonard Lee Rue III/Bruce Coleman

Now predominantly colonial backyard birds, purple martins once had a largely solitary life style.

UNWANTED VISITORS

Besides providing nesting sites, people have also provided martins with some nesting-site competitors. House sparrows and starlings were introduced into North America and have spread phenomenally from coast to coast. Both species use holes for nesting sites and appear to relish martin houses. Rarely is a martin house not also occupied by house sparrows, and starlings are a problem in some areas. These species fill martin-house rooms with bulky straw nests and sometimes actively chase purple martins away.

Bluebirds and wrens also often usurp birdhouses erected for purple martins. Some people assist martins by destroying sparrow and starling nests as they are built, and others resort to trapping these interloping species.

AND NEXT?

The purple martin, regarded by some as the premier backyard dweller in North America, actually has been nesting in large colonies only a short time. People have provided martins with an abundance of new nesting sites; they have also provided pest species that compete for those nesting sites. The purple martin thus presents an opportunity for evolutionary study: over time, we can observe whether these birds adapt further to a colonial life style □

INDEX

CONTRIBUTORS

LAWRENCE K. ALTMAN, M.D., *Medical reporter, The New York Times*
REVIEW OF THE YEAR: HEALTH & DISEASE

NATALIE ANGIER, *Staff writer, Discover magazine*
SPORTS SCIENCE
MARIJUANA: BAD NEWS AND GOOD

ERWIN AND PEGGY BAUER, *Free-lance writers and photographers*
THE TOTEMS OF ALASKA

J. KELLY BEATTY, *Staff member, Sky & Telescope*
A LAST LOOK AT SATURN

JERRY E. BISHOP, *Staff reporter, The Wall Street Journal*
MONOCLONAL ANTIBODIES

ERIK J. BITTERBAUM, *Free-lance writer*
co-author MARTIN HOUSES

STEPHEN BOOTH, *Senior Editor, Audio Times*
BLANK AUDIO TAPES

BRUCE BOWER, *Writer, Science News*
AUTISM: A WORLD APART

WILLIAM J. BROAD, *Member of News and Comment staff, Science magazine*
SCIENCE FRAUDS

JANE E. BRODY, *Science writer and Personal Health columnist, The New York Times*
THE BEAUTIFUL PEOPLE
STROKES

CHARLES R. BROWN, *Free-lance writer*
co-author MARTIN HOUSES

ANNETTE BURDEN, *Free-lance writer and editor of Santa Barbara Magazine*
SHROUD OF MYSTERY

JEFFREY BURROUGHS, *Assistant Professor of Psychology, Juniata College, Huntingdon, PA*
YOU ARE WHAT YOU EAT

PETER D. CAPEN, *Free-lance writer and photographer*
SEA ANEMONES

JOEL DAVIS, *Free-lance science writer*
ASTEROIDS

FAROUK EL-BAZ, *Director, Center for Earth and Planetary Studies, National Air and Space Museum, Washington, D.C.*
DESERT BUILDERS

TIMOTHY FOOTE, *Senior Editor, Time magazine; author of The Great Ringtail Garbage Caper, a children's book; free-lance writer*
RACCOONS

LINDA GARMON, *Chemistry Editor, Science News*
co-author NUCLEAR WASTE DISPOSAL

ROBERT GEBALLE, *Free-lance writer*
FREUDIAN SLIPS

DENISE GRADY, *Staff writer, Discover magazine*
ZEROING IN ON ALLERGIES

KENNETH GRAY, *Free-lance writer*
co-author THE MONTE CARLO METHOD

PETER GWYNNE, *Science editor, Newsweek magazine; free-lance science writer*
PROTON DECAY

FRED HAPGOOD, *Free-lance writer*
THE GHOSTLY WINGS OF NIGHT

KATHERINE HARAMUNDANIS, *Research Associate, Smithsonian Astrophysical Observatory; co-author of An Introduction to Astronomy*
REVIEW OF THE YEAR: ASTRONOMY
THE DINOSAUR AND THE ASTEROID

WILLIAM K. HARTMANN, *Senior Scientist, Planetary Science Institute, Tucson, Arizona; author of Astronomy: The Cosmic Journey*
THE VIEW FROM IO

ROBIN MARANTZ HENIG, *Free-lance science writer*
THE PLACEBO EFFECT

GLADWIN HILL, *Free-lance writer; former Environment editor of The New York Times*
REVIEW OF THE YEAR: THE ENVIRONMENT

LARRY L. HOUSER, *Free-lance writer*
sub-author THE MONTE CARLO METHOD

JAMES JACKSON, *Free-lance writer and photographer; author of Pulse of the Forest*
RIVER IN A STRAIGHTJACKET

KEVIN JONES, *Visiting Research Fellow, Department of Music, City University, London*
COMPUTER MUSIC

LARRY KAHANER, *Washington-based free-lance writer*
ELECTRONIC MAIL

CORLISS KARASOV, *Science writer; Representative, National Audubon Society*
THE BOWERBIRD

FREDERICK C. KLEIN, *Staff reporter, The Wall Street Journal*
TEENAGE SUICIDE

GINA BARI KOLATA, *Staff writer, Science magazine*
LOW CHOLESTEROL AND CANCER

MARC KUSINITZ, *Staff member, Science World*
REVIEW OF THE YEAR: PHYSICAL SCIENCES

ROBIN LANIER, *Free-lance writer*
BACKYARD SATELLITE TV
VIDEOCASSETTE RECORDERS

RICHARD S. LAZARUS, *Professor of Psychology, University of California at Berkeley*
HASSLES

BENEDICT LEERBURGER, *Free-lance science writer*
THE SPACE SHUTTLE

WILLIAM MATTHEWS III, *Regents Professor of Geology. Lamar State University, Texas; Director of Education, American Geological Institute*
REVIEW OF THE YEAR: EARTH SCIENCES

HELLER MCALPIN, *Free-lance writer*
DOWN

MARTIN MCLAUGHLIN, *Vice President for Education, Overseas Development Council, Washington, D.C.*
co-author REVIEW OF THE YEAR: PAST, PRESENT, & FUTURE

JEANNE O'NEILL, *Associate Editor, Science World*
REVIEW OF THE YEAR: COMPUTERS & MATHEMATICS

RICHARD M. PRESTON, *Free-lance writer.*
LIFE OF A SNOW CRYSTAL

CARL PROUJAN, *Executive Editor, Science Dept., Educational Book Division, Prentice-Hall, Inc.; free-lance writer*
REVIEW OF THE YEAR: TECHNOLOGY

JOHN J. PULLEN, *Free-lance writer specializing in energy topics*
ELECTRICITY FROM THE WIND

JANET RALOFF, *Policy/Technology editor, Science News*
ELECTROMAGNETIC PULSE
REVIEW OF THE YEAR: ENERGY

EDWARD SADALLA, *Associate Professor, Environmental Psychology, Arizona State University*
YOU ARE WHAT YOU EAT

DAVID SCHAFFER, *Radio astronomer with NASA's Very Long Baseline Interferometry Group*
co-author QUASARS

DON SHARP, *Free-lance writer specializing in automotive writing; winner of International Motor Press Association's Ken W. Purdy Award for 1981*
WHAT A DRAG!

GREG SHIELDS, *Associate Professor of Astronomy, University of Texas at Austin*
co-author QUASARS

JOANNE SILBERNER, *Free-lance science writer*
REVIEW OF THE YEAR: BIOLOGY

HOWARD SINER, *News Editor, Newspaper Enterprise Association*
THE 1981 NOBEL PRIZES IN PHYSICS AND CHEMISTRY

PETER STEINHART, *Free-lance writer concentrating on energy and wildlife topics*
THE BIRD BEHIND THE SYMBOL

BOB STROHM, *Executive Editor, National Wildlife magazine*
REVIEW OF THE YEAR: WILDLIFE

WALTER SULLIVAN, *Science reporter, The New York Times*
TAKING AIM AT TORNADOES

ROGER SWAIN, *Science editor of Horticulture magazine; author of Earthly Pleasures: Tales from a Biologist's Garden*
OUR TROUBLED LAKES

BARBARA TCHABOVSKY, *Free-lance science writer and editor*
THE 1981 NOBEL PRIZE IN PHYSIOLOGY OR MEDICINE
IN MEMORIAM
REVIEW OF THE YEAR: BEHAVIORAL SCIENCES
co-author REVIEW OF THE YEAR: PAST, PRESENT, & FUTURE

MATHEW TEKULSKY, *Free-lance writer specializing in science*
LIGHT WAVES OF THE FUTURE

BILL THOMAS, *Free-lance writer*
sub-author PEATLANDS

PAUL TRACHTMANN, *Editor, Smithsonian magazine; free-lance writer*
COMPUTER GAMES

KENNETH TRAVERS, *Free-lance writer*
co-author THE MONTE CARLO METHOD

JAMES TREFIL, *Professor of Physics, University of Virginia; author of From Atoms to Quarks*
NOTHING

LANSING WAGNER, *Free-lance science writer*
SCIENCE BOOKS OF THE YEAR

W. E. WALLACE, *Distinguished Service Professor in Chemistry Department, University of Pittsburgh*
MAGNETIC DOMAINS

FRED WARSHOFSKY, *Free-lance science writer*
RUBIK'S CUBE

MARK WEXLER, *Free-lance writer; Senior Editor, National Wildlife magazine*
TEN ENDANGERED HABITATS

JOHN NOBLE WILFORD, *Science writer, The New York Times*
REVIEW OF THE YEAR: SPACE SCIENCE

ALLEN YOUNG, *Curator and Head of Department of Invertebrate Zoology, Milwaukee Public Museum*
CHOCOLATE GROWS ON TREES

PATRICK YOUNG, *Free-lance science writer*
LIFE AT THE END OF THE EARTH

LISA YOUNT, *Free-lance writer*
THE FLY IN OUR FRUIT